Art of Problem Solving Presents:

BEAST ACADEMY

MATH
PRACTICE
4B

Aligned to the Common Core State Standards

Jason Batterson
Shannon Rogers

Published by: AoPS Incorporated
                       P.O. Box 2185
                       Alpine, CA 91903-2185
                       (619) 659-1612
                       info@BeastAcademy.com

ISBN: 978-1-934124-53-6

Written by Jason Batterson and Shannon Rogers
Book Design by Lisa T. Phan
Illustrations by Erich Owen
Grayscales by Greta Selman
Special thanks to Palmer Mebane for his puzzle contributions.

Visit the Beast Academy website at www.BeastAcademy.com.
Visit the Art of Problem Solving website at www.artofproblemsolving.com.
Printed in the United States of America.
First Printing 2014.

Contents:

How to Use This Book   4

Chapter 4: Counting   6

Chapter 5: Division   38

Chapter 6: Logic   64

Hints for Selected Problems   96

Solutions   100

This is Practice Book 4B in a four-book series for 4th grade.

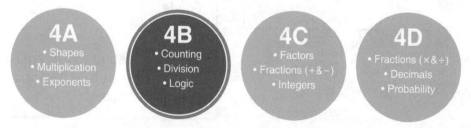

For more resources and information, visit BeastAcademy.com.

This is
Beast Academy
Practice Book
4B.

Each
chapter of this
Practice book
corresponds to
a chapter from
Beast Academy
Guide 4B.

The first page of
each chapter includes a
recommended sequence
for the Guide and
Practice book.

You may also read
the entire chapter in the
Guide before beginning
the Practice chapter.

Use this Practice book with
Guide 4B from BeastAcademy.com.

Recommended Sequence:

Book	Pages
Guide:	12–22
Practice:	7–19
Guide:	23–35
Practice:	20–31
Guide:	36–45
Practice:	32–37

You may also read the entire chapter
in the Guide before beginning the
Practice chapter.

Some problems in this book are very challenging. These problems are marked with a ★. The hardest problems have two stars!

Every problem marked with a ★ has a *hint!*

Hints for the starred problems begin on page 96.

Other problems are marked with a ✎. For these problems, you should write an explanation for your answer.

Some pages direct you to related pages from the Guide.

None of the problems in this book require the use of a calculator.

Solutions are in the back, starting on page 100.

A complete explanation is given for every problem!

CHAPTER 4
Counting

Use this Practice book with
Guide 4B from BeastAcademy.com.

Recommended Sequence:

Book	Pages:
Guide:	12-22
Practice:	7-19
Guide:	23-35
Practice:	20-31
Guide:	36-45
Practice:	32-37

You may also read the entire chapter
in the Guide before beginning the
Practice chapter.

EXAMPLE | How many numbers are in the list below?

23, 24, 25, 26, …, 61, 62, 63

The three dots (…) mean that the pattern continues. We want to count how many whole numbers there are starting from 23, counting by ones, and ending with 63.

To make the list easier to count, we subtract 22 from each number in the list:

$$
\begin{array}{cccccccc}
23, & 24, & 25, & 26, & …, & 61, & 62, & 63 \\
-22 & -22 & -22 & -22 & & -22 & -22 & -22 \\
\hline
1, & 2, & 3, & 4, & …, & 39, & 40, & 41
\end{array}
$$

Now, we have a list of numbers from 1 to 41.
The numbers are counted for us!
There are **41** numbers in the list.

It's easy to tell how many numbers are in a list if we can turn it into a list that starts at 1 and doesn't skip any numbers.

PRACTICE | How many numbers are in each list below?

1. 1, 2, 3, 4, 5, …, 17, 18, 19

1. _____

2. 16, 17, 18, …, 73, 74, 75

2. _____

3. 111, 112, 113, …, 225, 226, 227

3. _____

4. 20, 40, 60, …, 340, 360, 380

4. _____

5. 10, 15, 20, …, 65, 70, 75

5. _____

6. 3, 5, 7, …, 21, 23, 25

6. _____

7. 13, 18, 23, …, 88, 93, 98
★

7. _____

EXAMPLE | How many whole numbers are there from 70 to 90, inclusive?

If you are counting numbers in a list, sometimes you want to *include* the first and last numbers.

Other times, you want to *exclude* the first and last numbers.

The word *inclusive* means that we include the first and last numbers in the list. So, we want to know how many numbers are in the list below:

$$70, 71, 72, \ldots, 88, 89, 90.$$

If we subtract 69 from each number in the list, we get a list from 1 to 21. So, there are **21** numbers in the list.

EXAMPLE | How many numbers are there from 70 to 90, exclusive?

The word *exclusive* means that we exclude (don't count) the first and last numbers from the list. So, we want to know how many numbers are in the list below:

$$71, 72, 73, \ldots, 87, 88, 89.$$

If we subtract 70 from each number in the list, we get a list from 1 to 19. So, there are **19** numbers in the list.

This means there are 19 numbers *between* 70 and 90.

PRACTICE | Solve each counting problem below.

8. How many whole numbers are there from 100 to 200 inclusive?

8. _____

9. How many whole numbers are there from 100 to 200 exclusive?

9. _____

10. How many whole numbers are there between 50 and 200?

10. _____

11. How many odd numbers are there from 1 to 99 inclusive?

11. _____

PRACTICE | Solve each counting problem below.

12. How many 2-digit numbers are multiples of 5?

12. _____

13. Lizzie reads chapter 4 of her math textbook, beginning at the top of page 25 and finishing at the bottom of page 47. How many pages does Lizzie read?

13. _____

14. Barney skip-counts out loud by fives from 135 to 535, inclusive. How many numbers does Barney say?

14. _____

15. ★ Winnie has a list of numbers from 20 to 200, inclusive. If Winnie erases every multiple of 4 from the list, how many numbers will remain on the list?

15. _____

16. ★ ★ How many multiples of 3 between 0 and 300 have units digit 7?

16. _____

EXAMPLE | Ms. Q. is fencing her square garden. She uses 24 equally-spaced fence posts, including the four corner posts. How many fence posts are along each side of her garden?

Since the garden is a square, there are an equal number of fence posts along each side. You may guess that there are $24 \div 4 = 6$ posts along each side, as shown on the right.

6 posts

However, if you count the posts in this diagram, you will find that there are only 20 posts, not 24. Each corner post is counted along two sides!

Since we still have 4 posts left, we place one more on each side of the square for a total of $6 + 1 = \textbf{7 posts}$ along each side of the garden, as shown to the right.

7 posts

— *or* —

Since the corner posts are counted along two sides, we begin by placing the four corner posts.

That leaves $24 - 4 = 20$ posts. We can place $24 \div 4 = 5$ more posts on each side for a total of **7 posts** along each side of the square garden, as shown below.

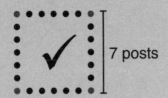

7 posts

PRACTICE | Use the information given below to answer the questions that follow.

Students arrange themselves around a 25 foot by 50 foot rectangular field. One student stands at each corner, and the remaining students are spaced 5 feet apart along the sides.

17. How many students stand along one long side of the rectangle?

17. _____

18. How many total students surround the rectangular field?

18. _____

19. ★ The same number of students arrange themselves to form a regular hexagon with one student at each corner and the remaining students spaced 5 feet apart along the sides. How many students stand along each side of the hexagon?

19. _____

PRACTICE | The little monsters create polygons by connecting gumdrops with toothpicks. Answer the questions about their creations below.

For example, Winnie creates the rectangle below with 5 gumdrops along each long side and 3 gumdrops along each short side.

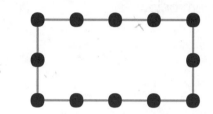

20. Lizzie wants to make a square using 8 gumdrops. How many toothpicks will she need?

20. _____

21. Cammie makes a rectangle that has 10 gumdrops along each long side and 4 gumdrops along each short side. How many toothpicks does she use?

21. _____

22.
★ Ralph makes the triangle below with 3 gumdrops along each side.

22. _____

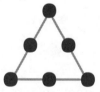

How many gumdrops does Ralph need to make an equilateral triangle that has 12 gumdrops on each side?

23.
★ Grogg makes a rectangle with 38 gumdrops. The long sides of Grogg's rectangle have twice as many gumdrops as the short sides. How many gumdrops are on a short side of Grogg's rectangle?

23. _____

PRACTICE | Solve each counting problem below.

24. At the park near Alex's house, there is a straight path that is lit by twelve lampposts, spaced 10 feet apart. If Alex walks from the first lamppost on the path to the last, how far does he walk?

24. _____

25. A second straight path is lit by twenty-one lampposts, spaced 15 feet apart. If Alex walks from the first lamppost on the path to the last, how far does he walk?

25. _____

26. The Beast Island Parkway has signs that mark each mile of the road. If Jenny drives from mile marker 18 to mile marker 95, how many mile marker signs does she pass, including the first and last signs?

26. _____

27. ★ If Jenny drives from mile marker 18 to mile marker 95, how many miles does she drive?

27. _____

EXAMPLE

Every day at summer camp, Will chooses one morning activity and one afternoon activity from the list below. How many different combinations of one morning activity and one afternoon activity can Will choose?

Activities
Morning: Basketball, Crafts, or Swimming
Afternoon: Archery, Canoeing, or Volleyball

We can use a tree diagram to help us solve counting problems!

We create a tree diagram to show all of the possible combinations. For example, the first combination on the list is basketball/archery:

Morning	**Afternoon**	
Basketball	Archery	1
	Canoeing	2
	Volleyball	3
Crafts	Archery	4
	Canoeing	5
	Volleyball	6
Swimming	Archery	7
	Canoeing	8
	Volleyball	9

Will can choose one of **9** different combinations of activities.

PRACTICE | Create a tree diagram to help you answer the question below.

28. At Frosty's Ice Cream Shop, there are four ice cream flavors: vanilla, chocolate, mango, and berry. There are two topping choices: caramel and sprinkles. How many different single-scoop one-topping ice cream cones are available at Frosty's?

28. _____

PRACTICE | Create a tree diagram that will help you answer each question below.

29. Ms. Q. assigns each student in her class a special code. The code
includes an *odd* digit inside a shape. There are 3 available shapes:
triangle, square, and circle. For example, one code is ⑦.
How many different codes are possible?

29. _____

30. Bridget's basketball team is choosing team jerseys. They can choose
one of three mascots: Lions, Tigers, or Bears. They can also choose
a jersey color: red, orange, blue, or green. How many different
choices of jersey does Bridget's team have?

30. _____

PRACTICE | Create a tree diagram that will help you answer each question below.

---

31. If Kamal flips a coin **three** times and records the results, how many possible sequences of heads and tails are possible? For example, one possible sequence is heads-tails-heads.

31. _____

32. Alex's dad is shopping for a car. The car he wants comes in five different colors: red, grey, green, blue, and black. He can choose either 2 or 4 doors. For a little extra money, he can get a sunroof installed. How many different versions of the car are available?

32. _____

PRACTICE | Use the information below to answer the questions that follow.

Grogg is making a sandwich. He has three types of bread: white, wheat, and rye. He has both Swiss and cheddar cheese, and both ham and bologna.

33. Draw a tree diagram below to show all of the possible sandwiches that use one type of bread, one cheese, and one meat. How many sandwich options are there?

33. _____

34. How many of Grogg's sandwich options *do not* have rye bread?

34. _____

35. How many of Grogg's sandwich options *do not* have Swiss cheese?

35. _____

36. If we add salami to Grogg's list of meat choices, how many different sandwich options are available?

36. _____

EXAMPLE

Emma has 5 shirts, 6 pairs of shorts, and 3 pairs of shoes. How many different outfits can she make that include one pair of shorts, one shirt, and one pair of shoes?

We can count the total number of possibilities *without* using a tree diagram.

Emma can pair any one of her 5 shirts with any one of her 6 pairs of shorts. This gives her a total of $5 \times 6 = 30$ possible outfits that consist of one shirt and one pair of shorts.

Emma has 3 choices for the shoes she will wear with each of these 30 shirt-shorts combinations. This makes a total of $30 \times 3 = \mathbf{90}$ possible outfits Emma can make.

PRACTICE | Solve each counting problem below.

37. Brandon has six ties and three hats. In how many different ways can he choose a hat and tie to wear to dinner?

37. _____

38. Lizzie is choosing new frames for her glasses. The frames come in 7 different styles. Each style comes in black, brown, gray, or burgundy. How many choices of new frames does Lizzie have?

38. _____

39. There are 5 third graders, 8 fourth graders, and 6 fifth graders in a math club. The club must select a team to compete in a local contest. The 3-monster team must include one third grader, one fourth grader, and one fifth grader. How many different teams can be selected to compete for the math club?

39. _____

PRACTICE | Solve each counting problem below.

40. Vinny's Pizza offers 12 different pizza toppings: pepperoni, pineapple, sausage, tomatoes, mushrooms, chicken, peppers, onions, anchovies, garlic, bacon, and artichokes. Vinny has thin, deep-dish, and hand-tossed crusts. Pizzas are available in two sizes. How many different 1-topping pizzas can be ordered from Vinny's Pizza?

40. _____

41. If Winnie flips a coin six times and record the results, how many sequences of heads and tails are possible? For example, one possible sequence is tails-heads-tails-heads-tails-tails.

41. _____

42. Every bicycle at Beast Academy is given a tag. Below are a few examples. Beast Island bicycle tags all begin with a letter and end with a digit. The letter and the digit are separated by either a hyphen (-) or an ampersand (&). How many bicycle tags are available for use at Beast Academy?

42. _____

| M&8 | B&1 | E-0 |

PRACTICE | Solve each counting problem below.

43. To travel from Sandlake to Titansville, Xue can take a bus, a train, or a plane. Then, to get from Titansville to Dunkledorf, Xue can hire a taxi, rent a car, ride a bike, or take the trolley. How many different transportation combinations can Xue use to get from Sandlake to Dunkledorf through Titansville?

43. _____

44. Plunk rides his bike to school. He secures his bike with a lock that has a 4-digit combination. Plunk cannot remember his combination, but he knows that all four digits are odd. How many possible combinations include only odd digits? For example, 5353 and 7513 are two such combinations.

44. _____

45. ★ On Beast Island, dates are written in the form month/day. For example, August 1st is written 8/1. On other islands, the day is written before the month, so August 1st would be written 1/8. This can cause confusion. For example, 3/4 might mean March 4th, or it might mean April 3rd. For how many different dates is it impossible to tell the date if we don't know which system was used to write it?

45. _____

We can use a Venn Diagram to organize things into overlapping categories.

You can review lines of symmetry in Chapter 1 of Guide 4A!

PRACTICE

Some letters, like X, have a horizontal line of symmetry (X).
Some letters, like Y, have a vertical line of symmetry (Y).
Use the letters written below to place each letter of the alphabet in the proper region of the Venn diagram.
X, Y, and Z are already placed for you.

A B C D E F G H I J K L M N O P Q R S T U V W X Y Z

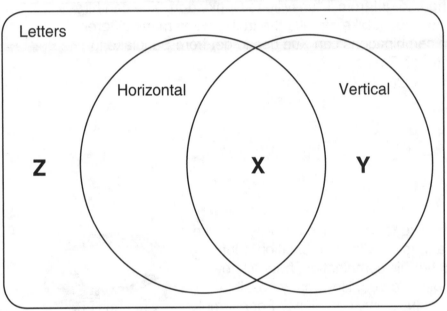

46. How many letters have a vertical line of symmetry?

46. _____

47. How many letters have a horizontal line of symmetry?

47. _____

48. How many letters have both a horizontal line of symmetry and a vertical line of symmetry?

48. _____

49. How many letters have neither a horizontal line of symmetry nor a vertical line of symmetry?

49. _____

50. How many letters have either a horizontal line of symmetry or a vertical line of symmetry, but not both?

50. _____

COUNTING

Venn Diagrams

PRACTICE | Use the sentence below to complete the Venn diagrams that follow.

A few of the words in this sentence are at least five letters long, and some contain two or more vowels.

51. Write each of the twenty-one words from the sentence above in the correct region of the Venn diagram below.

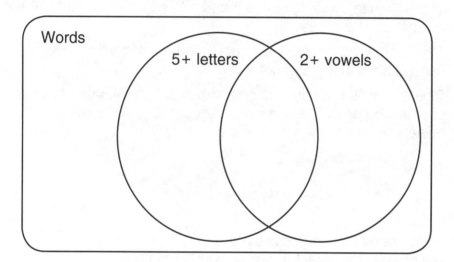

52. Fill in the blanks of the Venn diagram below to show **how many** of the twenty-one words in the sentence above belong in each region.

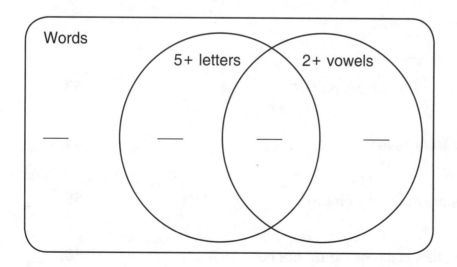

EXAMPLE

The Venn diagram below shows the results of a survey of 20 pet owners. How many pet owners have both a cat and a dog? How many have a pet cat? How many have a dog but not a cat? How many have neither a cat nor a dog?

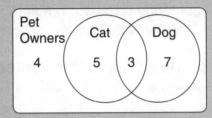

The area where the two circles overlap contains the number of people who have both a cat and a dog. So, **3** of the pet owners have both a cat and a dog.

The left circle contains both a 5 and a 3. All together, $5+3=8$ pet owners have a pet cat.

The 7 in the right circle that is not in the overlap tells us that **7** pet owners have a dog, but not a cat.

Finally, the number outside both circles tell us the number of people who do not have a cat or a dog. So, **4** of the pet owners have neither a cat nor a dog.

PRACTICE

The Venn diagram below organizes a group of monsters based on whether they have fur, horns, both, or neither.

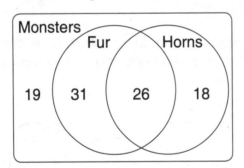

53. How many of the furry monsters have horns?

53. _____

54. How many of the monsters have fur?

54. _____

55. How many total monsters are in the group?

55. _____

56. How many of the monsters in the group *do not* have fur?

56. _____

PRACTICE | Use a Venn diagram to help you answer each of the following questions about 2-digit numbers.

57. ★ Some two-digit numbers are even. Some are multiples of 5. Complete the Venn diagram below to help you determine how many 2-digit numbers are *neither even nor multiples of 5*.

57. _____

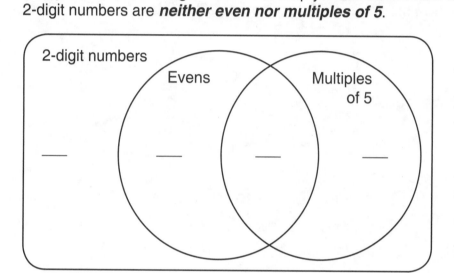

58. ★ Complete the Venn diagram below to help you figure out how many 2-digit numbers are *either perfect squares or odd, but not both*.

58. _____

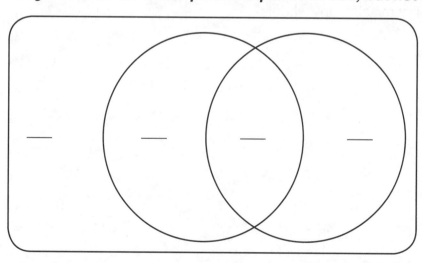

PRACTICE | Use a Venn diagram to help you answer each of the following.

59. Grogg's mom looks at his kindergarten class picture and counts 11 monsters that no wings and no tail, 5 monsters that have wings but no tail, and 3 monsters that have wings and a tail. If there are 25 monsters in the photo, how many have a tail but no wings?

59. _____

60. Drew has a box of 50 toy cars. There are 18 toy cars that are red, and there are 7 toy cars that are missing at least one wheel. Three of the red cars are missing a wheel. How many of the cars in Drew's box are not red and are not missing any wheels?

60. _____

PRACTICE | Use a Venn diagram to help you answer each of the following.

61. In today's Beast Academy cafeteria lunch line, every student took at least one fruit or vegetable. If 27 students took a vegetable, 35 students took a fruit, and 22 students took both a fruit and a vegetable, how many students passed through the Beast Academy lunch line?

61. _____

62. How many 2-digit numbers are not multiples of 3 and do not have
★ units digit 3?

62. _____

PRACTICE | Use a Venn diagram to help you answer each of the following.

63. Last Monday, all thirty little monsters in study hall finished their
★ math homework, their history homework, or both. Eighteen of those
students finished their history homework. Twenty-two of those
students finished their math homework. How many students in study
hall finished both their history and math homework?

63. _____

64. In Lizzie's weekend dragon classes, there are twenty little dragons.
★ Nine of the little dragons in her class can breathe fire. Fifteen of the
little dragons can fly. Four little dragons cannot fly or breathe fire yet.
How many of the twenty little dragons can fly *and* breathe fire?

64. _____

EXAMPLE In how many different ways can the digits 5, 6, and 7 be arranged to make a 3-digit number?

We create a tree diagram to show our choices for each place value.

Hundreds digit	Tens digit	Ones digit		
5	6	7	**1.**	567
	7	6	**2.**	576
6	5	7	**3.**	657
	7	5	**4.**	675
7	5	6	**5.**	756
	6	5	**6.**	765

We find **6** ways to arrange the three digits to make a 3-digit number.

PRACTICE Answer each of the following.

65. Create a tree diagram to show the six different ways that the letters A, B, and C can be arranged in some order.

Below, list the six arrangements in alphabetical order.

_____ _____ _____ _____ _____ _____

66. On a separate piece of paper, draw a tree diagram to show the ways that the digits 1, 2, 3, and 4 can be arranged to create a 4-digit number. In how many ways can we arrange these four digits?

66. _____

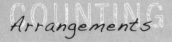
EXAMPLE | In how many different ways can Alvin, Biff, Cam, and Doug be seated in a row of 4 chairs?

We *could* list all of the arrangements as we did on the previous page, but there is a quicker way to count the total number of seating arrangements.

To seat four students, we begin by choosing one student to sit on the left. There are 4 choices for the student who sits in the chair farthest to the left.

Once we have chosen the student who sits on the left, we choose the student who sits in the next chair. No matter who is in the first chair, there are only 3 students who can fill the second chair, since one student is already seated. So, there are $4 \times 3 = 12$ ways to fill the first two seats.

After we have seated the first two students, we have 2 choices for the student who sits in the next chair. So, there are $12 \times 2 = 24$ ways to fill the first three chairs.

With the first three chairs filled, there is only 1 choice for the student who sits in the last chair.

We can multiply the number of choices we have at each step to get the total number of arrangements.

So, there are $4 \times 3 \times 2 \times 1 = \mathbf{24}$ possible seating arrangements.

PRACTICE | Answer each of the following.

67. How many three-digit numbers can be made by arranging the digits 5, 6, and 8 in some order?

67. _____

68. In how many ways can five students be seated in a row of 5 chairs?

68. _____

69. _____

69. ★ In how many ways can Kim, Lisa, Mandy, Nellie, and Olivia be seated in a row of 5 chairs if Mandy is seated in the middle chair?

70. ★ In how many different ways can the digits 0, 1, 2, and 3 be arranged to make a 4-digit number? Remember that zero cannot be used as the thousands digit.

70. _____

There be a special shortcut for writin' 4×3×2×1.

We put an exclamation point after a 4 to mean 4×3×2×1.

EXAMPLE | Compute the value of 2×(6!).

An exclamation point after a number tells us to multiply the number by each of the numbers less than it, all the way down to 1.

For example, 6! (called "6 factorial") equals 6×5×4×3×2×1 = 720.

So, we have 2×(6!) = 2×(6×5×4×3×2×1)
$$= 2×720$$
$$= \mathbf{1,440}.$$

PRACTICE | Answer each of the following.

71. Write 8×7×6×5×4×3×2×1 using factorial notation.

71. _____

72. Write 5×4×1×3×6×2 using factorial notation.

72. _____

73. Given that 9! = 362,880, find 10!.

73. _____

74. If 10!×n = 12!, what is the value of n?

74. $n =$ _____

75. Compute 5×(4!) − 5!.

75. _____

76. Find the units digit of 77!.

76. _____

77. Compute 7! ÷ 5!.

77. _____

EXAMPLE | Use factorial notation to express the number of ways 7 students can be arranged in a line.

There are 7 choices for the student who stands first in line. After the first student is chosen, 6 students remain.

We choose one of the remaining 6 students to stand second in line. So, there are 7×6 ways to choose the first two students in line.

We choose one of the remaining 5 students to stand third in line. So, there are 7×6×5 ways to pick the first three students.

We continue this way until there is only one student remaining to stand at the end of the line.

This gives us 7×6×5×4×3×2×1 = **7!** ways to arrange all 7 students in line.

PRACTICE | Answer each of the following *using factorial notation*.

78. Each of Ned, Jon, Rob, and Theo prepares his boat to go sailing. If each boat leaves at a different time, in how many different orders could the boats leave?

78. _____

79. How many different arrangements of the letters in the word BEAST are possible, including B-E-A-S-T?

79. _____

80. In how many different ways can the digits 1-9 be placed in the circles shown so that each digit is in one of the circles?

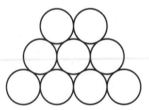

80. _____

81. How many different arrangements of the letters in the word
★ ACADEMY are possible if the two A's must be next to each other?
★ For example, AACDEMY and MYDEAAC are counted, but ACADEMY is not.

81. _____

PRACTICE | You may use the list of factorials below to help you answer each question that follows.

$$1! = 1 \qquad\qquad 5! = 120$$
$$2! = 2 \qquad\qquad 6! = 720$$
$$3! = 6 \qquad\qquad 7! = 5,040$$
$$4! = 24 \qquad\qquad 8! = 40,320$$

82. In how many different ways can 7 little monsters finish in order from 1st through 7th in the 100-yard dash at Beast Academy? (Assume that no two monsters finish at the same time.)

82. _____

83. In how many different ways can the letters in the word QUESTION be arranged, *not* including Q-U-E-S-T-I-O-N?

83. _____

84. In how many different ways can the digits 0, 1, 2, 3, 4, and 5 be arranged to make a 6-digit number? Zero cannot be used as the hundred-thousands digit.

84. _____

85. ★ The number of hours in September can be written as $n!$. Find n.

85. $n =$ _____

86. ★ Lizzie has 4 different math books and 4 different history books that she wants to arrange on her book shelf. In how many different ways can she arrange the books if she wants all four math books on the left and all four history books on the right?

86. _____

EXAMPLE

Alex, Grogg, Lizzie, Ralph, and Winnie need to choose a team of two participants to run in a sack race. List every possible two-person team they can make. How many teams are possible?

We organize our work by looking at one monster at a time. To begin, Alex can be paired with any of the other four monsters. This gives us four teams that include Alex.

Alex & Grogg
Alex & Lizzie
Alex & Ralph
Alex & Winnie

Then, we make teams that include Grogg. We already counted the team of Alex and Grogg. We can pair Grogg with each of Lizzie, Ralph, and Winnie to make 3 more possible teams.

Alex & Grogg   Grogg & Lizzie
Alex & Lizzie   Grogg & Ralph
Alex & Ralph   Grogg & Winnie
Alex & Winnie

We can then pair Lizzie with each of Ralph and Winnie, and finally Ralph with Winnie. Winnie has already been paired with each of the other four monsters. So, there are no more teams to count. This makes a total of **10** possible teams, as listed below.

Alex & Grogg   Grogg & Lizzie   Lizzie & Ralph   Ralph & Winnie
Alex & Lizzie   Grogg & Ralph   Lizzie & Winnie
Alex & Ralph   Grogg & Winnie
Alex & Winnie

PRACTICE | Answer each the following.

87. Grogg has a bag of jellybeans. There are 5 different flavors in the bag: banana, caramel, donut, elderberry, and fudge. Eating two different-flavored jellybeans at once creates a new flavor, as long as the two are not the same flavor. List all 10 **new** flavors that Grogg can make by combining two jellybeans.
(You may use B, C, D, E, and F to represent the flavors.)

87. _____ & _____ , _____ & _____ ,

_____ & _____ , _____ & _____ ,

_____ & _____ , _____ & _____ ,

_____ & _____ , _____ & _____ ,

_____ & _____ , _____ & _____ .

PRACTICE | Answer each of the following.

88. There are seven points below. How many straight lines must be drawn so that each point is directly connected to every other point by a line?

88. _____

C
•

B
•

D
•

A •

• E

•
G

•
F

89. In a card game, James must choose two of the five cards below to keep in his hand. How many different hands of two cards can James choose from the set of five cards below?

89. _____

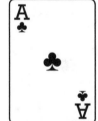 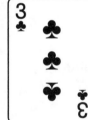   

90. How many different shaded diagrams can Alex make by shading two of the six circles in the large diagram below?
You might try out some possibilities in the smaller versions of the diagram.

90. _____

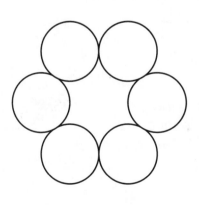 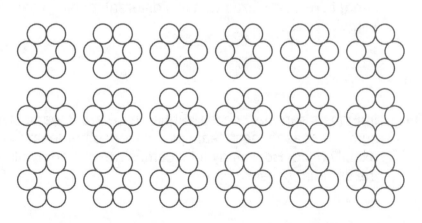

EXAMPLE

Professor Grok's class of 10 little monsters must select 2 little monsters to represent the class at the science fair. How many different pairs of two little monsters are possible?

We can count the total number of pairs without listing all the possibilities.

You might guess that since there are 10 monsters to select to be the first representative, and 9 monsters to select to be the second representative, there are $10 \times 9 = 90$ possible pairs.

However, the order in which we choose the monsters does not matter! For example, choosing Grogg first and Winnie second creates the same pair as choosing Winnie first and Grogg second. When we multiply 10×9 to get 90, every possible pair of monsters is counted twice!

Since $10 \times 9 = 90$ counts each pair of monsters twice, we must divide by 2 to get the actual number of possible pairs.

So, there are $90 \div 2 = \textbf{45}$ possible pairs of monsters.

PRACTICE | Answer each of the following.

91. A chemistry club has 11 members, and they choose 2 members to be the co-captains of the club. How many different pairs of members could be chosen as co-captains?

91. _____

92. Vinny's Pizza offers 12 different pizza toppings. How many different large, thin-crust pizzas with two different toppings can Jeff order from Vinny's Pizza?

92. _____

93. In Fiona's summer soccer league, there are 8 teams. During the summer season, each team plays every other team in the league exactly once. How many total games are played by all of the teams in the summer season?

93. _____

PRACTICE | Answer each of the following.

94. Before a Beastball game, each of the 9 members of the Minotaurs team high-fives every other Minotaur team member exactly once. How many high-fives occur between Minotaurs before the game?

94. _____

95. Ms. Q. assigns a class project to be worked on by groups of students. After she assigns some groups, the only students left without a group are Lizzie, Grogg, Alex, Winnie, and Ralph. In how many ways could Ms. Q. split these five students into one group of 2 and one group of 3?

95. _____

96. Six slips of papers with the numbers 1, 10, 100, 1,000, 10,000, and 100,000 are placed in a hat. Two of the numbers are chosen and added. How many different sums are possible?

96. _____

97. ★ A ***diagonal*** connects two vertices of a polygon that are not already connected by a side. For example, the square below has two diagonals, shown with dotted lines. The pentagon below has five diagonals. How many diagonals does a regular decagon have?

97. _____

  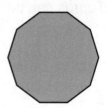

In a standard deck of cards, each card has a **suit** and a **rank**.

There are 4 suits: clubs (♣), diamonds (◊), hearts (♡), and spades (♠).

There are 13 ranks: 2, 3, 4, 5, 6, 7, 8, 9, 10, Jack (J), Queen (Q), King (K), and Ace (A).

Each suit has one card of each rank.

For example, the "5 of spades" is shown to the right. We use 5♠ to represent this card.

Hearts and diamonds are red. Clubs and spades are black.

Each card is different from every other card in the deck.

PRACTICE | Answer each of the following questions about a standard card deck.

98. All together, how many cards are in a standard deck of cards?

98. _____

99. Paul picks a card from a complete standard deck and says "My card is not a number!" How many possible cards could Paul's be?

99. _____

100. Grogg draws Q♡, 7♠, 4♣, 3♣, and 10♡ from a standard deck. How many different ways can Grogg arrange the five cards in his hand from left to right?

100. _____

101. How many different pairs of cards can be selected from a complete standard deck of cards?

101. _____

PRACTICE | Answer each of the following questions about a standard card deck.

102. Winnie picks a card from a complete standard deck and says, "My card is not a heart, and it is not a Jack." How many different cards could be Winnie's?

102. _____

103. Winnie puts her card back. Lizzie draws a card and says, "My card is not red, but it is a number." How many different cards could be Lizzie's?

103. _____

104. Grogg picks a hand of two cards from a complete standard deck. Both of his cards are spades. How many possible hands of two spades could Grogg have?

104. _____

105. ★ Alex picks two cards from a complete standard deck. One card is a diamond, and the other card is a spade. How many different hands of two cards could Alex have?

105. _____

106. ★★ Professor Grok picks two cards from a complete standard deck. One card is a diamond, and the other card is a Jack. How many possible hands of 2 cards could Professor Grok have?

106. _____

CHAPTER 5
Division

Use this Practice book with
Guide 4B from BeastAcademy.com.

Recommended Sequence:

Book	Pages:
Guide:	47-59
Practice:	39-45
Guide:	60-66
Practice:	46-55
Guide:	67-75
Practice:	56-63

You may also read the entire chapter
in the Guide before beginning the
Practice chapter.

PRACTICE | Write a division equation that answers each of the questions below.

1. If 54 little monsters are divided into teams of 6 little monsters, how many teams are made?

1. _____ ÷ _____ = _____ teams

2. If 42 coins are divided equally among seven pirates, how many coins will each pirate get?

2. _____ ÷ _____ = _____ coins

3. Alex has a bag of nickels worth a total of 75 cents. How many nickels are in Alex's bag?

3. _____ ÷ _____ = _____ nickels

4. Lizzie reads 30 pages of a book each day. How many days does it take her to finish a 150-page book?

4. _____ ÷ _____ = _____ days

5. What number, when multiplied by 4, gives a product of 48?

5. _____ ÷ _____ = _____

Division by zero is **undefined**. That just means it doesn't make sense.

Here are a few other special quotients you should know.

Division by zero is undefined.
For example, $73 \div 0$ is undefined.
For any number n,

$$n \div 0 \text{ is undefined}.$$

Zero divided by any nonzero number is zero.
For example, $0 \div 73 = 0$.
For any number n except 0,

$$0 \div n = 0.$$

Any number divided by 1 is itself.
For example, $73 \div 1 = 73$.
For any number n,

$$n \div 1 = n.$$

Dividing any nonzero number by itself equals 1.
For example, $73 \div 73 = 1$.
For any number n except 0,

$$n \div n = 1.$$

PRACTICE | Evaluate each expression below. If the expression is undefined, write "undefined" in the answer space.

6. $54{,}321 \div 1 = $ _____

7. $888 \div 888 = $ _____

8. $0 \div 1{,}000{,}000 = $ _____

9. $8{,}765{,}432 \div 0 = $ _____

10. $0 \div 0 = $ _____

11. $2{,}468 \div 1 = $ _____

12. $(2-2) \div (2+2) = $ _____

13. $(2+2) \div (2+2) = $ _____

14. $(2 \div 2) \div (2-2) = $ _____

15. $(2+2) \div (2 \div 2) = $ _____

16. $((2+2) \div 2) \div 2 = $ _____

17. $(2-2) \div (2-2) = $ _____

PRACTICE | Some expressions can be evaluated without knowing the values of the variables. Evaluate each expression below. If the expression is undefined, write "undefined" in the answer space.

Each variable in the expressions below represents a **nonzero** number.

18. Evaluate $(a-a) \div a$.   18. _____

19. Evaluate $b \div (b \div b)$.   19. _____

20. Evaluate $c \div (c-c)$.   20. _____

21. Evaluate $(d+d) \div (d+d)$.   21. _____

22. Evaluate $(m \div 1) \div (m \div m)$.   22. _____

23. Evaluate $(x \div y) \div (x \div y)$.   23. _____

24. What value of n makes $n \div (n-1)$ undefined?   24. _____

DIVISION

We can use multiplication to solve division problems!

EXAMPLE | Compute $72{,}000 \div 8$.

To compute $72{,}000 \div 8$, we find the number that is multiplied by 8 to get 72,000.

Since $9 \times 8 = 72$,

$\boxed{9{,}000} \times 8 = 72{,}000$.

So, $72{,}000 \div 8 = \mathbf{9{,}000}$.

PRACTICE | Find each quotient.

25. $54{,}000 \div 6 =$ _____

26. $6{,}300 \div 9 =$ _____

27. $4{,}000 \div 8 =$ _____

28. $900{,}000 \div 3 =$ _____

29. $4{,}200 \div 7 =$ _____

30. $8{,}100{,}000 \div 9 =$ _____

31. $64{,}000 \div 8 =$ _____

32. $20{,}000 \div 5 =$ _____

33. $720{,}000 \div 12 =$ _____

34. $660{,}000 \div 33 =$ _____

EXAMPLE | Compute 5,600 ÷ 700.

5,600 is 56 hundreds.
700 is 7 hundreds.

We can divide 56 hundreds into groups of 7 hundreds to make 56 ÷ 7 = 8 groups of 7 hundreds.

So, 5,600 ÷ 700 = 56 ÷ 7 = **8**.

We can remove the same number of zeros from the end of each number in a division problem without changing the quotient! Learn more about why this works on pages 53-59 of Guide 4B.

PRACTICE | Find each quotient.

35. 9,000 ÷ 3,000 = _____

36. 35,000 ÷ 5,000 = _____

37. 80,000 ÷ 200 = _____

38. 280,000 ÷ 400 = _____

39. 21,000 ÷ 300 = _____

40. 4,900,000 ÷ 7,000 = _____

41. 600,000 ÷ 1,500 = _____

42. 200,000 ÷ 25,000 = _____

43. 125,000 ÷ 500 = _____

44. 330,000 ÷ 1,100 = _____

PRACTICE | Answer each question below.

45. What is the height of a rectangle whose area is 18,000 square centimeters and whose width is 600 centimeters?

45. _____

46. Liam the truck driver drives the same number of miles each day. In a 30-day month, he drives 6,300 miles. How many miles does Liam drive each day?

46. _____

47. Winnie has a box of 24,000 tiny beads. It takes 400 beads to make one necklace. How many necklaces can she make with her box of beads?

47. _____

48. One of the public libraries on Beast Island houses 340,000 books. There are an equal number of books on each of the library's 1,700 bookshelves. How many books are on each bookshelf?

48. _____

PRACTICE | Answer each question below.

49. What is the side length of a regular 700-sided polygon that has a perimeter of 630,000,000 millimeters?

49. _____

50. Thirty-one thousand little monsters and nineteen thousand adult monsters attended the Titansville County Fair. All together, the fair sold $200,000 worth of tickets. Each ticket to the fair cost the same amount. What was the cost of a ticket to the fair?

50. _____

Use the following statements for the next two problems:
Captain Kraken finds a chest full of gold coins worth a total of 480,000 dollars. Each coin in the chest is worth 300 dollars.

51. How many coins are in the chest?

51. _____

52. Captain Kraken and his crew decide to share the gold coins in the chest equally. How many dollars worth of coins does each of the 20 pirates receive?

52. _____

EXAMPLE | Estimate 1,412÷21. Then, find the quotient and remainder of 1,412÷21.

We begin by estimating the quotient. Since 21 is close to 20, and 1,412 is close to 1,400, we estimate that 1,412÷21 is about 1,400÷20 = **70**.

To find out exactly how many times 21 goes into 1,412, we subtract 21's from 1,412 until we have a number that is less than 21. We look for a number that is easy to multiply by 21 that gives us a product less than 1,412.

$$21\overline{)1{,}412}$$

21×50 = 1,050. So, 21 can go into 1,412 at least 50 times. We subtract 1,050 from 1,412, and have 362 left over. Since 362 is more than 21, we keep dividing.

$$\begin{array}{r} 50 \\ 21\overline{)1{,}412} \\ -1{,}050 \\ \hline 362 \end{array}$$

21×10 = 210. So, 21 can go into 362 at least 10 times. We subtract 210 from 362, and have 152 left over. Since 152 is more than 21, we keep dividing.

$$\begin{array}{r} 10 \\ 50 \\ 21\overline{)1{,}412} \\ -1{,}050 \\ \hline 362 \\ -210 \\ \hline 152 \end{array}$$

21×5 = 105. So, 21 can go into 152 at least 5 times. We subtract 105 from 152, and have 47 left over. Since 47 is more than 21, we keep dividing.

$$\begin{array}{r} 5 \\ 10 \\ 50 \\ 21\overline{)1{,}412} \\ -1{,}050 \\ \hline 362 \\ -210 \\ \hline 152 \\ -105 \\ \hline 47 \end{array}$$

21×2 = 42. So, 21 can go into 47 at least 2 times. We subtract 42 from 47, and have 5 left over. Since 5 is less than 21, we can't subtract any more 21's.

All together, we subtracted 50+10+5+2 = 67 twenty-ones from 1,412. So, the quotient of 1,412÷21 is **67**, and the remainder is **5**.

We use our estimate to check that our answer makes sense. The quotient 67 is very close to our estimate of 70. ✓

$$\left.\begin{array}{r} 2 \\ 5 \\ 10 \\ 50 \end{array}\right\}67$$

$$\begin{array}{r} 21\overline{)1{,}412} \\ -1{,}050 \\ \hline 362 \\ -210 \\ \hline 152 \\ -105 \\ \hline 47 \\ -42 \\ \hline 5 \end{array}$$

Long division is used to compute a quotient and remainder!

Review the division algorithm beginning on page 60 of Guide 4B.

Here, we keep track of how many 21's we subtract. This is the quotient.

This is the remainder.

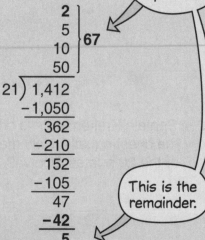

PRACTICE | Estimate each quotient below. Then, use long division to find the quotient and remainder in each problem.

53. 671÷9 is closest to: (circle one)

    20   70   150   500

9) 671

quotient = _____

remainder = _____

54. 822÷32 is closest to: (circle one)

    30   90   210   500

32) 822

quotient = _____

remainder = _____

55. 654÷12 is closest to: (circle one)

    5   15   55   155

12) 654

quotient = _____

remainder = _____

56. 4,123÷40 is closest to: (circle one)

    11   30   100   1,000

40) 4,123

quotient = _____

remainder = _____

PRACTICE | Estimate each quotient below. Then, use long division to find the quotient and remainder in each problem.

57.   1,312÷52 is closest to: (circle one)

     25   80   150   500

$52 \overline{)\,1,312}$ quotient = _____

                                   remainder = _____

58.   1,953÷21 is closest to: (circle one)

     9   50   100   900

$21 \overline{)\,1,953}$ quotient = _____

                                   remainder = _____

59.   15,000÷96 is closest to: (circle one)

     15   150   500   1,500

$96 \overline{)\,15,000}$ quotient = _____

                                   remainder = _____

60.   31,975÷77 is closest to: (circle one)

     14   40   120   400

$77 \overline{)\,31,975}$ quotient = _____

                                   remainder = _____

PRACTICE | Estimate each quotient below. Then, use long division to find the quotient and remainder in each problem.

61. 5,091÷67 is closest to: (circle one)

15   70   200   700

67) 5,091   quotient = _____

remainder = _____

62. 9,551÷28 is closest to: (circle one)

30   80   150   320

28) 9,551   quotient = _____

remainder = _____

63. 1,282÷19 is closest to: (circle one)

6   65   125   605

19) 1,282   quotient = _____

remainder = _____

64. 40,196÷86 is closest to: (circle one)

50   200   500   4,000

86) 40,196   quotient = _____

remainder = _____

EXAMPLE

If 63,042 marbles are divided equally into 7 buckets, how many marbles will there be in each bucket?

We begin by splitting 63,000 of the marbles into 7 buckets, which gives us $63,000 \div 7 = 9,000$ marbles in each bucket.

We divide the remaining 42 marbles among the 7 buckets, which gives us $42 \div 7 = 6$ more marbles in each bucket.

So, each bucket has a total of $9,000 + 6 = $ **9,006 marbles**.

In math, we write:

$$63,042 \div 7 = (63,000 + 42) \div 7$$
$$= (63,000 \div 7) + (42 \div 7)$$
$$= 9,000 + 6$$
$$= 9,006.$$

We can split numbers to divide them one part at a time.

PRACTICE | Try to find each quotient without using long division.

65. $36,036 \div 9 = $ _____

66. $2,840 \div 4 = $ _____

67. $490,014 \div 7 = $ _____

68. $4,032 \div 8 = $ _____

69. $5,412 \div 6 = $ _____

70. $205,015 \div 5 = $ _____

71. $640,400 \div 8 = $ _____

72. $2,701,800 \div 9 = $ _____

EXAMPLE | A 92-foot rope is cut into four pieces of equal length. What is the length of each piece of rope?

To cut a rope into four equal pieces, we can cut it into two equal pieces, then cut each of those pieces into two equal pieces.

Similarly, to divide a number by 4, we can divide that number by 2 twice.

So, to divide 92 by 4, we can compute $(92 \div 2) \div 2$.

$$92 \div 4 = (92 \div 2) \div 2$$
$$= 46 \div 2$$
$$= 23.$$

Each of the four pieces of rope is $92 \div 4 = $ **23 feet** long.

PRACTICE | Try to find each quotient without using long division.

73. $180 \div 4 = $ _____

74. $252 \div 4 = $ _____

75. $560 \div 4 = $ _____

76. $2,500 \div 4 = $ _____

77. $4,900 \div 4 = $ _____

78. $2,108 \div 4 = $ _____

79.
★   Fill in the blank in the following statement: Dividing by sixteen is the same as dividing by two _____ times.

DIVISION
Mental Division

Sometimes it is helpful to double both numbers in a division problem before dividing.

In a division problem, we can double both the dividend and the divisor without changing the quotient.

For example, dividing $65 \div 5$ gives the same result as dividing $(65 \times 2) \div (5 \times 2) = 130 \div 10 = 13$.

If we divide 65 items into 5 groups, there are $65 \div 5 = 13$ items in each group. If we divide twice as many items (130) into twice as many groups (10), we still get 13 items in each group.

Another way to explain why doubling both the dividend and divisor doesn't change the quotient is by using a fraction to represent our division.

$65 \div 5$ can be written as a fraction: $\frac{65}{5}$.

As we learned in Beast Academy 3D, we can use multiplication to find equivalent fractions:

$$65 \div 5 = \frac{65}{5} \overset{\times 2}{\underset{\times 2}{=}} \frac{130}{10} = 130 \div 10 = 13.$$

PRACTICE | Practice dividing by 5 without using long division.

80. $325 \div 5 =$ _____

81. $445 \div 5 =$ _____

82. $220 \div 5 =$ _____

83. $185 \div 5 =$ _____

84. $2{,}300 \div 5 =$ _____

85. $315 \div 5 =$ _____

86. $3{,}335 \div 5 =$ _____

87. $1{,}745 \div 5 =$ _____

88. ★ Without using long division, find the quotient and remainder when 1,463 is divided by 5. For an added challenge, try to find the quotient and remainder without writing anything down.

88. quotient = _____

remainder = _____

The method we learned on the previous page is often useful for dividing by **any** multiple of 5.

EXAMPLE | Compute $275 \div 55$.

We can divide $275 \div 55$ by doubling both numbers as we did in the problems on the previous page. This gives us $(275 \times 2) \div (55 \times 2) = 550 \div 110$.

$$550 \div 110 = 5, \text{ so}$$
$$275 \div 55 = 550 \div 110 = \textbf{5}.$$

PRACTICE | Try to find each quotient without using long division.

89. $270 \div 45 = \underline{\hspace{1.5cm}}$

90. $175 \div 35 = \underline{\hspace{1.5cm}}$

91. $1,650 \div 55 = \underline{\hspace{1.5cm}}$

92. $32,600 \div 50 = \underline{\hspace{1.5cm}}$

93. $465 \div 15 = \underline{\hspace{1.5cm}}$

94. $1,300 \div 65 = \underline{\hspace{1.5cm}}$

95. $31,500 \div 350 = \underline{\hspace{1.5cm}}$

96. $120,000 \div 150 = \underline{\hspace{1.5cm}}$

97. ★ ✎ The dividend and the divisor in each problem above are both multiples of 5. Why is doubling both numbers often useful when working with numbers that are multiples of 5?

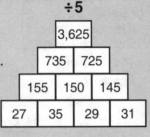

In a Division Pyramid puzzle, the goal is to find a path of touching blocks, one per row, from the top to the bottom of the pyramid.

The divisor is given above the puzzle.

Beginning at the top block, divide the number in the block by the divisor, and travel to the block below that contains the quotient.

EXAMPLE | Complete the Division Pyramid puzzle to the right.

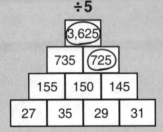

In this puzzle, the divisor is 5.

We start at the top block, which contains 3,625.

$3625 \div 5 = \boxed{725}$, so we move to the block that contains 725.

We continue to divide by 5 until we arrive at the bottom. The completed puzzle is shown below.

$725 \div 5 = \boxed{145}$.

$145 \div 5 = \boxed{29}$.

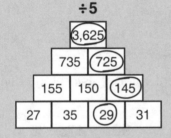

Try to find all quotients with mental division!

PRACTICE | Complete each Division Pyramid puzzle below.

98.

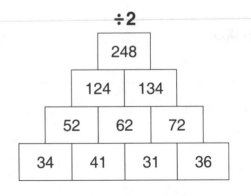

99.

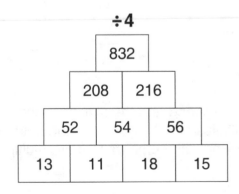

PRACTICE | Complete each Division Pyramid puzzle below.

100.

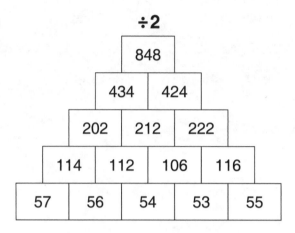

101.

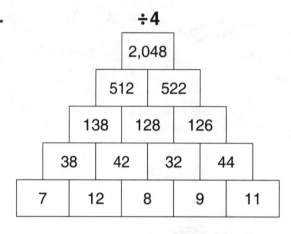

102.

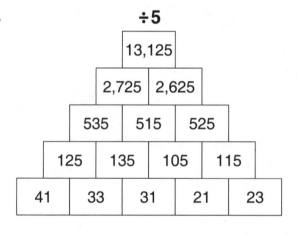

103.

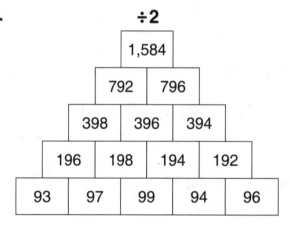

104.

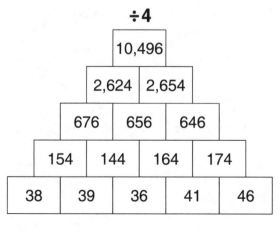

105.

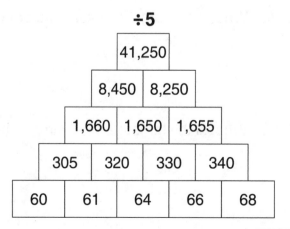

When one whole number can be divided by another with no remainder...

...we say that the first number is *divisible* by the second.

Since 3×5 = 15, we say that 15 is a multiple of both 3 and 5. Another way to say that 15 is a multiple of 3 and of 5 is to say that 15 is *divisible* by 3 and by 5.

EXAMPLE | How many 2-digit numbers are divisible by 7?

The 2-digit numbers that are divisible by 7 are the 2-digit multiples of 7:

14, 21, 28, 35, 42, 49, 56, 63, 70, 77, 84, 91, and 98.

All together, there are **13** two-digit numbers that are divisible by 7.

PRACTICE | Answer each question below.

106. Circle each number below that is divisible by 9.

81 27 78 63 57 45 9 3

107. Circle each number below that 60 is divisible by.

0 1 11 12 18 60 120

108. What is the largest 2-digit number that is divisible by 8? **108.** _____

109. What is the largest 2-digit number that is not divisible by 2 or by 3? **109.** _____

PRACTICE | Answer each question below.

110. Find a number between 40 and 50 that is divisible by 6 but not by 7.

110. _____

111. How many 2-digit numbers are divisible by 10 but not by 20?

111. _____

112. What is the smallest number besides 0 that is divisible by 5 and by 6?

112. _____

113. If $\boxed{2}\,\boxed{9}\,\boxed{A}$ is a three-digit number that is divisible by 13, find the value of the digit A.

113. $A =$ _____

114. ★ If $\boxed{8}\,\boxed{1}\,\boxed{B}$ is a three-digit number that is divisible both by 4 and by 7, find the value of the digit B.

114. $B =$ _____

115. ★ The number 36 is divisible by 9 different numbers! List them all below.

_____, _____, _____, _____, _____, _____, _____, _____, _____

If a is divisible by b, and b is divisible by c, then a is divisible by c.

For example,

$42 = 6 \times 7$, so 42 is divisible by 6.

$6 = 3 \times 2$, so 6 is divisible by 3.

Therefore, $42 = 6 \times 7$
$= (3 \times 2) \times 7$
$= 3 \times (2 \times 7)$
$= 3 \times 14,$

and 42 is divisible by 3.

In short, 42 is divisible by 6, and 6 is divisible by 3. So, 42 is divisible by 3.

PRACTICE | Circle true or false for each statement below. Try to answer each problem without using long division.

116. 156 is divisible by 12, so 156 is definitely divisible by 4.

116. true / false

117. A number x is divisible by 15, so x is definitely divisible by 3.

117. true / false

118. A number y is divisible by 22, so y is definitely divisible by 44.

118. true / false

119. Every number that is divisible by 3 is divisible by 6.

119. true / false

120. Every multiple of 21 is divisible by 7.

120. true / false

121. Every number that is divisible by 4 and by 6 is divisible by $4 \times 6 = 24$.

121. true / false

122. ★ ✎ How can you quickly tell that 5,971 is definitely not divisible by 14?

PRACTICE | Solve each problem below.

123. Winnie writes down a number. She tells Grogg, "My number is divisible by 100." List 8 other numbers that Winnie's number is definitely divisible by.

_____, _____, _____, _____, _____, _____, _____, _____

124. Is 5,100 divisible by 25? If so, how can you tell?

125. ***Without dividing 25 into each number***, find and circle the number below that is divisible by 25.

5,105   5,115   5,125   5,135   5,145

126. Is 1,234,567,890 divisible by 25? How can you tell?

127. Is 678,900 divisible by 4? How can you tell?

128. ***Without dividing 4 into each number***, find and circle the number below that is divisible by 4.

710   720   725   734   750

129. Is 98,765,432 divisible by 4? How can you tell?
★

DIVISION
Divisibility Rules

The descriptions below give ways to recognize divisibility by 2, 5, 10, 100, 25, and 4.

Find out more about these rules and why they work in Guide 4B on pages 67-75.

2: A number is divisible by **2** if and only if its units digit is even.
For example, 408 and 602 are divisible by 2, but 985 and 513 are not.

5: A number is divisible by **5** if and only if its units digit is 0 or 5.
For example, 985 and 630 are divisible by 5, but 231 and 5,936 are not.

10: A number is divisible by **10** if and only if its units digit is 0.
For example, 740 and 20,680 are divisible by 10, but 787 and 10,099 are not.

100: A number is divisible by **100** if and only if it ends in 00.
For example, 9,200 and 12,600 are divisible by 100, but 407 and 7,090 are not.

25: A number is divisible by **25** if and only if the number formed by its last two digits is divisible by 25. A number that ends in 00, 25, 50, or 75 is divisible by 25.
For example, 275 and 12,625 are divisible by 25, but 257 and 1,715 are not.

4: A number is divisible by **4** if and only if the number formed by its last two digits is divisible by 4. A number that ends in 00, 04, 08, …, 88, 92, or 96 is divisible by 4.
For example, 608 and 8,960 are divisible by 4, but 1,826 and 4,062 are not.

For one-digit numbers, we can add as many leading zeros as we need in order to use these tests. For example, 0 = 00 and 8 = 08 are divisible by 4.

PRACTICE | Answer each question below.

130. Circle all of the numbers below that are divisible by 25:

9,855   5,485   10,025   1,400

131. Circle all of the numbers below that are divisible by 5 but ***not*** by 2:

5,553   65,800   1,395   6,480

132. Circle all of the numbers below that are divisible by 4:

6,700   2,196   5,018   5,434

PRACTICE | Answer each question below.

133. What is the smallest number you can add to 19,056 that will make the sum divisible by 25?

133. _____

134. Circle the two numbers below whose *sum* is divisible by 25:

9,802   1,488   4,137   5,135

135. Arrange the squares below so that the digits form a 4-digit number that is divisible by 4. Write the 4-digit number you create.

135. _____

| 4 | 5 | 62 |

136. ★ Arrange the squares below into pairs to create two 3-digit numbers such that one of the numbers is divisible by 4 and the other is divisible by 25. Write both numbers you create.

136. _____

| 4 | 5 | 18 | 47 |

_____

137. ★ Arrange the squares below into pairs to create two 3-digit numbers such that one of the numbers is divisible by 4 and the other is divisible by 25. Write both numbers you create.

137. _____

| 5 | 6 | 75 | 82 |

_____

138. ✏ | 4 | 1 | A | 6 | is a four-digit number that is divisible by 4. What digit (or digits) could A be?

PRACTICE | Answer each question below.

139. Joey makes 134 mini-muffins to share with his chess team. The chess team has 14 members (including Joey). How many muffins will be left over after all of the mini-muffins are shared equally among the members of the chess team?

139. _____

140. A dodecagon is a polygon with 12 sides. What is the side length of a regular dodecagon that has a perimeter of 2,184 millimeters?

140. _____

141. Beast Academy orders 1,800 packs of pencils for its students. Each shipping box can hold 450 packs. How many boxes will it take to ship the entire order of pencils?

141. _____

142. Right triangle ABC has an area of 4,720 square meters. The
★ length of leg AB is 40 meters. What is the length of leg BC?

142. _____

143. The oldest yeti on Beast Island is named Herbert. Herbert is
★ between 800 and 900 years old. When Herbert's age is divided by 25, the remainder is 1. When his age is divided by 4, the remainder is 2. How old is Herbert the yeti?

143. _____

PRACTICE | Answer each question below.

144. Zack's station wagon can carry up to 1,800 pounds, including the driver and passengers. Zack weighs 176 pounds. How many 35-pound sacks of flour can Zack transport in his station wagon without exceeding the 1,800-pound weight limit?

144. _____

145. School buses for Beast Academy can hold up to 25 monsters, including the driver and one additional adult to supervise the students on the bus. How many school buses are needed to take 785 students on a field trip?

145. _____

146. What is the remainder of $(43 \times 225) \div 42$?
★

146. _____

147. When Amy divides her favorite three-digit number by 11, she gets a remainder that is greater than the quotient. What is Amy's favorite three-digit number?
★
★

147. _____

CHAPTER 6
Logic

Use this Practice book with
Guide 4B from BeastAcademy.com.

Recommended Sequence:

Book	Pages:
Guide:	77-89
Practice:	65-77
Guide:	90-109
Practice:	78-95

You may also read the entire chapter
in the Guide before beginning the
Practice chapter.

When we take given information and use it to reach a valid conclusion, we are using *logic*.

EXAMPLE

Max, Buzz, Gene, and Lumpy each have some coins. Buzz has more coins than Gene. Max and Gene each have more coins than Lumpy. Which of the statements below are *definitely* true?

     1. Buzz has more coins than Lumpy.

     2. Lumpy has the fewest coins.

     3. Max has the most coins.

We begin by organizing what we know in a diagram. Arrows point from the monster with more coins to the monster with fewer coins.

Buzz has more coins than Gene.

Max and Gene each have more coins than Lumpy.

We can combine the first two diagrams into one as shown.

1. Buzz has more coins than Gene, and Gene has more coins than Lumpy. So, Buzz has more coins than Lumpy. **Statement 1 is true.**

2. Each of Max, Gene, and Buzz has more coins than Lumpy. So, Lumpy has the fewest coins. **Statement 2 is true.**

3. We don't know whether Max has more coins than Gene or Buzz. So, we can't tell whether statement 3 is true.

Only **statements 1 and 2** are definitely true.

PRACTICE

Fring is 5 years older than his sister, Kim, who is older than her other brother, Wicket. Elmore is 4 years older than his sister, Zoe. Kim is older than Zoe. Circle True, False, or Can't Tell for each statement below.

1. Fring is older than Zoe.

    1. True   False   Can't Tell

2. Wicket is older than Fring.

    2. True   False   Can't Tell

3. Elmore is older than Wicket.

    3. True   False   Can't Tell

4. ★ Fring is older than Elmore.

    4. True   False   Can't Tell

PRACTICE	Ella is taller than Dave, who is taller than Carl. Ben is taller than Anna, who is taller than Frank. Dave is taller than Ben. Carl is taller than Anna. Circle True, False, or Can't Tell for each statement below.

5.   Ella is taller than Carl.

5. True   False   Can't Tell

6.   Dave is taller than Anna.

6. True   False   Can't Tell

7.   Frank is taller than Carl.

7. True   False   Can't Tell

8.   Dave is taller than Frank.

8. True   False   Can't Tell

9.   Carl is taller than Ben.

9. True   False   Can't Tell

10.   Anna is taller than Ella.

10. True   False   Can't Tell

11.   If Carl, Ella, and Frank stand in a line from tallest to shortest, can you tell who would be in the middle? If so, who? If not, why not?

12.   If all six monsters named above stand in a line from tallest (first) to shortest (last), can you tell which monsters will stand first and last? If so, who stands first and who stands last? If not, why not?

13.   If all six monsters named above stand in a line from tallest to shortest, can you tell which monster will stand third, and which will stand fourth? If so, who stands third and who stands fourth? If not, why not?

EXAMPLE

Brian and Roger are playing jump rope with Roger's sister, Isabella. One monster has red fur, one has green fur, and one has blue fur. The boy monster with blue fur is older than the monster with red fur. Isabella is the oldest, and Brian is the youngest. Which monster has which color fur?

One way to organize our work for logic puzzles like these is to make a chart like the one on the right. If a clue lets us know that a monster does not have a particular fur color, we place an ✘ by that monster's name under that color. Once we know a monster's fur color, we use a ✓ by the monster's name under that color.

	red	grn	blue
Bri			
Rog			
Isa			

One clue starts "The boy monster with blue fur..." This tells us that Isabella does not have blue fur. We put an ✘ by Isabella under blue.

Then, we use some clues about ages.

We are told the monster with blue fur is older than the one with red fur and that Isabella is the oldest. Since the monster with red fur is not the oldest, Isabella does not have red fur.

Similarly, we are told that Brian is the youngest. Since the monster with blue fur is not the youngest, Brian does not have blue fur.

	red	grn	blue
Bri			✘
Rog			
Isa	✘		✘

Since Isabella does not have red fur or blue fur, her fur must be the only color left: green. We put a ✓ in the box for Isabella under green. Then, we know that neither Brian nor Roger has green fur, so we ✘ those boxes.

	red	grn	blue
Bri		✘	✘
Rog		✘	
Isa	✘	✓	✘

Neither Brian nor Isabella has blue fur. So, Roger has blue fur. That leaves red for Brian. Our chart is complete.

Brian has red fur, Roger has blue fur, and Isabella has green fur.

	red	grn	blue
Bri	✓	✘	✘
Rog	✘	✘	✓
Isa	✘	✓	✘

PRACTICE | Solve each logic puzzle using the clues given.

14. Ms. Maple has three grandchildren: Sam, Ann, and Lou. They are 5, 7, and 10 years old. When 36 is divided by Sam's age, the remainder is 1. Ann is younger than Sam. How old is each grandchild?

	5	7	10
Sam			
Ann			
Lou			

14. Sam: _____

Ann: _____

Lou: _____

15. Three of the teachers at Beast Academy are named Mr. Red, Mr.
★   Green, and Mr. Blue.
     One day, as they are strolling the halls, Mr. Red says, "It's interesting that one of us has red fur, one has green fur, and one has blue fur."
     "Yes, but none of our names matches the color of our fur," replies the monster with blue fur. What color is each monster's fur?

	red	grn	blue
Mr. Red			
Mr. Green			
Mr. Blue			

15. Mr. Red's fur is _____.

Mr. Green's fur is _____.

Mr. Blue's fur is _____.

PRACTICE | Solve each logic puzzle using the clues given.

16. Three boys, Tosh, Jun, and Van, along with one girl, Kim, race across a field. Jun finishes two places ahead of his younger brother, Tosh. Boys finish first and last. The youngest runner wins the race. Who placed 1st, 2nd, 3rd, and 4th?

	1st	2nd	3rd	4th
Tosh				
Jun				
Van				
Kim				

16. 1st: _____

2nd: _____

3rd: _____

4th: _____

17. Lisa, Ellie, Sophia, Madison, and Samantha are sisters who are 4, 5, 6, 7, and 8 years old. No girl is the same age as the number of letters in her name. If they line up alphabetically (Ellie, Lisa, Madison, Samantha, Sophia), no girl stands in the same position as when they line up from youngest to oldest. Sophia is older than Ellie, and Samantha is older than Madison. Find the age of each sister.

	4	5	6	7	8
Lisa					
Ellie					
Sophia					
Madison					
Samantha					

17. Lisa: _____

Ellie: _____

Sophia: _____

Madison: _____

Samantha: _____

Logic Puzzles

EXAMPLE | Two girls, Nat and Jan, and a boy, Reed, each bring an item to present for show-and-tell. The student who brings a bike goes after the student who brings a family photograph. The girl who brings her favorite book is last to present her show-and-tell item. Jan was happy to go first. Who brings which item, and in what order do they present?

Since there are **three** things to match in this problem (student, item, and order), we could use three charts to organize our data.

	1st	2nd	3rd
Nat			
Jan			
Reed			

	book	bike	photo
Nat			
Jan			
Reed			

	1st	2nd	3rd
book			
bike			
photo			

Instead, we combine the three charts as shown on the right. As in our previous charts, we use ✓'s and ✗'s to mark what we know.

We look at our clues:
"The student who brings a bike goes after the student who brings a family photograph."
This tells us that the person who brought a bike did not go first, and the person who brought a photo did not go last. We mark our chart as shown.

	1st	2nd	3rd	book	bike	photo
Nat						
Jan						
Reed						
book						
bike	✗					
photo			✗			

Next, *"The girl who brings her favorite book is last to present her show-and-tell item."*
This gives us three pieces of information:
1. The book presenter is a girl and therefore not Reed.
2. The book presenter went last.
3. Reed did not go last.
This allows us to figure out the order of all three items presented. We mark our chart as shown.

	1st	2nd	3rd	book	bike	photo
Nat						
Jan						
Reed			✗	✗		
book	✗	✗	✓			
bike	✗	✓	✗			
photo	✓	✗	✗			

Finally, *"Jan was happy to go first."*
Putting a check in the first column for Jan allows us to complete the chart. Since Jan goes first, Reed must go second (since he is not third). Nat goes third. We already know that the photo is presented first, the bike second, and the book third.

Jan goes first and brings a family photograph.
Reed goes second and brings his bike.
Nat goes third and brings her favorite book.

Notice that we did not need the section in the upper-right of our chart to complete the problem. We could fill in the missing entries, but it is not necessary for this problem.

	1st	2nd	3rd	book	bike	photo
Nat	✗	✗	✓			
Jan	✓	✗	✗			
Reed	✗	✓	✗	✗		
book	✗	✗	✓			
bike	✗	✓	✗			
photo	✓	✗	✗			

Logic Puzzles

PRACTICE | Solve each logic puzzle using the clues given.

18. Tommy has two sisters: Amy and Janice. Each of the three siblings has a different vehicle: a car, a truck, and a motorcycle. Janice parks her truck across from the white car. The girl with the red vehicle recently had both tires replaced. One vehicle is black. Match each sibling to the right vehicle and color.

	truck	car	motorcycle	red	white	black
Tommy						
Amy						
Janice						
red			
white			
black			

18. Tommy has a _____ _____.

Amy has a _____ _____.

Janice has a _____ _____.

19. Fred, Ned, and Ted were born on the 4th, 9th, and 18th of January, April, and November of the same year. Grogg cannot remember which day goes with which month or monster. However, he does remember a few things. He remembers giving one of the three monsters a ukulele for his birthday on April 4th. Fred and Ted were born on even-numbered days. Fred is the oldest of the three monsters. Find each monster's birthday.

	January	April	November	4th	9th	18th
Fred						
Ned						
Ted						
4th			
9th			
18th			

19. Fred's birthday is _____ _____.

Ned's birthday is _____ _____.

Ted's birthday is _____ _____.

Beast Academy Practice 4B

71

In a **Minesweeper** puzzle, the goal is to locate all of the mines in a grid of squares. Some of the empty squares in the grid contain a mine. Numbers within the grid give the total mines in the empty squares that surround the number (left, right, above, below, and diagonally).

EXAMPLE | Solve the following minesweeper puzzle.

3		4	
	2		1

The 3 in the upper left corner of the puzzle tells us that mines are in all three squares that surround the corner.
We mark the mines as shown.

3	●	4	
●	●		
	2		1

The number 2 touches two mines. So, none of the remaining six squares that surround the 2 contain mines. We mark these squares with an X to show that they do not contain mines.

3	●	4	
●	●	×	
×	2	×	1
×	×	×	

Finally, we need two more mines for the 4. We place a mine in each of the empty squares surrounding the 4. This takes care of the mine for the 1 as well, so the lower-right corner does not contain a mine.

3	●	4	●
●	●	×	●
×	2	×	1
×	×	×	×

Now, we have filled every empty square with a mine or an X. We check that the correct number of mines surround each number, and we are done!

Find more Minesweeper puzzles at *BeastAcademy.com*.

PRACTICE | Solve each Minesweeper puzzle below.

20.

2		4	
5			
		2	

21.

1		1	
2		2	
			2

22.

		3	
	2		
			4
		5	

PRACTICE | Solve each Minesweeper puzzle below.

23.

4	6		3
	2		1

24.

1			
2		5	
2			
2		2	

25.
★

1		2	
			3
3			
	2		1

26.
★

1		1	
		3	
1			1

27.
★

			2
	7		
			1
	3		

28.
★

2			1
	3		
		4	
2			2

PRACTICE | Each shape-number card has a **shape** on
one side and a **number** on the other side.

29. Faria places three shape-number cards in a row, as shown.

29. _____

She flips over some (maybe all) of the cards and mixes them
up. The new arrangement of the same cards is shown below.

What shape is on the other side of the 4 that Faria sees in
the first arrangement?

30. Anton places three shape-number cards in a row, as shown.

30. _____

He flips over some (maybe all) of the cards and mixes them up.
The new arrangement of the same cards is shown below.

What shape is on the other side of the 1 that Anton sees in the first
arrangement?

PRACTICE | Each shape-number card has a **shape** on one side and a **number** on the other side.

31. Yuki places four shape-number cards in a row, as shown.

He flips over some (maybe all) of the cards and mixes them up.
The new arrangement of the same cards is shown below.

What shape is on the other side of the 9?

32. Willa places four shape-number cards in a row, as shown.

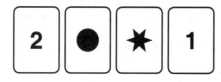

She flips over some (maybe all) of the cards and mixes them up.
The new arrangement of the same cards is shown below.

How many of these four cards have an odd number on one side?

In a 4×4 **Sudoku** puzzle, each empty square must be filled with a number so that every row and column contains each digit from 1 through 4. The grid is also broken into four 2×2 grids called boxes. Each box must contain every digit from 1 through 4.

EXAMPLE | Solve the following Sudoku puzzle.

The lower-right box has a 1 and a 3, so we need to place a 2 and a 4 in the shaded squares. Since there is already a 4 in the bottom row, the 4 cannot be placed in the bottom-right square. So, we place the 2 in the bottom-right square and the 4 in the other shaded square.

The bottom row is only missing a 3. So, we fill the bottom-left square with a 3.

The first column is missing a 4 and a 2. The second row already has a 2, so we place the 4 in the second row, and the 2 in the third row.

We use similar reasoning to fill the remaining squares in the grid as shown below.

PRACTICE | Solve each 4×4 Sudoku puzzle below.

33.

34.

35.

PRACTICE | Use the clues given in each Sudoku puzzle below to fill in the requested numbers.

36. What number belongs in the shaded square in the Sudoku below?

1			
		4	
	3		
			2

37. What number belongs in the shaded square in the Sudoku below?

			1
		3	
4		2	

38. Three of the 2's appear in the Sudoku below. Fill in the final 2.

	2		
2			
		2	

39. Two of the 3's appear in the Sudoku below. Fill in the remaining 3's.

		1	
			3
3			

40. Two of the 3's appear in the Sudoku below. Fill in the remaining 3's

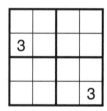

41. Fill in the remaining 2's and 4's in the Sudoku below.

		4	2
		2	
	4		

42. What number belongs in the shaded square in the Sudoku below?

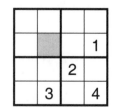

43. ★ What number belongs in the shaded square in the Sudoku below?

			4
			2
1			

Every monster who lives on a small island belongs to one of two tribes. Monsters in the liar tribe *always* lie. Monsters in the truth-teller tribe *always* tell the truth. The only way to tell which monsters are liars and which are truth-tellers is by listening to statements made by monsters who live on the island.

EXAMPLE

Alex encounters two islanders and asks which tribe they belong to. Yorp says, "We are both truth-tellers," to which Mags replies, "Yorp is lying." Which tribe does each monster belong to?

We don't know yet whether Yorp is telling the truth or lying. We consider both possibilities:

If Yorp is telling the truth when he says, "We are both truth-tellers," then Mags is also a truth-teller. But, if Mags is telling the truth when she says that Yorp is lying, then Yorp is a liar. Yorp can't be a both a liar and a truth-teller! This is called a **contradiction**. So, Yorp is not a truth-teller.

If Yorp is lying when he says, "We are both truth-tellers," then, since Mags says that Yorp is lying, Mags is a truth-teller. This works!

Only one of these two possibilities works. So, **Yorp is a liar and Mags is a truth-teller.**

PRACTICE

Use the information below to complete each statement and answer the questions that follow.

Alex is visiting the island of liars and truth-tellers. In line at the supermarket, Alex meets Bib and Loaf. Bib points to Loaf and says, "He's a liar." Loaf wraps his arm around Bib and says, "We're both liars!"

44. *Case 1*: Consider the possibility that Bib is telling the truth.

If Bib is telling the truth, then Loaf is a _____.
(liar/truth-teller)

45. *Case 2:* Consider the possibility that Bib is lying.

If Bib is lying, then Loaf is a _____.
(liar/truth-teller)

46. Which of the two cases above is impossible?   46. (circle one) Case 1   Case 2

47. Which tribe does each monster belong to?   47. Bib: _____

Loaf: _____

PRACTICE | Use the information below to complete each statement and answer the questions that follow.

Later in his visit, Alex meets Geoff, Huck, and Iggy.
Geoff says, "Huck is a liar."
Iggy says, "No, Huck is a truth-teller."
Huck says to Alex, "One of them is lying, but the other is telling the truth."
Which tribe does each monster belong to?

48. *Case 1:* Consider the possibility that Geoff is telling the truth.

If Geoff is telling the truth, then Iggy is a _____, and
(liar/truth-teller)

Huck's statement is _____.
(true/false)

49. *Case 2:* Consider the possibility that Geoff is lying.

If Geoff is lying, then Iggy is a _____, and
(liar/truth-teller)

Huck's statement is _____.
(true/false)

50. Which of the two cases above gives a *contradiction*?

50. (circle one) Case 1   Case 2

51. Which tribe does Huck belong to?

51. Huck: _____

52. Which tribe does Geoff belong to?

52. Geoff: _____

53. Which tribe does Iggy belong to?

53. Iggy: _____

PRACTICE | Answer each question about Alex's visit to the island of liars and truth-tellers below.

54. Alex finds Hurb and Gurk sitting on their front porch.
Alex asks Hurb, "Is **at least one** of you a truth-teller?"
Hurb says, "No."
Which tribe does each monster belong to?

54. Hurb: _____

Gurk: _____

55. Alex meets Oomlot for dinner. When Alex asks
Oomlot if he is a truth-teller, he says, "Urp,"
which Alex knows is the island's word for either
yes or no, but Alex can't remember which.
What does "urp" mean in the island language?

55. "Urp" means _____.

56. Alex meets a pair of monsters, Jo and Mo. Alex
asks Mo if he and Jo belong to the same tribe.
Mo says, "Of course!"
What tribe does Jo belong to?

56. Jo is a _____.

57. Bjorn, Corn, Dorn, and Gus are all having a picnic in the park. When
Alex approaches them, Bjorn speaks up, "Only one of us is a liar."
Corn says, "No, exactly two of us are liars."
"Wrong!" says Dorn, "Exactly three of us are liars."
Gus says "We're all liars!"
How many of the four picnicking monsters are liars?

57. _____

PRACTICE | Answer each question about Alex's visit to the island of liars and truth-tellers below.

58. Alex meets Jaggle, Kip, and Lyra at the park.
"Exactly one of us is a truth-teller," says Jaggle.
"Lyra and I are in the same tribe," says Kip.
Which tribe does each monster belong to?

58. Jaggle: _____

Kip: _____

Lyra: _____

59. Alex meets six islanders: Al, Bo, Cade, Dina, Eli, and Frey.
Al says, "Bo is a liar." Bo says, "Cade is a truth-teller."
Cade says, "Dina is a liar." Dina says, "Eli is a liar."
Eli says, "Frey is a liar." Frey says, "Al is a truth-teller."
How many of these islanders are truth-tellers?

59. _____

60. Alex meets Ak, Lief, and Quiggy.
★ Ak tells Alex that Lief and Quiggy are in the same tribe. Alex asks
✏ Quiggy if Ak and Lief are in the same tribe. Quiggy says, "Yes." Can you tell if Quiggy is a liar or a truth-teller? Why or why not?

61. A monster approaches Alex and says, "I am a liar."
✏ How can Alex tell that the monster does not live on the island?

As in Sudoku, in a 4×4 **Sum-doku** puzzle, every row and column must contain each digit from 1 to 4. However, in Sum-doku, the grid is broken into sections called *cages* instead of boxes. Each cage contains a small number in the top-left corner giving the sum of the digits in the cage.

EXAMPLE | Solve the following Sum-doku puzzle.

Since every row and column contains each of the digits 1 through 4, the sum of the numbers in any row or column is 1+2+3+4=10.

The cage with a sum of 13 includes all four numbers in the first column, plus one number in the second column. Since the sum of the numbers in the first column is 10, the number in the second column must be 13−10=3.

The sum of the numbers in the bottom row is 10. The two digits in the cage on the right end of the row sum to 5, and we have a 3 in the second column. So, the leftmost number in the bottom row is 10−5−3=2. This leaves 1 and 4 as the digits in the third and fourth columns, but we do not have enough information to place them yet.

The three numbers in the top-right cage have a sum of 5. There are only two ways to get a sum of 5 using three digits: 1+1+3, and 1+2+2. We cannot use the same digit twice in any row or column. So, the digits must be arranged in one of the two ways shown on the right.

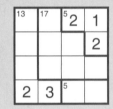

However, we need a 1 in the bottom row. The option on the left makes it impossible to place a 1 in the bottom row. So, we can only use the option on the right. Then, we place the 1 and the 4 on the bottom row as shown.

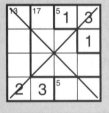

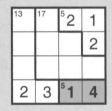

We use the same reasoning we learned when solving Sudoku puzzles to complete the remaining entries in the puzzle. Check to be sure that the sum in each cage equals the given clue.

Beast Academy Practice 4B

PRACTICE | Use the steps given below to solve the 4×4 Sum-doku puzzle.

62. The sum of the numbers in any row or column of a Sum-doku is always $1+2+3+4=10$. So, the sum of all eight numbers in the two left columns is $10+10=20$. Fill in the shaded square with the correct number.

63. Write your answer from the previous problem in the grid to continue solving the puzzle. Think about which two digits must be placed in the cage with a sum of 4, and how you can you arrange these digits. Place the digits in the correct shaded squares.

64. Write your answers from the previous problems in the grid to continue solving the puzzle. Think about which two digits must be placed in the cage with a sum of 7, and how you can arrange these digits. Place the digits in the correct shaded squares.

65. Complete the puzzle. It may help to start by finding the number that should be in the shaded square.

PRACTICE | Solve each 4×4 Sum-doku puzzle below. Some entries have been placed for you.

66.

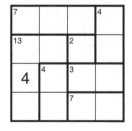

67.

68.

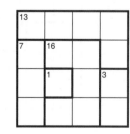

PRACTICE | Solve each 4×4 Sum-doku puzzle below.

69.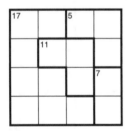

70.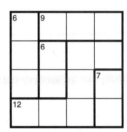

71.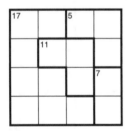

72.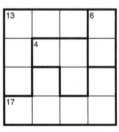

73.
★
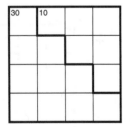

74.
★
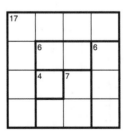

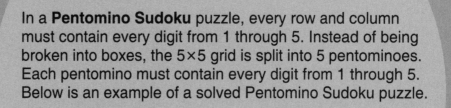

In a **Pentomino Sudoku** puzzle, every row and column must contain every digit from 1 through 5. Instead of being broken into boxes, the 5×5 grid is split into 5 pentominoes. Each pentomino must contain every digit from 1 through 5. Below is an example of a solved Pentomino Sudoku puzzle.

1	2	5	3	4
2	3	1	4	5
4	1	3	5	2
3	5	4	2	1
5	4	2	1	3

PRACTICE | Solve each Pentomino Sudoku puzzle below.

75.

4			1	
2				4
	3			
			5	2
1				

76.

		3		
			1	
4				2
2		1		
			5	

77. ★

1				5
			1	3
		1		
			4	

78. ★

			2	5
4				
		5		1

EXAMPLE

Three playing cards, two red aces and one black ace, are placed face down on a table. Grogg and Winnie each pick up a card and look at it. Grogg says to Winnie, "I know what color your card is." What color is Winnie's card?

If Grogg's card is red, then he can't know whether Winnie's card is red or black. But, if Grogg's card is black, then he knows that both of the remaining cards are red. So, Grogg's card must be black, and Winnie's card must be **red**.

PRACTICE

Use the information below to answer the questions that follow. For each problem, assume that all of the students are using perfect logic.

Professor Grok has four sticky notes, numbered 1 through 4. He puts one sticky note in his pocket. Then, he puts one sticky note on Alex's forehead, one on Lizzie's forehead, and one on Winnie's forehead. Monsters can see the numbers on the other two monsters' foreheads, but not their own number.

79. Professor Grok asks Alex, "Is your number odd or even?" Alex looks at the other cards and says, "Even!"

   a. What numbers must Alex see on the heads of Lizzie and Winnie to know that his number is even?

       79a. _____ & _____

   b. Is the number in Professor Grok's pocket odd or even?

       79b. _____

80. Professor Grok rearranges the four sticky notes and asks Lizzie, "Is your number greater than two?" Lizzie looks at the other little monsters' numbers and says, "Yes."

   a. What numbers must Lizzie see on the heads of Alex and Winnie to know that her number is greater than 2?

       80a. _____ & _____

   b. Professor Grok then asks Winnie, "What number is on your head?" Winnie looks at Alex's number, thinks carefully, and says "One." What number is on Alex's head?

       80b. _____

PRACTICE Use the information below to answer the questions that follow. For each problem, assume that all of the students are using perfect logic.

81. Professor Grok rearranges the four sticky notes. He then asks Winnie, "Which of you three little monsters has the biggest number?" After looking at Alex's number and Lizzie's number, Winnie says, "I can't tell."

    a. What number cannot be on Alex or Lizzie's head?

    81a. _____4_____

    b. Professor Grok then asks Lizzie which of the three little monsters' numbers is biggest. Lizzie thinks for a moment and then says, "Alex's!"
What number is in Professor Grok's pocket?

    81b. _____

    c. What number is on Alex's head?

    81c. _____

82. Professor Grok rearranges the four sticky notes. He then asks Winnie, "Is your number larger or smaller than Alex's?" After looking at Alex's number and Lizzie's number, Winnie says, "I can't tell."

    a. Which two numbers *cannot* be on Alex's head?

    82a. _____ & _____

    b. ★ Professor Grok then asks Lizzie, "What number is on your head?" Lizzie looks at Alex and Winnie then says, "Four!" What number is on Alex's head?

    82b. _____

    c. ★★ What number is in Professor Grok's pocket?

    82c. _____

PRACTICE | Use the information below to answer the questions that follow.

Captain Kraken places two gold coins and three silver coins in a satchel. The coins feel exactly the same. Students pull coins from the bag without looking into the bag.

83. Alex and Grogg each pull out two coins without showing each other.

    a. There are three possible combinations of coins that Alex could have drawn from the satchel. For example, he could have drawn two silver coins. What are the other two possible combinations?

    83a. <u>Silver & Silver</u>

            <u>   </u>

            <u>   </u>

    b. Captain Kraken asks Alex, "How many silver coins does Grogg have?" Alex looks at his coins and says, "I don't know."
One of the three possible combinations of coins above can be *ruled out* for Alex?

    83b. _____

    c. Captain Kraken asks Grogg, "How many *gold* coins does Alex have?" Grogg looks at his coins and says, "One."
Which of the three combinations of coins from part (a) does Grogg have?

    83c. _____

84. All the coins are returned to the satchel. Alex and Lizzie each pull out two coins. Captain Kraken asks Lizzie, "What type of coin is left in the satchel?"
Lizzie looks at her coins and says, "I don't know."
Captain Kraken asks Alex, "What type of coin is left in the satchel?"
Alex looks at his coins and says, "I don't know, either."
How many gold coins does Alex have?

    84. _____

PRACTICE | Use the information below to answer the questions that follow.

Ms. Q. places tokens numbered 1 through 5 in a bag. The tokens feel exactly the same. Students pull tokens from the bag without looking into the bag.

85. Grogg and Lizzie each pull two tokens from the bag. Ms. Q. asks Grogg, "Is the sum of Lizzie's numbers odd or even?"
"Definitely even," says Grogg.
What numbers did Grogg pull from the bag?

85. _____ & _____

86. ★ All the tokens are returned to the bag. Grogg and Winnie each pull out two tokens. Ms. Q. asks Winnie, "Is the sum of your numbers greater than the sum of Grogg's numbers?"
Winnie says, "No. It may be equal, but it's definitely not greater."
What is the sum of Winnie's numbers?

86. _____

87. ★ All the tokens are returned to the bag. Lizzie and Winnie each pull out two tokens. Ms. Q. asks Winnie, "Is the number on the token in the bag odd or even?"
Winnie looks at her tokens and says, "I don't know."
Ms. Q. asks Lizzie, "Do you know?"
Lizzie looks at her tokens and says, "I didn't know before Winnie said she didn't know, but now I know."
Is the numbered token in the bag odd or even?

87. _____

In a **Hive** puzzle, every hexagon is filled with a number from 1 to 7. Once every hexagon is filled, the number in each hexagon is the smallest number that does not appear in any of the hexagons that it touches.

Fill in the shaded hexagon in each Hive puzzle below to make sure you understand the rule. Answers are upside-down at the bottom of these instructions.

a.   **b.**   **c.** 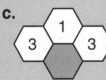 **d.**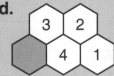

EXAMPLE | Solve the following Hive puzzle.

The 4 in the top-right hexagon tells us that the hexagons that touch it must contain a 1, a 2, and a 3. There is already a 2 touching the 4, so the shaded hexagons must contain a 1 and a 3.

We cannot place the 1 and the 3 as shown, because the 3 must touch both a 1 and a 2. In the diagram on the right, the 3 is not the smallest number that does not appear in any of the hexagons it touches.

So, the 3 and the 1 must be placed as shown. All that is left is the lower-left hexagon. The smallest number it does not touch is a 1. Note also that the 2 must touch a 1.

We place a 1 in the lower left hexagon to complete the puzzle.

We check our puzzle to see that the 2 touches a 1, the 3 touches a 1 and a 2, and the 4 touches a 1, a 2, and a 3.

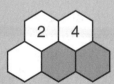

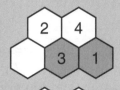

a. 3 b. 1 c. 2 d. 1

PRACTICE | Solve each Hive puzzle below.

88.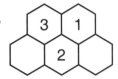

89.

90.

Beast Academy Practice 4B

PRACTICE | Solve each Hive puzzle below.

91.

92.

93.

94.

95.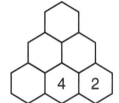

96.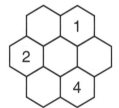

97.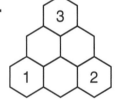

98.
★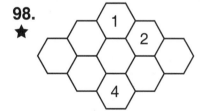

99.
★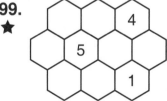

In a **Tents** puzzle, the goal is to attach one tent (△) to each tree (O) on the grid using the following rules:

1. Each tent must be connected to exactly one tree.
2. A connection can only be made between a tent and a tree that are next to each other horizontally or vertically (not diagonally).
3. No two tents may occupy squares that touch, even diagonally.

EXAMPLE | Solve the tents puzzle to the right.

There is only one place to attach a tent to the tree in row 4, column 3. We draw a triangle to represent the tree, and we connect the tent to the tree as shown. While solving the puzzle, we place X's in the squares where tents cannot be placed.

Now, there are two places where we can attach a tent to the tree in row 3, column 3. However, if we attach the tent to the left of the tree as shown, it blocks all of the squares around it. This makes it impossible to attach tents to the remaining trees!

So, we attach a tent above the tree as shown.

This leaves only one place to attach the tent to the tree in the bottom row, as shown in figure 5.

Finally, we attach the last tent to the tree in the first column.

The completed puzzle is shown on the right.

Beast Academy Practice 4B

PRACTICE | Solve each tents puzzle below.

100.

101.

102.

103.

104.

105.

106.

107.

108.

109.
★

110.
★

111.
★

In a **Times Out** puzzle, the goal is to place numbers in a square grid so that there are exactly two numbers in each row and two numbers in each column. Some of the rows and columns have clues. A number to the left of the grid gives the product of the two numbers in that row. Similarly, a number above the grid gives the product of the two numbers in that column.

In a 3×3 Times Out puzzle, you must use each of the digits 1-6 exactly once. In a 4×4 Times Out puzzle, you must use each of the digits 1-8 exactly once.

EXAMPLE | Solve the following Times Out puzzle.

First, we look for ways to make each product using two different numbers from 1-6, since each number can only appear once in the puzzle.

$$10 = 2\times5 \qquad 2 = 1\times2 \qquad 18 = 3\times6 \qquad 24 = 4\times6.$$

Since the column marked 10 must contain a 2, and the row marked 2 must contain a 2, we place the 2 in the top-left square. Similarly, since the column marked 18 needs a 6, and the row marked 24 needs a 6, we place a 6 in the middle of the bottom row.

We need a 3 in the center column, since $3\times6 = 18$. The 3 cannot be placed in the top row, since 2 is not divisible by 3.
So, the 3 must be placed in the second row. The top row needs a 1, and since the center column has two numbers already, we place the 1 in the top-right corner.

The left column needs a 5. Since 24 is not divisible by 5, we place the 5 in the middle row. Finally, the bottom row needs a 4, which can only be placed in the bottom-right corner.

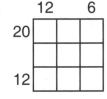

Find more helpful strategies for solving Times Out puzzles on pages 102-105 of the Guide.

PRACTICE | Use the numbers 1-6 to solve each Times Out puzzle below.

112.

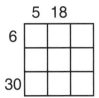

113.

	15	2
3		
12		

114.

	12	6
20		
12		

PRACTICE | Use the numbers 1-8 to solve each Times Out puzzle below.

115.

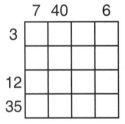

116.

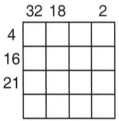

117.

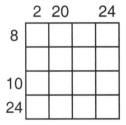

118.

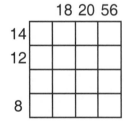

119.
★

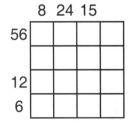

120.
★

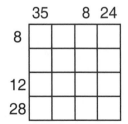

HINTS
For Selected Problems

Below are hints to every problem marked with a ★.
Work on the problems for a while before looking at the hints.
The hint numbers match the problem numbers.

CHAPTER 4
Counting

7. The numbers in this list count by fives, but they are not multiples of 5. How can you make this list easier to count?

15. How many numbers are in Winnie's original list? How many numbers does she erase?

16. What is the smallest multiple of 3 that has units digit 7? What is the next-smallest multiple of 3 that has units digit 7? The next? Can you find a pattern that will help you count them all?

19. How many of the students stand on corners of the hexagon? How many do not stand on corners?

22. If there are 12 gumdrops on each side, how many of those 12 gumdrops are *not* on the corners?

23. Start with an easy example and look for a pattern. How many gumdrops are used to make a rectangle that has short sides with 2 gumdrops and long sides with 4 gumdrops? Short sides with 3 gumdrops and long sides with 6 gumdrops?

27. Start with an easy example and look for a pattern. How many miles does Jenny drive from mile marker 18 to mile marker 19? From mile marker 18 to mile marker 20? From mile marker x to mile marker y?

45. Consider some example dates written in the day/month or month/day form:

9/7, 5/5, 15/10, 10/15, 4/12, 6/27, 2/2.

Which dates can you understand without knowing which system was used?

57. Start by filling in the overlapping region of the two circles. How many two-digit numbers are both even and a multiple of 5?

58. Label the diagram, then fill in the overlapping region of the two circles. How many 2 digit numbers are odd perfect squares?

62. How many 2-digit multiples of 3 have units digit 3?

63. In your Venn diagram, what number belongs outside both circles? Then, if 18 students finished their history homework, how many did not?

64. How many dragons have at least one of these skills? How many little dragons *cannot* breathe fire?

69. Begin by seating Mandy in the middle. Now, how many choices are there for the student who sits farthest to the left? Then, how many choices remain for the student who sits second from the left?

70. Which digits can be used as the thousands digit? For each of those choices, how many choices remain for the hundreds digit? The tens digit? The ones digit?

81. Since we only want to count the arrangements with the A's next to each other, we attach the A's to make a new "letter": AA. How many ways can we arrange our new group of "letters," with the A's attached?

85. How many days are in September? How many hours are in each day?

86. Lizzie will arrange the 4 math books in some order on the left, and the 4 history books in some order on the right.

| math | math | math | math | history | history | history | history |

How many ways can the math books be arranged? How many ways can the history books be arranged?

97. Label the vertices of the decagon:

How many diagonals include vertex A? How many diagonals include vertex B? Vertex C? Be careful not to count any diagonals twice!

105. While solving this problem, do you count any hands twice?

106. Careful! The Jack of diamonds is both a Jack and a diamond.

CHAPTER 5
Division

79. Each time we divide a number by 2, what happens to the number of equal parts we have? How many times do we need to divide a number by 2 to get 16 equal parts?

88. Find the remainder first. Then, find the quotient.

97. What is true about all of the numbers we get when we double multiples of 5?

114. Since we have a divisibility rule for 4, we start with 4. What digits can replace B to make $\boxed{8}\,\boxed{1}\,\boxed{B}$ divisible by 4?

115. Find pairs of numbers whose product is 36. How can you organize your work to make sure you don't miss any factors?

122. If a number *n* is divisible by 14, what other numbers must *n* be divisible by?

129. Is 98,765,400 divisible by 4? How can you tell?

136. Consider divisibility by 25 first. Where must the 5 be placed?

137. There are lots of ways to arrange the squares to create a 3-digit number that is divisible by 25. Consider divisibility by 4. What 3-digit number can you create that is divisible by 4?

142. The area of right triangle ABC is half the area of a rectangle that has the same height and base, as shown below.

143. When Herbert's age is divided by 25, the remainder is 1. What are the possible last two digits of Herbert's age?

146. Consider a related problem: If 43 boxes, each containing 225 donuts, are divided among 42 monsters so that each monster gets the same number of (whole) donuts, how many donuts are left over?

147. What is the greatest possible remainder?

CHAPTER 6
Logic   64

4. What is the relationship in age between Elmore and Kim?

15. Who speaks first? Who speaks second?

25. Each of the 1's is surrounded by 3 empty squares. What does this tell you about the location of the mines that surround the 3's?

26. The 1 in the third column is surrounded by 4 empty squares, and only 1 contains a mine. What does this tell you about the location of the mines that surround the 3?

27. Only one of the eight squares surrounding the 7 does *not* contain a mine. What does the 1 tell you about the location of the empty square?

28. Start with the top-left 2 and the bottom-right 2.

43. Where is the 1 in the lower-right box? How many more entries can you fill in?

60. If Ak is a truth-teller, then Lief and Quiggy are in the same tribe. However, if Ak is a liar, then Lief and Quiggy are in different tribes. What is Quiggy's response to Alex's question in every case? When will he say "Yes?"

73. Is 10 a large sum or a small sum for the six numbers in the shaded cage?

74. First, place the 4 as shown.

Can you place the other three 4's using the clues given? Start with the shaded cage shown.

77. The ⌐ pentomino needs a 1. Where can that 1 be placed?

Then, can you complete the fifth column?

78. The ⌐ pentomino needs a 5. Where must that 5 be placed?

Now, where can the other 5's go?

82. b. From part (a), which two numbers could be on Alex's head? Consider both cases. Which possibility does not allow Lizzie to have the 4? Which does?

Remember that Winnie cannot tell if her number is larger or smaller than Alex's after looking at both Alex's and Lizzie's numbers.

c. How could Lizzie have known she had the 4 on her head? Remember that Lizzie could see Alex's number. What number must Lizzie have seen on Winnie's head?

86. What are all the possible sums that Winnie could get with 2 of the 5 tokens?

For which sums would Winnie know that her sum is definitely less than Grogg's? For which sums would Winnie know that her sum is definitely greater than Grogg's? Which sum(s) could Winnie and Grogg both have?

87. Winnie doesn't know whether the number in the bag is odd or even. What does that tell us (and Lizzie) about Winnie's numbers?

Lizzie also doesn't know whether the number in the bag is odd or even until Winnie speaks. What does that tell us about Lizzie's numbers?

98. The 4 at the bottom must touch a 1, a 2, and a 3. Where must these numbers be placed?

99. The 5 must touch a 4. Where can the 4 be placed? Remember that every 4 must touch a 1, a 2, and a 3.

109. Where can the tent attached to the tree in row 4, column 3 be placed?

110. Where can the tent attached to the tree in row 3, column 2 be placed?

111. Where can the tent attached to the tree in row 4, column 2 be placed?

119. Record all of the possible products for each row and column by filling in the blanks as shown below. Which products cannot be used?

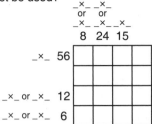

120. Record all of the possible products for each row and column by filling in the blanks as shown below. Can the same product be used for the 8 in the top row as for the 8 in the third column?

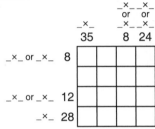

SOLUTIONS
Chapters 4-6

1. The numbers are counted for us! There are **19** numbers in the list.

2. To make this list easier to count, we subtract 15 from each number in the list.

$$
\begin{array}{ccccccc}
16, & 17, & 18, & \ldots, & 73, & 74, & 75 \\
-15 & -15 & -15 & \ldots & -15 & -15 & -15 \\
\hline
1, & 2, & 3, & \ldots, & 58, & 59, & 60
\end{array}
$$

Now, we have a list of numbers from 1 to 60. There are **60** numbers in the list.

3. To make the list easier to count, we subtract 110 from each number in the list.

$$
\begin{array}{ccccccc}
111, & 112, & 113, & \ldots, & 225, & 226, & 227 \\
-110 & -110 & -110 & \ldots & -110 & -110 & -110 \\
\hline
1, & 2, & 3, & \ldots, & 115, & 116, & 117
\end{array}
$$

Now, we have a list of numbers from 1 to 117. There are **117** numbers in the list.

4. All the numbers in this list are multiples of 20, so to make the list easier to count, we divide each number in the list by 20.

$$
\begin{array}{ccccccc}
20, & 40, & 60, & \ldots, & 340, & 360, & 380 \\
\div 20 & \div 20 & \div 20 & \ldots & \div 20 & \div 20 & \div 20 \\
\hline
1, & 2, & 3, & \ldots, & 17, & 18, & 19
\end{array}
$$

Now, we have a list of numbers from 1 to 19. There are **19** numbers in the list.

5. Each number in this list a multiple of 5. To make the list easier to count, we divide each number in the list by 5.

$$
\begin{array}{ccccccc}
10, & 15, & 20, & \ldots, & 65, & 70, & 75 \\
\div 5 & \div 5 & \div 5 & \ldots & \div 5 & \div 5 & \div 5 \\
\hline
2, & 3, & 4, & \ldots, & 13, & 14, & 15
\end{array}
$$

Subtracting 1 from each number in the list gives us a list from 1 to 14. So, there are **14** numbers on this list.

6. The numbers in this list count by twos, but they are not multiples of two. To make the list easier to count, we first subtract 1 from each number in the list.

$$
\begin{array}{ccccccc}
3, & 5, & 7, & \ldots, & 21, & 23, & 25 \\
-1 & -1 & -1 & \ldots & -1 & -1 & -1 \\
\hline
2, & 4, & 6, & \ldots, & 20, & 22, & 24
\end{array}
$$

Next, we divide each number in the list by 2.

$$
\begin{array}{ccccccc}
2, & 4, & 6, & \ldots, & 20, & 22, & 24 \\
\div 2 & \div 2 & \div 2 & \ldots & \div 2 & \div 2 & \div 2 \\
\hline
1, & 2, & 3, & \ldots, & 10, & 11, & 12
\end{array}
$$

Now, we have a list of numbers from 1 to 12. There are **12** numbers in the list.

7. The numbers in this list count by fives, but they are not multiples of 5. To make the list easier to count, we first subtract 8 from each number in the list.

$$
\begin{array}{ccccccc}
13, & 18, & 23, & \ldots, & 88, & 93, & 98 \\
-8 & -8 & -8 & \ldots & -8 & -8 & -8 \\
\hline
5, & 10, & 15, & \ldots, & 80, & 85, & 90
\end{array}
$$

Next, we divide each number in the list by 5.

$$
\begin{array}{ccccccc}
5, & 10, & 15, & \ldots, & 80, & 85, & 90 \\
\div 5 & \div 5 & \div 5 & \ldots & \div 5 & \div 5 & \div 5 \\
\hline
1, & 2, & 3, & \ldots, & 16, & 17, & 18
\end{array}
$$

Now, we have a list of numbers from 1 to 18. There are **18** numbers in the list.

8. The word "inclusive" means that we include the first and last numbers in the list. So, we want to know how many numbers are in this list: 100, 101, 102, …, 198, 199, 200.

If we subtract 99 from each number in the list, we get a list from 1 to 101. So, there are **101** numbers from 100 to 200 inclusive.

9. The word "exclusive" means that we exclude the first and last numbers in the list. So, we want to know how many numbers are in this list:

101, 102, 103, …, 197, 198, 199.

If we subtract 100 from each number in the list, we get a list from 1 to 99. So, there are **99** numbers from 100 to 200 exclusive.

— *or* —

We notice that the list above is the same list as in the previous problem, missing the first and last numbers (100 and 200). So, there are 2 fewer numbers in the list above than in the list in the previous problem. So, there are $101-2 = $ **99** numbers from 100 to 200 exclusive.

10. The word "between" means that we exclude the first and last numbers in the list. So, we want to know how many numbers are in this list:

51, 52, 53, …, 197, 198, 199.

If we subtract 50 from each number in the list, we get a list from 1 to 149. So, there are **149** numbers between 50 and 200.

11. We want to know how many numbers are in this list:

1, 3, 5, …, 95, 97, 99.

Adding 1 to each number in the list gives us a list from 2 to 100 that counts by twos:

2, 4, 6, …, 96, 98, 100.

Dividing each number on this list by 2 gives us a list from 1 to 50. So, there are **50** odd numbers from 1 to 99 inclusive.

12. We want to know how many numbers are in this list:

$$10, 15, 20, \ldots, 85, 90, 95.$$

Dividing each number in the list by 5 gives us a list from 2 to 19:

$$2, 3, 4, \ldots, 17, 18, 19.$$

Subtracting 1 from each number in the list gives us a list from 1 to 18. So, there are **18** two-digit multiples of 5.

13. Lizzie reads pages 25 to 47 inclusive. So, we want to know how many numbers are in the list

$$25, 26, 27, \ldots, 45, 46, 47.$$

Subtracting 24 from each number in the list, we get a list from 1 to 23. So, there are 23 numbers in the list, and Lizzie read **23** pages.

14. Barney says all of the numbers in the list below:

$$135, 140, 145, \ldots, 525, 530, 535.$$

Dividing each number in the list by 5 gives us a list from 27 to 107:

$$27, 28, 29, \ldots, 105, 106, 107.$$

Subtracting 26 from each number in the list gives us a list from 1 to 81. So, Barney says **81** numbers.

15. First, we count the numbers on Winnie's original list. Winnie's original list was 20, 21, 22, …, 198, 199, 200.

Subtracting 19 from each number in this list gives us a list from 1 to 181. So, Winnie's original list contained 181 numbers.

Next, we count the numbers Winnie erases from the list. We begin with the smallest multiple of four in the list (20) and count by fours until we reach the largest multiple of four in the list (200):

$$20, 24, 28, \ldots, 192, 196, 200.$$

Dividing each number by 4 gives us a list from 5 to 50:

$$5, 6, 7, \ldots, 48, 49, 50.$$

Subtracting 4 from each number in the list gives us a list from 1 to 46. So, Winnie erases 46 multiples of 4 from her original list.

Winnie erases 46 numbers from her original list of 181, and $181 - 46 = 135$. So, **135** numbers remain on her list.

16. We begin by listing the multiples of 3 to look for a pattern:

$$3, \ 6, \ 9, 12, 15, 18, 21, 24, \underline{27}, 30,$$
$$33, 36, 39, 42, 45, 48, 51, 54, \underline{57}, 60,$$
$$63, 66, 69, 72, 75, 78, 81, 84, \underline{87}, 90, \ldots$$

Based on the pattern above, multiples of 3 between 0 and 300 that have units digit 7 begin with 27 and occur every 30 numbers. We write out the list that begins with 27 and counts by thirties up to 297 (which is the largest multiple of 3 that is less than 300):

$$27, 57, 87, \ldots, 237, 267, 297.$$

To count the number of numbers in this list, we first add 3 to each number to get the following list:

$$30, 60, 90, \ldots, 240, 270, 300.$$

Then, dividing each number by 30 gives us a list from 1 to 10. So, there are **10** multiples of 3 between 0 and 300 that have units digit 7.

— *or* —

27 is the smallest multiple of 3 that ends in 7.

To get to the next multiple of 3 that ends in 7, we must add a number with units digit 0 to 27.

To get another multiple of 3, the number we add must be a multiple of 3.

$3 \times 10 = 30$ is the smallest multiple of 3 with units digit 0.

So, multiples of 3 between 0 and 300 that have units digit 7 begin with 27 and occur every 30 numbers. We write out the list that begins with 27 and counts by thirties up to 297.

$$27, 57, 87, \ldots, 237, 267, 297.$$

We count the numbers in this list as in the previous solution to find that there are **10** multiples of 3 between 0 and 300 that have units digit 7.

COUNTING
Geometric Arrangements 10-12

17. We draw a diagram.

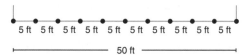

There are **11** students along each long side of the rectangle.

— *or* —

$50 \div 5 = 10$. So, we can divide a 50-foot side of the rectangle into 10 five-foot segments. However, 10 students is not enough for each long side of the rectangle. If we place a student at one corner, and then place another student every 5 feet, we need 1 more student to stand at the remaining corner.

So, there are $10 + 1 = $ **11** students along each long side of the rectangle.

18. In the previous problem, we found that there are 11 students along each long side of the rectangle.

Using the same strategies, we find that 6 students stand along each of the short sides of the rectangle.

```
  •   •   •   •   •   •
  5 ft  5 ft  5 ft  5 ft  5 ft
  |——————— 25 ft ———————|
```

To find the total number of students that surround the rectangle, we begin by placing one student at each corner:

Then, for there to be 11 students along each long side, we must place 9 more students along each long side.

Similarly, for there for be 6 students along each short side, we place 4 more students along each short side.

All together, $4+(9\times2)+(4\times2) = 4+18+8 = \textbf{30}$ students surround the rectangle.

— *or* —

We group the students so that each corner student is only counted once.

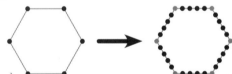

We circle two groups of 10 students and two groups of 5 students. All together, $(2\times10)+(2\times5) = 20+10 = \textbf{30}$ students surround the rectangle.

19. In the previous problem, we found that 30 students surround the rectangle. To arrange the same number of students around a hexagon, we begin by placing one student on each corner.

That leaves $30-6 = 24$ students. We place $24\div6 = 4$ more students along each side to make a regular hexagon.

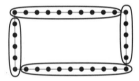

All together, there are $4+2 = \textbf{6}$ students along each side of the hexagon.

20. Lizzie can arrange the 8 gumdrops by placing the first 4 gumdrops on the corners of the square, and then placing 1 more gumdrop along each side, as shown.

Then, she can complete the polygon by connecting the gumdrops with **8 toothpicks**, as shown.

— *or* —

21. It takes 1 toothpick to connect 2 gumdrops in a row.
It takes 2 toothpicks to connect 3 gumdrops in a row.
It takes 3 toothpicks to connect 4 gumdrops in a row.
It takes $n-1$ toothpicks to connect n gumdrops in a row.

So, to connect 10 gumdrops along each long side of the rectangle requires 9 toothpicks, and to connect 4 gumdrops along each short side requires 3 toothpicks.

So, Cammie uses 9 toothpicks along each long side, and 3 toothpicks along each short side. All together, she uses $(2\times9)+(2\times3) = 18+6 = \textbf{24}$ toothpicks.

22. If Ralph's triangle has 12 gumdrops on each side, since 2 of the gumdrops on each side are on the corners, there are 10 gumdrops on each side that are *not* on the corners. So, there are $3\times10 = 30$ gumdrops on the triangle that are not on the corners, plus another 3 gumdrops that are on the corners, for a total of $30+3 = 33$ gumdrops.

— *or* —

We group the gumdrops so that each corner gumdrop is only counted once. For example, to count the total number of gumdrops on a triangle that has 5 gumdrops on each side, we can group the gumdrops as shown into 3 equal groups of 4 gumdrops for a total of $3\times4 = 12$ gumdrops.

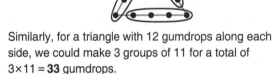

Similarly, for a triangle with 12 gumdrops along each side, we could make 3 groups of 11 for a total of $3\times11 = \textbf{33}$ gumdrops.

23. We begin with the smallest rectangle whose sides have twice as many gumdrops on the long sides as the short sides, with 2 gumdrops on each short side and 4 on each long side:

Then, for each gumdrop that we add to each short side, we must add two gumdrops to each long side so that the long sides still have twice as many gumdrops as the short sides. For example, a rectangle with $2+1 = 3$ gumdrops along its short side must have $4+2 = 6$ on its long side.

All together, we must add 6 more gumdrops to the whole rectangle to increase the length of the short sides by 1.

So, after placing the first 8 gumdrops, we can add gumdrops, 6 at a time, until we have a rectangle with $8+6+6+6+6 = 38$ gumdrops as shown.

There are 14 gumdrops along the long side and **7** gumdrops along the short side of Grogg's rectangle.

24. We draw a diagram of the 12 lampposts and find the total distance from the first to the last post.

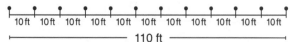

So, if Alex walks from the first lamppost to the last, he walks **110 feet**.

— *or* —

We number each lamppost from 1 to 12.

To walk from lamppost 1 to lamppost 2, we walk one length of 10 feet. To walk from lamppost 1 to lamppost 3, we walk two lengths of ten feet. To walk from lamppost 1 to lamppost 4, we walk three lengths of ten feet.

To walk from lamppost 1 to lamppost n, we walk $n-1$ lengths of ten feet. So, to walk from lamppost 1 to lamppost 12, we walk $12-1 = 11$ lengths of ten feet. $11 \times 10 = 110$, so Alex walks **110 feet**.

25. There are 21 lampposts, spaced 15 feet apart. To walk from lamppost 1 to lamppost n, we walk $n-1$ lengths of fifteen feet.

So, to walk from lamppost 1 to lamppost 21, we walk $21-1 = 20$ lengths of fifteen feet. $20 \times 15 = 300$, so Alex walks **300 feet**.

26. Jenny passes the mile markers numbered 18 to 95, inclusive: 18, 19, 20, ..., 93, 94, 95.

Subtracting 17 from each number in the list gives us a list from 1 to 78. So, Jenny drove past **78** mile markers.

27. To drive from mile marker 18 to mile marker 19, Jenny drives $19-18 = 1$ mile. To drive from mile marker 18 to mile marker 20, Jenny drives $20-18 = 2$ miles.
To drive from mile marker 18 to mile marker 21, Jenny drives $21-18 = 3$ miles.

To drive from mile marker x to mile marker y, Jenny drives $y-x$ miles.

So, to drive from mile marker 18 to mile marker 95, Jenny drives $95-18 = $ **77 miles**.

28. We create a tree diagram to show all of the possibilities.

Flavor	Topping	
vanilla	caramel	1
	sprinkles	2
chocolate	caramel	3
	sprinkles	4
mango	caramel	5
	sprinkles	6
berry	caramel	7
	sprinkles	8

All together, there are **8** different single-scoop one-topping cones available.

29. We create a tree diagram to show all of the possibilities.

Digit	Shape	
1	triangle △	1
	square ☐	2
	circle ○	3
3	triangle △	4
	square ☐	5
	circle ○	6
5	triangle △	7
	square ☐	8
	circle ○	9
7	triangle △	10
	square ☐	11
	circle ○	12
9	triangle △	13
	square ☐	14
	circle ○	15

All together, there are **15** different possible codes.

30. We create a tree diagram to show all of the possibilities.

Mascot	Color	
Lion	red	1
	orange	2
	blue	3
	green	4
Tiger	red	5
	orange	6
	blue	7
	green	8
Bear	red	9
	orange	10
	blue	11
	green	12

All together, there are **12** different jersey choices.

31. We create a tree diagram to show all of the possibilities.

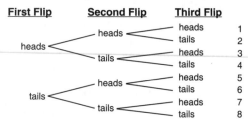

All together, there are **8** different possible sequences.

32. We create a tree diagram to show all of the possibilities.

Color	# Doors	Sunroof?	
red	2	yes	1
		no	2
	4	yes	3
		no	4
grey	2	yes	5
		no	6
	4	yes	7
		no	8
green	2	yes	9
		no	10
	4	yes	11
		no	12
blue	2	yes	13
		no	14
	4	yes	15
		no	16
black	2	yes	17
		no	18
	4	yes	19
		no	20

All together, **20** different versions of the car are available.

33. We create a tree diagram to show all of the possibilities.

Bread	Cheese	Meat	
white	Swiss	ham	1
		bologna	2
	cheddar	ham	3
		bologna	4
wheat	Swiss	ham	5
		bologna	6
	cheddar	ham	7
		bologna	8
rye	Swiss	ham	9
		bologna	10
	cheddar	ham	11
		bologna	12

Grogg can make **12** different sandwiches.

34. We use the same diagram from the previous problem, and remove the choices with rye bread.

Bread	Cheese	Meat	
white	Swiss	ham	1
		bologna	2
	cheddar	ham	3
		bologna	4
wheat	Swiss	ham	5
		bologna	6
	cheddar	ham	7
		bologna	8
rye	Swiss	ham	
		bologna	
	cheddar	ham	
		bologna	

So, **8** of the sandwich options do not have rye bread.

35. We use our original tree diagram, and we remove the choices with Swiss cheese.

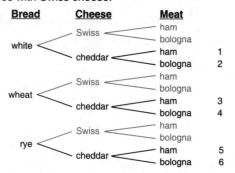

Bread	Cheese	Meat	
white	Swiss	ham	
		bologna	
	cheddar	ham	1
		bologna	2
wheat	Swiss	ham	
		bologna	
	cheddar	ham	3
		bologna	4
rye	Swiss	ham	
		bologna	
	cheddar	ham	5
		bologna	6

So, **6** of Grogg's sandwich options do not have Swiss cheese.

36. We add salami as a third meat option to our original tree diagram and count the total number of sandwich options.

Bread	Cheese	Meat	
white	Swiss	ham	1
		bologna	2
		salami	3
	cheddar	ham	4
		bologna	5
		salami	6
wheat	Swiss	ham	7
		bologna	8
		salami	9
	cheddar	ham	10
		bologna	11
		salami	12
rye	Swiss	ham	13
		bologna	14
		salami	15
	cheddar	ham	16
		bologna	17
		salami	18

Including the sandwiches with salami, Grogg can make **18** different sandwiches.

COUNTING
Possibilities

17–19

37. Brandon can pair any one of his 6 ties with any one of his 3 hats. This gives him a total of $6×3 = $ **18** different ways to a choose a hat and tie to wear to dinner.

38. Lizzie can choose any one of the 7 styles in any one of 4 colors. This gives her a total of $7×4 = $ **28** different choices for new frames.

39. The club can choose any one of the 5 third graders, any one of the 8 fourth graders, and any one of the 6 fifth graders. This gives a total of $5×8×6 = $ **240** possible teams.

40. To order a one-topping pizza from Vinny's, we choose any one of the 12 toppings, any one of 3 crust types, and any one of 2 sizes. All together, we can order $12×3×2 = $ **72** different pizzas from Vinny's.

41. Each time Winnie flips a coin, it will land on heads or tails. So, the first flip lands on one of 2 sides, the second flip lands on one of 2 sides, and so on until the sixth flip.

All together, there are $2×2×2×2×2×2 = 2^6 = $ **64** possible sequences.

42. To create a bicycle tag we choose any one of 26 letters, any one of 2 symbols (- or &), and any one of 10 digits. All together, $26×2×10 = $ **520** different bicycle tags are available for use at Beast Academy.

43. To travel from Sandlake to Dunkeldorf through Titansville, Xue must choose any one of 3 transportation options from Sandlake to Titansville and any one of 4 transportation options from Titansville to Dunkeldorf. All together, there are $3×4 = $ **12** different transportation combinations.

44. Since all of the digits of Plunk's combination are odd (1, 3, 5, 7, 9), each of the digits is one of 5 possible choices.

All together, there are $5×5×5×5 = 5^4 = $ **625** possible combinations that include only odd digits.

45. We begin by looking at some example dates:

* 4/12 is April 12th on Beast Island but is the 4th of December on islands using the day/month system.

* 10/15 is October 15 on Beast Island. However, 10/15 would not be used in a day/month system, because there are only 12 months in a year.

Similarly, 15/10 is the 15th of October on islands using the day/month system, but would not be used on Beast Island.

So, if a number greater than 12 appears on either side of the date, then we know which system is being used, and we can figure out the date.

* 5/5 is May 5 in both systems! If the day and month numbers are the same, we always know the date.

So, if two different numbers 1 through 12 appear on both sides of the date, then it is impossible to tell the date if we do not know which system is being used.

There are 12×12 = 144 dates for which the numbers 1 through 12 appear on both sides of the date.

There are 12 dates on which the day and month number are the same (1/1, 2/2, and so on, to 12/12).

Therefore, there are 144−12 = **132** dates for which it is impossible to tell the date if we do not know which system is being used.

— or —

For each of the 12 months, there are 11 days that will give us an unclear date. For example, the Beast Island dates 2/1, 2/3, 2/4, 2/5, 2/6, 2/7, 2/8, 2/9, 2/10, 2/11, and 2/12 would all be unclear if we didn't know which system was used.

All together, there are 12×11 = **132** dates for which it is impossible to tell the date if we do not know the system.

COUNTING
Venn Diagrams   20-26

To help us answer the next five questions, we add the remaining letters to the Venn diagram as shown.

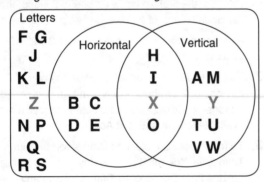

46. The number of letters that have a vertical line of symmetry is the total number of letters in the circle labeled "Vertical."

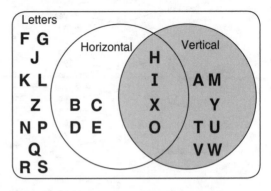

All together, **11** letters have a vertical line of symmetry: A, H, I, M, O, T, U, V, W, X, and Y.

47. The number of letters that have a horizontal line of symmetry is the total number of letters in the circle labeled "Horizontal."

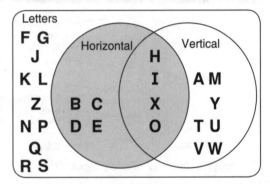

All together, **8** letters have a vertical line of symmetry: B, C, D, E, H, I, O, and X.

48. The area where the two circles overlap contains the letters that have both horizontal and vertical lines of symmetry.

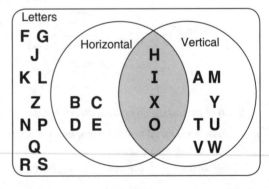

There are **4** letters have both horizontal and vertical lines of symmetry: H, I, O, and X.

49. The area outside of both circles contains the letters that have neither a horizontal nor a vertical line of symmetry.

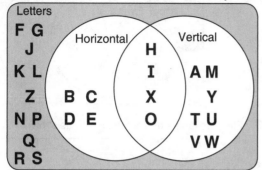

There are **11** letters that have neither a vertical nor a horizontal line of symmetry: F, G, J, K, L, N, P, Q, R, S, and Z.

50. There are 4 letters that have a horizontal but not a vertical line of symmetry. There are 7 letters that have a vertical but not a horizontal line of symmetry.

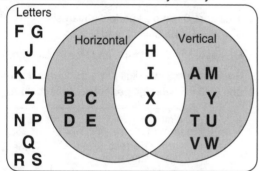

All together, 4+7 = **11** letters have a horizontal or vertical line of symmetry, but not both: A, B, C, D, E, M, T, U, V, W, and Y.

51. We place each of the words in the diagram as shown:

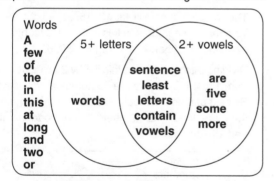

52. Using our Venn diagram from the previous problem, we count the number of words in each region to label the diagram as shown.

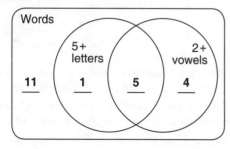

All of the words in the sentence should be counted exactly one time in one of the four regions. So, we check that the sum of the four numbers above is the same as the number of words in the sentence: 11+1+5+4 = 21. ✓

53. The area where the two circles overlap gives us the number of monsters that have both fur and horns.

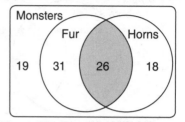

So, **26** of the furry monsters have horns.

54. 26 monsters have fur and horns, and 31 monsters have fur but not horns.

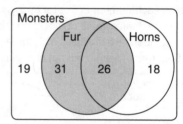

All together, 31+26 = **57** monsters have fur.

55. Each monster in the group is counted exactly one time in one of the four regions in the diagram. So, we add up the numbers in each region.

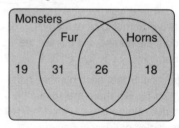

All together, there are 19+31+26+18 = **94** monsters in the group.

56. Monsters in the shaded regions below do not have fur.

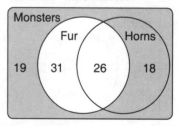

All together, 19+18 = **37** of the monsters do not have fur.
— *or* —

We previously calculated that there are 94 monsters in the group and that 57 of the monsters have fur. This leaves 94−57 = **37** monsters with no fur.

57. We begin by counting the number in the overlap of even numbers and multiples of 5. The two-digit even multiples of 5 are 10, 20, 30, ..., 70, 80, 90.

All together, there are 9 two-digit numbers that are even multiples of 5.

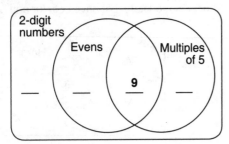

The two-digit evens are 10, 12, 14, 16, ..., 94, 96, 98. To count the numbers in this list, we first subtract 2 from each number: 2, 4, 6, ..., 86, 88, 90.

Dividing each number in this list by 2 gives us a list from 1 to 45. So, there are 45 numbers on this list. Since 9 of these numbers are multiples of 5, there are $45-9=36$ numbers that are even but not multiples of 5.

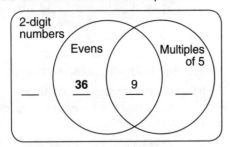

The two-digit multiples of 5 are 10, 15, 20, ..., 85, 90, 95. To count the numbers in this list, we first divide each number in the list by five: 2, 3, 4, ..., 17, 18, 19.

Subtracting 1 from each number in this list gives us a list from 1 to 18. So, there are 18 numbers on this list. Since 9 of these numbers are even, $18-9=9$ of these numbers are multiples of 5 but not even.

You may have instead listed the 9 odd two-digit multiples of five: 15, 25, 35, ..., 75, 85, 95.

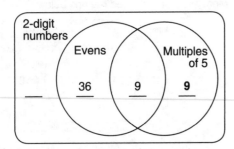

All together, there are 90 two-digit numbers (10, 11, 12, ..., 97, 98, 99).

36 are even but not multiples of 5,
9 are both even and multiples of 5, and
9 are multiples of 5 but not even.

This leaves $90-36-9-9=$ **36** two-digit numbers that are neither even nor a multiple of 5.

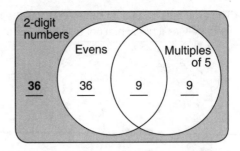

58. First, we label our Venn diagram, as shown.

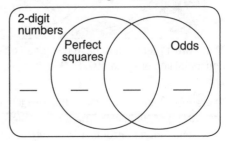

There are 6 two-digit perfect squares: $4^2=16$, $5^2=25$, $6^2=36$, $7^2=49$, $8^2=64$, and $9^2=81$.

Of these, $5^2=25$, $7^2=49$, and $9^2=81$ are odd.

So, there are 3 two-digit perfect squares that are odd, and $6-3=3$ two-digit perfect squares that are not odd.

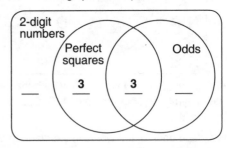

The two-digit odds are 11, 13, 15, ..., 95, 97, 99. To count the numbers in this list, we first subtract 9 from each number: 2, 4, 6, ..., 86, 88, 90.

Dividing each number in this list by 2 gives us a list from 1 to 45. So, there are 45 numbers on this list. Since 3 of these numbers are also perfect squares, there are $45-3=42$ numbers that are odd but not perfect squares.

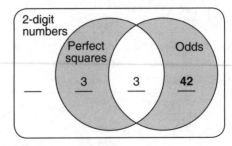

There are 3 two-digit perfect squares that are not odd, and there are 42 odd numbers that are not perfect squares. All together, $3+42=$ **45** two-digit numbers are either perfect squares or odd, but not both.

Note that we did not need to determine the number that is outside the circles to answer this question.

59. First, we label our Venn diagram as shown. We use the information given in the problem to label some regions of the Venn diagram as shown:

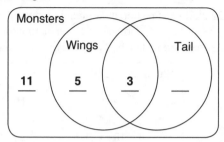

All together, there are 25 monsters in the picture. We know 11 do not have wings or a tail, 5 have wings but no tail, and 3 have both wings and a tail. This leaves $25-11-5-3=$ **6** monsters in the picture that have a tail but no wings.

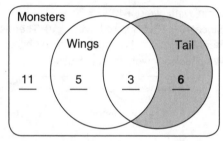

60. We label our Venn diagram as shown. Three of the red toy cars are missing a wheel.

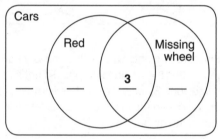

Drew has 18 red toy cars. Since 3 of those red toy cars are missing a wheel, $18-3=15$ red toy cars are not missing a wheel.

Also, 7 of Drew's toy cars are missing a wheel. Since 3 of those toy cars missing wheels are red, $7-3=4$ toy cars are missing wheels but are not red.

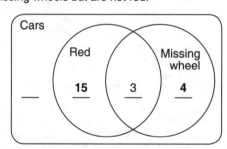

All together, Drew has 50 toy cars.

15 are red but not missing a wheel,
3 are red and missing a wheel, and
4 are missing a wheel but not red.

This leaves $50-15-3-4=$ **28** toy cars that are not red and not missing any wheels.

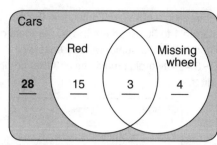

61. We label our Venn diagram as shown. Since every student took at least one fruit or vegetable, we know that there are 0 students in the region outside of the two circles. Also, 22 students took both a fruit and a vegetable.

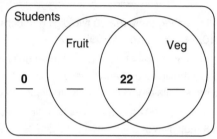

27 students took a vegetable. Since 22 of those students also took a fruit, $27-22=5$ students took only a vegetable.

35 students took a fruit. Since 22 of those students also took a vegetable, $35-22=13$ students took only a fruit.

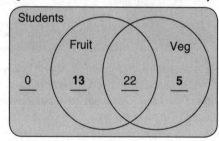

All together, $0+13+22+5=$ **40** students passed through the Beast Academy lunch line.

62. We label our Venn diagram as shown. There are 9 two-digit numbers with units digit 3:

$$13, 23, 33, ..., 73, 83, 93.$$

Of these, only 33, 63, and 93 are multiples of 3.

So, there are 3 two-digit multiples of 3 that have units digit 3, and $9-3=6$ two-digit numbers that have units digit 3 but are not multiples of 3.

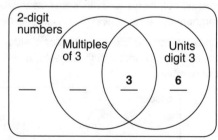

The two-digit multiples of 3 are 12, 15, 18, ..., 93, 96, 99. To count the numbers in this list, we first divide each number by three: 4, 5, 6, ..., 31, 32, 33.

Subtracting 3 from each number in the list gives us a list from 1 to 30. So, there are 30 numbers on this list. Since 3 of these numbers have units digit 3, there are $30-3=27$ two-digit multiples of 3 that do not have units digit 3.

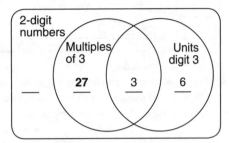

All together, there are 90 two-digit numbers (10, 11, 12, …, 97, 98, 99).

27 are multiples of 3 but do not have units digit 3, 3 are multiples of 3 and have units digit 3, and 6 have units digit 3 but are not multiples of 3.

This leaves $90-27-3-6=\textbf{54}$ two-digit numbers that are not multiples of 3 nor have units digit 3.

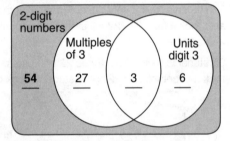

63. We label our Venn diagram as shown below. Since each of the 30 students finished homework for at least one subject, we know that there are 0 students in the region outside of the two circles.

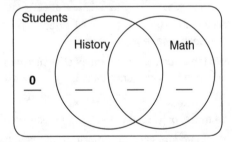

Since we don't know how many students finished homework for *only one* subject, or how many students finished homework for *both*, it isn't clear what the numbers in the remaining regions should be.

Since we want to know the number of students who finished homework for both subjects, we let x represent that number.

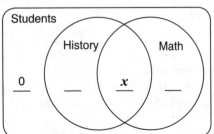

18 students finished their history homework. Since x of those also finished their math homework, $18-x$ students finished only their history homework.

22 students finished their math homework. Since x of those students also finished their history homework, $22-x$ students finished only their math homework.

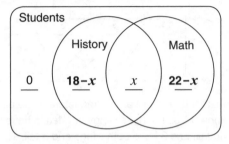

All together, there were 30 students in study hall. So, we have $0+(18-x)+x+(22-x)=30$.

Simplifying, we get $40-x=30$.
Since $40-\boxed{10}=30$, we have $x=10$. Therefore, **10** students finished both their math and history homework. We check our work by substituting 10 for x:

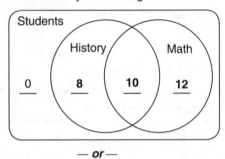

— *or* —

Since 18 students finished their history homework, there were $30-18=12$ students who did not finish their history homework. Since every student finished at least one of the two assignments, these 12 students finished only their math homework.

Then, since 22 students finished their math homework and 12 students finished only their math homework, there were $22-12=\textbf{10}$ students who finished both assignments.

64. We label our Venn diagram as shown below. Four of the dragons cannot fly or breathe fire yet.

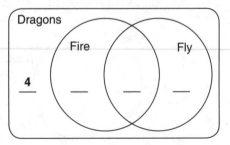

Since we want to know the number of dragons who can breathe fire *and* fly, we let x represent that number.

9 dragons can breathe fire. Since x of those can also fly, $9-x$ of the little dragons only breathe fire.

15 little dragons can fly. Since x of those can also breathe fire, $15-x$ of the little dragons only fly.

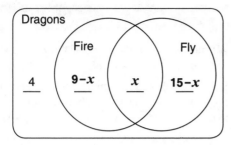

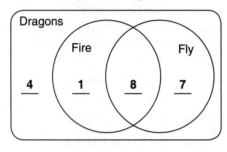

All together, there are 20 little dragons in Lizzie's class. So, we have $4+(9-x)+x+(15-x)=20$.

Simplifying the left side of the equation, we have $28-x=20$. So, $x=8$. Therefore, **8** of the little dragons in Lizzie's weekend class can both fly and breathe fire.

We check our work by substituting 8 for x:

— *or* —

There are $20-4=16$ dragons who have at least one of the two skills. Since 9 of the little dragons can breathe fire, $16-9=7$ dragons can fly but cannot breathe fire.

There are a total of 15 little dragons who can fly, so $15-7=8$ of the dragons who can fly can also breathe fire. So, there are **8** dragons who can fly and breathe fire.

COUNTING

Arrangements   27–28

65. We create the tree diagram.
If A comes first, then the second letter could be B or C. If the first letter is A and the second letter is B, then the third letter can only be C.

1st	2nd	3rd	
A	B	C	1. ABC
	C	B	2. ACB
B	A	C	3. BAC
	C	A	4. BCA
C	A	B	5. CAB
	B	A	6. CBA

Then, we list the six different arrangements in alphabetical order: **ABC ACB BAC BCA CAB CBA**.

66. We create a diagram to organize which digit comes first, second, third, and fourth in the number.

For example, if 1 comes first, then the second digit could be 2, 3, or 4. If the first two digits are 1 and 2, then the third digit could be 3 or 4. If the first three digits are 1, 2, and 3, then the fourth digit can only be 4.

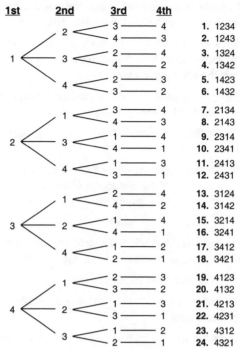

1st	2nd	3rd	4th		
1	2	3	4	1.	1234
		4	3	2.	1243
	3	2	4	3.	1324
		4	2	4.	1342
	4	2	3	5.	1423
		3	2	6.	1432
2	1	3	4	7.	2134
		4	3	8.	2143
	3	1	4	9.	2314
		4	1	10.	2341
	4	1	3	11.	2413
		3	1	12.	2431
3	1	2	4	13.	3124
		4	2	14.	3142
	2	1	4	15.	3214
		4	1	16.	3241
	4	1	2	17.	3412
		2	1	18.	3421
4	1	2	3	19.	4123
		3	2	20.	4132
	2	1	3	21.	4213
		3	1	22.	4231
	3	1	2	23.	4312
		2	1	24.	4321

All together, there are **24** ways to arrange these four digits into a four-digit number.

67. We can count the arrangements without listing them all. To arrange the digits into a number, we first choose a digit to use as the hundreds digit. There are 3 choices for the hundreds digit (5, 6, or 8).

Once we have chosen the hundreds digit, we choose the tens digit. No matter which digit we use as the hundreds digit, there are only 2 digits that can be chosen as the tens digit.

With the hundreds and tens digits selected, there is only 1 choice for the ones digit.

All together, there are $3\times2\times1=$ **6** ways to arrange the three digits in some order.

68. To seat five students, we begin by choosing one student to sit on the left. There are 5 choices for the student who sits in the chair farthest to the left.

Once we have chosen the student who sits on the left, there are only 4 students who can fill the second chair.

Similarly, once we have seated the first two students, we have 3 choices for the student who sits in the third chair.

Once we have seated the first three students, we have 2 choices for the student who sits in the fourth chair.

Finally, with the first four chairs filled, there is only 1 choice for the student who sits in the last chair.

All together, there are $5\times4\times3\times2\times1=$ **120** possible seating arrangements.

69. We place Mandy in the middle seat and count the remaining seating choices.

_____   _____   _Mandy_   _____   _____

We still must seat Kim, Lisa, Nellie, and Olivia.

To seat the four remaining students, we first choose one of the four to sit farthest to the left. There are 4 choices.

Once we have chosen the student who sits farthest to the left, there are 3 choices for the student who sits second from the left, next to Mandy.

Then, there are 2 choices for the student who sits on the other side of Mandy.

Finally, the 1 student who remains sits farthest to the right.

All together, there are $4\times3\times2\times1 =$ **24** possible arrangements of the 5 students in a row of chairs if Mandy is seated in the middle chair.

— *or* —

We first seat Mandy in the middle seat. Then, we seat Kim, then Lisa, then Nellie, and then Olivia.

We have 4 choices for Kim's seat.

No matter where Kim sits, we have 3 choices remaining for Lisa's seat.

No matter where Kim and Lisa sit, we have 2 choices for Nellie's seat, which leaves the 1 remaining seat for Olivia.

All together, there are $4\times3\times2\times1 =$ **24** possible arrangements.

70. Since 0 cannot be used as the thousands digit, we have 3 choices for the first digit: 1, 2 or 3.

Then, once we have chosen the thousands digit, there are 3 choices for the hundreds digit. (For example, if the thousands digit is 1, then the hundreds digit could be 0, 2, or 3.)

Then, there are 2 choices for the tens digit.

Finally, the 1 digit that remains will be the ones digit.

All together, there are $3\times3\times2\times1 =$ **18** ways to arrange these four digits into a four-digit number.

We can confirm this with a tree diagram that shows all 18 arrangements.

1st	2nd	3rd	4th		
	0	2	3	**1.**	1023
		3	2	**2.**	1032
1	2	0	3	**3.**	1203
		3	0	**4.**	1230
	3	0	2	**5.**	1302
		2	0	**6.**	1320
	0	1	3	**7.**	2013
		3	1	**8.**	2031
2	1	0	3	**9.**	2103
		3	0	**10.**	2130
	3	0	1	**11.**	2301
		1	0	**12.**	2310
	0	1	2	**13.**	3012
		2	1	**14.**	3021
3	1	0	2	**15.**	3102
		2	0	**16.**	3120
	2	0	1	**17.**	3201
		1	0	**18.**	3210

71. We multiply numbers from 8 all the way down to 1:
$8\times7\times6\times5\times4\times3\times2\times1 =$ **8!**.

72. Since multiplication is commutative and associative, we begin by reordering the numbers in order from greatest to least: $5\times4\times1\times3\times6\times2 = 6\times5\times4\times3\times2\times1$.

$6\times5\times4\times3\times2\times1 =$ **6!**.

73. We know $9! = 9\times8\times7\times6\times5\times4\times3\times2\times1$, and
$10! = 10\times9\times8\times7\times6\times5\times4\times3\times2\times1$
$ = 10\times(9\times8\times7\times6\times5\times4\times3\times2\times1)$.
So, $10! = 10\times(9!)$.
We are told that $9! = 362,880$, so we have
$10! = 10\times(9!) = 10\times362,880 =$ **3,628,800**.

74. We know $10! = 10\times9\times8\times7\times6\times5\times4\times3\times2\times1$.
Also, $12! = 12\times11\times10\times9\times8\times7\times6\times5\times4\times3\times2\times1$
$ = 12\times11\times(10\times9\times8\times7\times6\times5\times4\times3\times2\times1)$.
So, $12! = 12\times11\times(10!)$.

We rewrite this as $12! = 10!\times(11\times12)$.

$11\times12 = 132$, so $12! = 10!\times132$.

Since $10!\times n = 12!$, we have $n =$ **132**.

75. We know $4! = 4\times3\times2\times1$, and $5! = 5\times4\times3\times2\times1$.
So, $5! = 5\times(4!)$.

Therefore, $5\times(4!)-5! = 5!-5! =$ **0**.

76. To evaluate 77!, we multiply numbers from 77 all the way down to 1. One of the numbers we multiply is 10:

$$77! = 77\times76\times75\times\cdots\times10\times\cdots\times3\times2\times1$$

So, 77! is a multiple of ten. Since all multiples of ten have a units digit of 0, the units digit of 77! is **0**.

77. We know $7! = 7\times6\times5\times4\times3\times2\times1 = 5,040$, and
$5! = 5\times4\times3\times2\times1 = 120$.

$7!\div5! = 5,040\div120 =$ **42**.

— *or* —

$7! = 7\times6\times5!$. To compute $7!\div5!$, we rewrite 7! to get $7!\div5! = 7\times6\times5!\div5!$. Multiplying by 5! and then dividing by 5! is the same as doing nothing.

So, $7\times6\times5!\div5! = 7\times6 =$ **42**.

78. There are 4 choices for the boat that leaves first (Ned's, Jon's, Rob's, or Theo's). Once that boat leaves, we have 3 choices for the boat that leaves second. Then, we have 2 choices for the boat that leaves third. Finally, the 1 remaining boat leaves last.

This gives us $4\times3\times2\times1 =$ **4!** different orders in which the boats can leave.

79. There are 5 different letters: B, E, A, S, and T.

We have 5 choices for the first letter in the arrangement. Once we have chosen the first letter, we choose one of the 4 remaining letters as the second letter. Then, we choose one of the 3 remaining letters as the third letter.

One of the 2 remaining letters is chosen as the fourth letter, and the 1 letter that remains must be the fifth letter of the arrangement.

This gives us $5\times4\times3\times2\times1 = $ **5!** different arrangements of the letters B, E, A, S and T.

80. There are 9 digits that can be placed in the top-left circle.

Once we have placed a digit in the top-left circle, there are 8 digits that can be placed in the top-right circle.

Next, we choose one of the remaining 7 digits to place in the next circle.

We continue this way until there is only 1 choice for the digit that can be placed in the last circle.

This gives us $9\times8\times7\times6\times5\times4\times3\times2\times1 = $ **9!** different ways to place the digits 1 through 9 in the circles.

— *or* —

We choose the circle each digit will be placed in. We choose from nine circles to place the 1. Once the 1 is placed, we choose from eight circles to place to 2. Then, we choose from seven remaining circles for the 3. We continue until there is only one circle left for the 9.

This gives us $9\times8\times7\times6\times5\times4\times3\times2\times1 = $ **9!** different ways to place the digits 1 through 9 in the circles.

81. There are 7 letters in ACADEMY. In each new arrangement, the A's must be next to each other. So, we attach the two A's to make one new "letter": AA.

Now, we have six "letters" to arrange: AA, C, D, E, M, and Y. In every arrangement, the two A's will be next to each other. There are 6! ways to arrange these 6 "letters."

Therefore, there are **6!** ways to arrange the letters of ACADEMY so that the two A's are next to each other.

82. There are 7! ways to order the 7 little monsters from first to last. So, there are 7! = **5,040** different orders in which the little monsters could finish.

83. There are 8 different letters to arrange: Q, U, E, S, T, I, O, and N.

We can arrange these 8 different letters in 8! = 40,320 different orders. However, one of these arrangements is Q-U-E-S-T-I-O-N, which we cannot include.

So, we subtract one arrangement. All together, there are $40,320 - 1 = $ **40,319** different ways to arrange the letters in the word QUESTION, not including Q-U-E-S-T-I-O-N.

84. Since 0 cannot be used as the first (hundred-thousands) digit, there are 5 digits (1, 2, 3, 4, or 5) that can be used as the hundred-thousands digit of the number.

Once we have chosen the first digit, there are still 5 choices for the second digit. For example, if 2 is the first digit, then the second digit could be 0, 1, 3, 4, or 5.

Once we have chosen the first and second digits, we choose one of the 4 remaining digits as the third.

We continue this way until there is only one digit remaining to be the sixth (ones) digit of the number.

All together, this gives us $5\times5\times4\times3\times2\times1 = 5\times(5!)$ ways to arrange these digits into a 6-digit number.

Since 5! = 120, we have $5\times(5!) = 5\times120 = $ **600** ways to arrange the digits 0, 1, 2, 3, 4, and 5 into a six-digit number.

85. There are 24 hours in one day, and there are 30 days in September. So, there are $30\times24 = 720$ hours in September. Using the numbers at the top of the page, we see that 720 = 6!, so $n = $ **6**.

— *or* —

There are $24 = 4\times3\times2\times1$ hours in a day.

There are $30 = 6\times5$ days in September.

So, there are $30\times24 = 6\times5\times4\times3\times2\times1 = 6!$ hours in September, and we have $n = $ **6**.

86. Lizzie will arrange the 4 math books in some order on the left, and the 4 history books in some order on the right.

math	math	math	math	history	history	history	history

There are 4! ways to arrange the four math books. For each arrangement of the math books, there are 4! ways to arrange the four history books. This gives a total of $4!\times4! = 24\times24 = $ **576** possible arrangements of all eight books.

COUNTING
Counting Pairs 32-35

87. To organize our work, we begin by listing the 4 new flavors that can be made with the banana jellybean: banana-caramel, banana-donut, banana-elderberry, and banana-fudge.

Next, we list the 3 additional flavors that can be made with the caramel jellybean: caramel-donut, caramel-elderberry, and caramel-fudge. The caramel-banana flavor was listed earlier with the banana combinations.

Then, we list the 2 additional flavors that can be made with the donut jellybean: donut-elderberry and donut-fudge. The donut-banana and donut-caramel flavors were listed earlier.

Finally, we list the 1 additional flavor that can be made with elderberry: elderberry-fudge. Every other combination that included elderberry was already listed.

There are no additional flavors that can be made with fudge, since they were all listed earlier.

Using B, C, D, E, and F to represent the flavors, we get the following list of new flavors:

B&C, B&D, B&E, B&F, C&D, C&E, C&F, D&E, D&F, and E&F.

88. We draw 6 lines to connect dot A to each other dot.

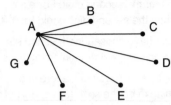

Next, we draw 5 new lines to connect dot B to each other dot. (The line connecting B to A was already drawn above.)

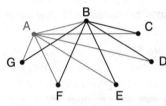

Next, we draw 4 new lines to connect dot C to each other dot. (The lines connecting C to A and C to B were already drawn earlier.)

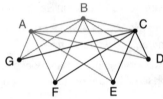

We continue this way, drawing all of the remaining lines to connect D, E, F, and G to each other dot.

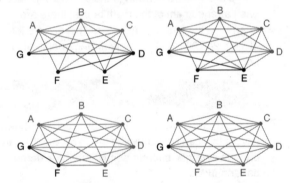

All together, we drew 6+5+4+3+2+1+0 = **21** lines.

89. We will note the cards by the letter or number on the card and the suit. For example, we use A♣ to represent the card below.

To organize our work, we begin by listing the 4 hands that include the A♣:

(A♣, 3♣), (A♣, 5♠), (A♣, 7♠), and (A♣, 9♠).

Next, we list the 3 additional hands that include the 3♣. The hand (3♣, A♣) was already counted above.

(3♣, 5♠), (3♣, 7♠), and (3♣, 9♠).

Next, we list the 2 additional hands that include the 5♠:

(5♠, 7♠) and (5♠, 9♠).

Finally, we list the 1 remaining hand: (7♠, 9♠).

All together 4+3+2+1 = **10** hands of two cards can be chosen from the set of five.

90. To organize our work, we label the circles A, B, C, D, E, and F.

We begin by counting the shaded pairs of circles that include circle A. There are 5 pairs of circles that include circle A, as shown below.

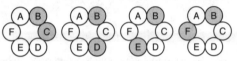

Next, there are 4 additional pairs of circles that include circle B, since the pair (A, B) was already counted above.

Next, there are 3 additional pairs of circles that include circle C, since the pairs (A, C) and (B, C) were counted above.

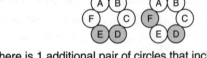

There are 2 additional pairs of circles that include circle D, since the pairs (A, D), (B, D), (C, D) were counted above.

There is 1 additional pair of circles that includes circle E, since the pairs (A, E), (B, E), (C, E), and (D, E) were counted above.

All together, we can make 5+4+3+2+1 = **15** different circle diagrams by shading two of the circles.

91. If the team picks one co-captain first and then another co-captain second, there are 11 choices for the first co-captain and 10 choices for the second co-captain. However, the order in which we choose the co-captains doesn't matter! Since 11×10 = 110 counts each possible pair of co-captains twice, the team can choose 110÷2 = **55** pairs of co-captains.

92. If Jeff chooses toppings one at a time, there are 12 choices for the first topping and 11 choices for the second topping. However, the order in which we select the toppings doesn't matter! Since 12×11 = 132 counts each possible pair of toppings twice, Jeff can order 132÷2 = **66** thin-crust two-topping large pizzas from Vinny's Pizza.

93. Each game is played by one pair of teams. In choosing a pair of teams, we have 8 choices for the "first" team and 7 choices for the "second" team in the game. Then, since the order of the teams does not matter, $8\times7=56$ counts each game twice.

So, there are $56\div2=$ **28** games in the summer season.

94. Each high-five happens between a pair of Minotaur teammates. We have 9 choices for the "first" teammate, and 8 choices for a "second" teammate in a high-five. Then, since order does not matter, $9\times8=72$ counts each high-five twice. So, there are $72\div2=$ **36** high-fives before the game.

95. To split the remaining students into one group of 2 and one group of 3, Ms. Q. just needs to choose the two students who will be in the pair. Then, the remaining 3 students will form the group of 3.

Ms. Q. has 5 choices for the first little monster in the pair and 4 choices for the second little monster in the pair. Then, since the order does not matter, $5\times4=20$ counts each possible pair of students twice. So, there are $20\div2=$ **10** pairs of students that Ms. Q. can select from five, leaving the three remaining students a group of 3.

96. Adding the numbers on any two pieces of paper will give a different sum. The order in which we add the numbers does not matter. So, we count the number of pairs of numbers we can choose:

$$(6\times5)\div2=30\div2=15.$$

All together, there are **15** different possible sums.

97. Each of the 10 vertices of a decagon can be connected to one of 7 other vertices to create a diagonal (a vertex cannot be connected to itself, or to either of the vertices it is already connected to by a side). For example, vertex A can be connected to vertex C, D, E, F, G, H, or I.

However, the order in which we choose the vertices does not matter when drawing a diagonal. For example, connecting A to E creates the same diagonal as connecting E to A.

So, we have counted each diagonal twice.

Connecting each of 10 vertices to 7 other vertices creates $(10\times7)\div2=$ **35** diagonals in a regular decagon.

98. There are 4 suits and 13 ranks. There is one card of each rank in each suit. All together, a standard deck has $4\times13=$ **52** cards.

99. Paul's card is not a number, so it is a Jack, Queen, King, or Ace. We do not know anything about the suit. So, there are 4 possible ranks, and 4 possible suits. Paul has one of $4\times4=$ **16** possible cards.

100. There are 5! ways to order Grogg's five cards. So, Grogg could arrange his cards in $5!=5\times4\times3\times2\times1=$ **120** different orders.

101. If we select cards from a deck one at a time, the first card can be any one of the 52 cards. The second card can be any one of the remaining 51 cards. So, there are $52\times51=2,652$ ways to pick two cards from the deck in order. However, the order in which we pick the cards does not matter. For example, picking A♣ then J♢ gives the same pair of cards as picking J♢ then A♣.

So, there are $(52\times51)\div2=$ **1,326** different pairs of cards that can be selected from a standard deck.

102. Winnie's card is not a heart, so her card is either a club, a diamond, or a spade.

Winnie's card is not a Jack, so it is a 2, 3, 4, 5, 6, 7, 8, 9, 10, Q, K, or A.

There are 3 possible suits, and 12 possible ranks for Winnie's card. So, Winnie has one of $3\times12=$ **36** possible cards.

103. Since Lizzie's card is not red, it is black. So, Lizzie's card is a club or a spade. Lizzie's card is a number, so its rank is 2, 3, 4, 5, 6, 7, 8, 9, or 10. There are 2 possibilities for the card's suit, and 9 possible ranks. So, Lizzie has one of $2\times9=$ **18** possible cards.

104. There are 13 spades in a standard deck of cards. So, we have 13 choices for the "first" spade and 12 choices for the "second" spade in Grogg's hand. Then, since the order of the cards in his hand does not matter, $13\times12=156$ counts each pair of spades twice.

So, Grogg has one of $156\div2=$ **78** hands.

105. One of Alex's cards is a diamond, so it could be any one of 13 ranks. Alex's other card is a spade, so it could also be any one of 13 ranks. So, Alex has one of $13\times13=$ **169** possible pairs of cards.

Note that in this case we never assumed an order to the cards. So, we have not counted each pair of cards twice. Be careful not to divide this by 2, even though the question asks about "pairs" of cards.

106. A Jack of diamonds is both a Jack and a diamond. We do not want to mistakenly count the impossible pair (J♢,J♢). So, we first count all of the pairs that do not include the Jack of diamonds. In this case, there are 12 choices for the card that is a diamond, and 3 choices for the card that is a Jack. This gives us $12\times3=36$ possible pairs that do not include the Jack of diamonds.

Then we count the possible pairs that include the Jack of diamonds. Grok's second card could be one of the 3 remaining Jacks, or one of the 12 remaining diamonds This gives us an additional $3+12 = 15$ pairs of cards.

So, Grok could have $36+15 = \mathbf{51}$ possible pairs of cards.

— *or* —

There are 13 diamonds and 4 jacks in a standard deck. So, it would at first appear that Professor Grok could have one of $13\times4 = 52$ different pairs of cards. However, when we count the pairs this way, we include the impossible pair with two Jacks of diamonds (J$\diamond$,J$\diamond$).

We subtract this impossible pair to leave $52-1 = \mathbf{51}$ possible pairs.

DIVISION
Basics

page 39

1. We make $54 \div 6 = 9$ teams.

2. Each pirate gets $42 \div 7 = 6$ coins.

3. A nickel is worth 5 cents, so Alex has $75 \div 5 = 15$ nickels.

4. Lizzie will finish her book in $150 \div 30 = 5$ days.

5. We divide 48 by 4 to get $48 \div 4 = 12$.

DIVISION
Special Quotients

40-41

6. Any number divided by 1 is itself, so $54{,}321 \div 1 = \textbf{54,321}$.

7. Dividing any nonzero number by itself equals 1. So, $888 \div 888 = \textbf{1}$.

8. Zero divided by any nonzero number is 0, so $0 \div 1{,}000{,}000 = \textbf{0}$.

9. Division by 0 is undefined, so $8{,}765{,}432 \div 0$ is **undefined**.

10. Division by 0 is undefined, so $0 \div 0$ is **undefined**.

11. Any number divided by 1 is itself, so $2{,}468 \div 1 = \textbf{2,468}$.

12. We first simplify the expression: $(2-2) \div (2+2) = 0 \div 4$. Since $0 \div 4 = 0$, we have $(2-2) \div (2+2) = \textbf{0}$.

13. We first simplify the expression: $(2+2) \div (2+2) = 4 \div 4$. Since $4 \div 4 = 1$, we have $(2+2) \div (2+2) = \textbf{1}$.

— *or* —

In the expression, we divide $(2+2)$ by itself. Dividing any nonzero number by itself equals 1. Since $2+2$ is not equal to zero, $(2+2) \div (2+2) = \textbf{1}$.

14. We first simplify the expression: $(2 \div 2) \div (2-2) = 1 \div 0$. Division by 0 is undefined, so $(2 \div 2) \div (2-2)$ is **undefined**.

15. We first simplify the expression: $(2+2) \div (2 \div 2) = 4 \div 1$. $4 \div 1 = 4$, so $(2+2) \div (2 \div 2) = \textbf{4}$.

16. We first simplify the expression:
$((2+2) \div 2) \div 2 = (4 \div 2) \div 2 = 2 \div 2$.
Since $2 \div 2 = 1$, we have $((2+2) \div 2) \div 2 = \textbf{1}$.

17. We first simplify the expression: $(2-2) \div (2-2) = 0 \div 0$. Division by zero is undefined, so $(2-2) \div (2-2)$ is **undefined**.

18. We first simplify the expression: $(a-a) \div a = 0 \div a$. Since a is not zero, $(a-a) \div a = 0 \div a = \textbf{0}$.

19. We first evaluate the expression in parentheses. Since b is not zero, $b \div b = 1$.
So, $b \div (b \div b) = b \div 1 = \boldsymbol{b}$.

20. We first simplify the expression: $c \div (c-c) = c \div 0$. Division by zero is undefined, so $c \div (c-c)$ is **undefined**.

21. In the expression, we divide $(d+d)$ by itself. Dividing any nonzero number by itself equals 1. Since d is not zero, $d+d$ is not 0. So, $(d+d) \div (d+d) = \textbf{1}$.

22. We first simplify the expression. No matter what m is, $m \div 1 = m$. Since m is not zero, $m \div m = 1$.

So, $(m \div 1) \div (m \div m) = m \div 1$.

Since $m \div 1 = m$, we have $(m \div 1) \div (m \div m) = \boldsymbol{m}$.

23. In the expression, we divide $(x \div y)$ by itself. Dividing any nonzero number by itself equals 1. Since y is not 0, $x \div y$ is not undefined. Since x is not 0, $x \div y$ is not 0.

So, $(x \div y) \div (x \div y) = \textbf{1}$.

24. A division expression is only undefined if we divide by 0. So, the expression $n \div (n-1)$ is undefined when $n-1 = 0$.
$n-1 = 0$ when $n = 1$. So, $n \div (n-1)$ is undefined when $n = 1$.

We check our answer. When $n = 1$, we have $n \div (n-1) = 1 \div (1-1) = 1 \div 0$, which is undefined.

DIVISION
Multiples of Ten

42-45

25. Since $9 \times 6 = 54$, we have $\boxed{9{,}000} \times 6 = 54{,}000$.
So, $54{,}000 \div 6 = \textbf{9,000}$.

26. Since $7 \times 9 = 63$, we have $\boxed{700} \times 9 = 6{,}300$.
So, $6{,}300 \div 9 = \textbf{700}$.

27. Since $5 \times 8 = 40$, we have $\boxed{500} \times 8 = 4{,}000$.
So, $4{,}000 \div 8 = \textbf{500}$.

28. Since $3 \times 3 = 9$, we have $\boxed{300{,}000} \times 3 = 900{,}000$.
So, $900{,}000 \div 3 = \textbf{300,000}$.

29. Since $6 \times 7 = 42$, we have $\boxed{600} \times 7 = 4{,}200$.
So, $4{,}200 \div 7 = \textbf{600}$.

30. Since $9 \times 9 = 81$, we have $\boxed{900{,}000} \times 9 = 8{,}100{,}000$.
So, $8{,}100{,}000 \div 9 = \textbf{900,000}$.

31. Since $8 \times 8 = 64$, we have $\boxed{8{,}000} \times 8 = 64{,}000$.
So, $64{,}000 \div 8 = \textbf{8,000}$.

32. Since $4 \times 5 = 20$, we have $\boxed{4{,}000} \times 5 = 20{,}000$.
So, $20{,}000 \div 5 = \textbf{4,000}$.

33. Since $6 \times 12 = 72$, we have $\boxed{60{,}000} \times 12 = 720{,}000$.
So, $720{,}000 \div 12 = \textbf{60,000}$.

34. Since $2 \times 33 = 66$, we have $\boxed{20{,}000} \times 33 = 660{,}000$.
So, $660{,}000 \div 33 = \textbf{20,000}$.

35. We can divide 9 thousands into groups of 3 thousands to make $9 \div 3 = 3$ groups of 3 thousands.

So, $9{,}000 \div 3{,}000 = 9 \div 3 = \textbf{3}$.

36. We can divide 35 thousands into groups of 5 thousands to make $35 \div 5 = 7$ groups of 5 thousands.

So, $35{,}000 \div 5{,}000 = 35 \div 5 = \textbf{7}$.

37. We remove two zeros from both the dividend and the divisor, then compute: $80,000 \div 200 = 800 \div 2 = \textbf{400}$.

38. $280,000 \div 400 = 2,800 \div 4 = \textbf{700}$.

39. $21,000 \div 300 = 210 \div 3 = \textbf{70}$.

40. $4,900,000 \div 7,000 = 4,900 \div 7 = \textbf{700}$.

41. $600,000 \div 1,500 = 6,000 \div 15 = \textbf{400}$.

42. $200,000 \div 25,000 = 200 \div 25 = \textbf{8}$.

43. $125,000 \div 500 = 1,250 \div 5 = \textbf{250}$.

44. $330,000 \div 1,100 = 3,300 \div 11 = \textbf{300}$.

45. We find the height of the rectangle by dividing its area by its width: $18,000 \div 600 = 180 \div 6 = \textbf{30 centimeters}$.

46. In 30 days, Liam drives 6,300 miles. So, each day, Liam drives $6,300 \div 30 = 630 \div 3 = \textbf{210 miles}$.

47. We can divide the 24,000 beads into groups of 400 to find the number of necklaces Winnie can make: $24,000 \div 400 = 240 \div 4 = \textbf{60 necklaces}$.

48. We divide the 340,000 books into 1,700 groups to find the number of books on each bookshelf: $340,000 \div 1,700 = 3,400 \div 17 = \textbf{200 books}$.

49. We divide the perimeter of the regular polygon by the number of sides to find the length of each side: $630,000,000 \div 700 = 6,300,000 \div 7 = \textbf{900,000 millimeters}$.

50. All together, $31,000 + 19,000 = 50,000$ tickets were sold. We find the cost of each ticket by dividing the total ticket sales by the number of tickets sold: $200,000 \div 50,000 = 20 \div 5 = \textbf{4 dollars}$.

51. We find the number of coins by dividing the total worth of the coins in the chest by the worth of each coin: $480,000 \div 300 = 4,800 \div 3 = \textbf{1,600 coins}$.

52. We calculate the worth of each group of coins by dividing the total worth of the coins in the chest by the number of pirates who split the coins: $480,000 \div 20 = 48,000 \div 2 = \textbf{24,000 dollars}$.

— or —

In the previous problem, we found that there are 1,600 coins in the chest. Each of the 20 pirates receives $1,600 \div 20 = 160 \div 2 = 80$ coins. Since each coin is worth 300 dollars, each group of 80 coins is worth $80 \times 300 = \textbf{24,000 dollars}$.

DIVISION
Long Division
46-49

For each long division problem below, we show some steps you may have taken to estimate and divide. You may have taken different steps to find the same estimate, quotient, and remainder.

53. 9 is close to 10, and 671 is close to 700. So, we estimate that $671 \div 9$ is about $700 \div 10 = \textbf{70}$.

$9 \times 70 = 630$. So, 9 can go into 671 at least 70 times. We subtract 630 from 671 and have 41 left over. Since 41 is more than 9, we keep dividing.

$$\begin{array}{r} 70 \\ 9\,)\overline{671} \\ -630 \\ \hline 41 \end{array}$$

$9 \times 4 = 36$, so 9 can go into 41 at least 4 times. We subtract 36 from 41 and have 5 left over. Since 5 is less than 9, we can't subtract any more 9's.

All together, we subtracted $70 + 4 = 74$ nines.

$$\begin{array}{r} 4\rceil 74 \\ 70 \\ 9\,)\overline{671} \\ -630 \\ \hline 41 \\ -36 \\ \hline 5 \end{array}$$

So, the quotient of $671 \div 9$ is **74** and the remainder is **5**.

54. 32 is close to 30, and 822 is close to 810. So, we estimate that $822 \div 32$ is about $810 \div 30 = 27$. We circle the closest answer choice, **30**.

$32 \times 20 = 640$. So, 32 can go into 822 at least 20 times. We subtract 640 from 822 and have 182 left over. Since 182 is more than 32, we keep dividing.

$$\begin{array}{r} 20 \\ 32\,)\overline{822} \\ -640 \\ \hline 182 \end{array}$$

$32 \times 5 = 160$, so 32 can go into 182 at least 5 times. We subtract 160 from 182 and have 22 left over. Since 22 is less than 32, we can't subtract any more 32's.

All together, we subtracted $20 + 5 = 25$ thirty-twos.

$$\begin{array}{r} 5\rceil 25 \\ 20 \\ 32\,)\overline{822} \\ -640 \\ \hline 182 \\ -160 \\ \hline 22 \end{array}$$

So, the quotient of $822 \div 32$ is **25** and the remainder is **22**.

55. We know that $12 \times 50 = 600$, so $600 \div 12 = 50$. Since 654 is more than 600, we know $654 \div 12$ is a little more than $600 \div 12 = 50$. We circle the closest answer choice, **55**.

$12 \times 50 = 600$. So, 12 can go into 654 at least 50 times. We subtract 600 from 654 and have 54 left over. Since 54 is more than 12, we keep dividing.

$$\begin{array}{r} 50 \\ 12\,)\overline{654} \\ -600 \\ \hline 54 \end{array}$$

$12 \times 4 = 48$, so 12 can go into 54 at least 4 times. We subtract 48 from 54 and have 6 left over. Since 6 is less than 12, we can't subtract any more 12's.

All together, we subtracted $50 + 4 = 54$ twelves.

$$\begin{array}{r} 4\rceil 54 \\ 50 \\ 12\,)\overline{654} \\ -600 \\ \hline 54 \\ -48 \\ \hline 6 \end{array}$$

So, the quotient of $654 \div 12$ is **54** and the remainder is **6**.

56. 4,123 is close to 4,000. So, we estimate that $4,123 \div 40$ is about $4,000 \div 40 = \textbf{100}$.

$40 \times 100 = 4,000$. So, 40 can go into 4,000 at least 100 times. We subtract 4,000 from 4,123 and have 123 left over. Since 123 is more than 40, we keep dividing.

$$\begin{array}{r} 100 \\ 40\,)\overline{4,123} \\ -4,000 \\ \hline 123 \end{array}$$

$40 \times 3 = 120$, so 40 can go into 123 at least 3 times. We subtract 120 from 123 and have 3 left over. Since 3 is less than 40, we can't subtract any more 40's.

$$\begin{array}{r} 3\rceil 103 \\ 100 \\ 40\,)\overline{4,123} \\ -4,000 \\ \hline 123 \\ -120 \\ \hline 3 \end{array}$$

All together, we subtracted $100 + 3 = 103$ forties. So, the quotient of $4,123 \div 40$ is **103** and the remainder is **3**.

57. 52 is close to 50, and 1,312 is close to 1,300. So, we estimate that $1,312 \div 52$ is about $1,300 \div 50 = 26$. We circle the closest answer choice, **25**.

$$\begin{array}{r} 5 \\ 20 \end{array} \bigg\} 25$$
$$52 \overline{)\,1,312}$$
$$\underline{-1,040}$$
$$272$$
$$\underline{-260}$$
$$12$$

All together, we subtracted $20+5 = 25$ fifty-twos.

So, the quotient of $1,312 \div 52$ is **25** and the remainder is **12**.

58. 21 is close to 20, and 1,953 is close to 2,000. So, we estimate that $1,953 \div 21$ is about $2,000 \div 20 = \mathbf{100}$.

$$\begin{array}{r} 3 \\ 40 \\ 50 \end{array} \bigg\} 93$$
$$21 \overline{)\,1,953}$$
$$\underline{-1,050}$$
$$903$$
$$\underline{-840}$$
$$63$$
$$\underline{-63}$$
$$0$$

All together, we subtracted $50+40+3 = 93$ twenty-ones.

So, the quotient of $1,953 \div 21$ is **93** and the remainder is **0**.

59. 96 is close to 100, so we estimate that $15,000 \div 96$ is about $15,000 \div 100 = \mathbf{150}$.

$$\begin{array}{r} 1 \\ 5 \\ 50 \\ 100 \end{array} \bigg\} 156$$
$$96 \overline{)\,15,000}$$
$$\underline{-9,600}$$
$$5,400$$
$$\underline{-4,800}$$
$$600$$
$$\underline{-480}$$
$$120$$
$$\underline{-96}$$
$$24$$

All together, we subtracted $100+50+5+1 = 156$ ninety-sixes.

So, the quotient of $15,000 \div 96$ is **156** and the remainder is **24**.

60. 77 is close to 80, and 31,975 is close to 32,000. So, we estimate that $31,975 \div 77$ is close to $32,000 \div 80 = \mathbf{400}$.

$$\begin{array}{r} 5 \\ 10 \\ 200 \\ 200 \end{array} \bigg\} 415$$
$$77 \overline{)\,31,975}$$
$$\underline{-15,400}$$
$$16,575$$
$$\underline{-15,400}$$
$$1,175$$
$$\underline{-770}$$
$$405$$
$$\underline{-385}$$
$$20$$

All together, we subtracted $200+200+10+5 = 415$ seventy-sevens.

So, the quotient of $31,975 \div 77$ is **415** and the remainder is **20**.

61. We know that $70 \times 70 = 4,900$, so $4,900 \div 70 = 70$. 67 is close to 70, and 5,091 is close to 4,900, so we estimate that $5,091 \div 67$ is about $4,900 \div 70 = \mathbf{70}$.

$$\begin{array}{r} 5 \\ 10 \\ 10 \\ 50 \end{array} \bigg\} 75$$
$$67 \overline{)\,5,091}$$
$$\underline{-3,350}$$
$$1,741$$
$$\underline{-670}$$
$$1,071$$
$$\underline{-670}$$
$$401$$
$$\underline{-335}$$
$$66$$

All together, we subtracted $50+10+10+5 = 75$ sixty-sevens.

So, the quotient of $5,091 \div 67$ is **75** and the remainder is **66**.

62. 9,551 is close to 9,600, and 28 is close to 30. So, we estimate that $9,551 \div 28$ is about $9,600 \div 30 = \mathbf{320}$.

$$\begin{array}{r} 1 \\ 20 \\ 20 \\ 100 \\ 200 \end{array} \bigg\} 341$$
$$28 \overline{)\,9,551}$$
$$\underline{-5,600}$$
$$3,951$$
$$\underline{-2,800}$$
$$1,151$$
$$\underline{-560}$$
$$591$$
$$\underline{-560}$$
$$31$$
$$\underline{-28}$$
$$3$$

All together, we subtracted $200+100+20+20+1 = 341$ twenty-eights.

So, the quotient of $9,551 \div 28$ is **341** and the remainder is **3**.

63. 19 is close to 20, and 1,282 is close to 1,300. So, we estimate that $1,282 \div 19$ is close to $1,300 \div 20 = \mathbf{65}$.

$$\begin{array}{r} 2 \\ 5 \\ 10 \\ 50 \end{array} \bigg\} 67$$
$$19 \overline{)\,1,282}$$
$$\underline{-950}$$
$$332$$
$$\underline{-190}$$
$$142$$
$$\underline{-95}$$
$$47$$
$$\underline{-38}$$
$$9$$

All together, we subtracted $50+10+5+2 = 67$ nineteens.

So, the quotient of $1,282 \div 19$ is **67** and the remainder is **9**.

64. 86 is close to 80, and 40,196 is close to 40,000. So, we estimate that $40,196 \div 86$ is about $40,000 \div 80 = \mathbf{500}$.

$$\begin{array}{r} 2 \\ 5 \\ 10 \\ 50 \\ 200 \\ 200 \end{array} \bigg\} 467$$
$$86 \overline{)\,40,196}$$
$$\underline{-17,200}$$
$$22,996$$
$$\underline{-17,200}$$
$$5,796$$
$$\underline{-4,300}$$
$$1,496$$
$$\underline{-860}$$
$$636$$
$$\underline{-430}$$
$$206$$
$$\underline{-172}$$
$$34$$

All together, we subtracted $200+200+50+10+5+2 = 467$ eighty-sixes, and we have 34 left over.

So, the quotient of $40,196 \div 86$ is **467** and the remainder is **34**.

65. Consider dividing 36,036 marbles into 9 buckets.

We begin by dividing 36,000 of the marbles into 9 buckets, which gives us $36,000 \div 9 = 4,000$ marbles in each bucket.

Then, we divide the remaining 36 marbles among the 9 buckets, which gives us $36 \div 9 = 4$ more marbles in each bucket. So, each bucket has a total of $4,000 + 4 = 4,004$ marbles.

Therefore, $36,036 \div 9 = \mathbf{4,004}$.

— *or* —

$$\begin{aligned} 36,036 \div 9 &= (36,000 + 36) \div 9 \\ &= (36,000 \div 9) + (36 \div 9) \\ &= 4,000 + 4 \\ &= 4,004. \end{aligned}$$

Therefore, $36,036 \div 9 = \mathbf{4,004}$.

66. $$\begin{aligned} 2,840 \div 4 &= (2,800 + 40) \div 4 \\ &= (2,800 \div 4) + (40 \div 4) \\ &= 700 + 10 \\ &= 710. \end{aligned}$$

Therefore, $2,840 \div 4 = \mathbf{710}$.

67. $$\begin{aligned} 490,014 \div 7 &= (490,000 + 14) \div 7 \\ &= (490,000 \div 7) + (14 \div 7) \\ &= 70,000 + 2 \\ &= 70,002. \end{aligned}$$

Therefore, $490,014 \div 7 = \mathbf{70,002}$.

68. $$\begin{aligned} 4,032 \div 8 &= (4,000 + 32) \div 8 \\ &= (4,000 \div 8) + (32 \div 8) \\ &= 500 + 4 \\ &= 504. \end{aligned}$$

Therefore, $4,032 \div 8 = \mathbf{504}$.

69. $$\begin{aligned} 5,412 \div 6 &= (5,400 + 12) \div 6 \\ &= (5,400 \div 6) + (12 \div 6) \\ &= 900 + 2 \\ &= 902. \end{aligned}$$

Therefore, $5,412 \div 6 = \mathbf{902}$.

70. $$\begin{aligned} 205,015 \div 5 &= (200,000 + 5,000 + 15) \div 5 \\ &= (200,000 \div 5) + (5,000 \div 5) + (15 \div 5) \\ &= 40,000 + 1,000 + 3 \\ &= 41,003. \end{aligned}$$

Therefore, $205,015 \div 5 = \mathbf{41,003}$.

71. $$\begin{aligned} 640,400 \div 8 &= (640,000 + 400) \div 8 \\ &= (640,000 \div 8) + (400 \div 8) \\ &= 80,000 + 50 \\ &= 80,050. \end{aligned}$$

Therefore, $640,400 \div 8 = \mathbf{80,050}$.

72. $$\begin{aligned} 2,701,800 \div 9 &= (2,700,000 + 1,800) \div 9 \\ &= (2,700,000 \div 9) + (1,800 \div 9) \\ &= 300,000 + 200 \\ &= 300,200. \end{aligned}$$

Therefore, $2,701,800 \div 9 = \mathbf{300,200}$.

73. Consider cutting a 180-inch rope into 4 equal pieces. We begin by cutting the rope into two equal pieces, each of length 90 inches. Then, we cut each of those pieces into two equal pieces for a total of 4 equal pieces, each with length $90 \div 2 = 45$ inches. Therefore, $180 \div 4 = \mathbf{45}$.

— *or* —

$180 \div 4 = (180 \div 2) \div 2 = 90 \div 2 = 45.$

Therefore, $180 \div 4 = \mathbf{45}$.

74. $$\begin{aligned} 252 \div 4 &= (252 \div 2) \div 2 \\ &= 126 \div 2 \\ &= 63. \end{aligned}$$

Therefore, $252 \div 4 = \mathbf{63}$.

75. $$\begin{aligned} 560 \div 4 &= (560 \div 2) \div 2 \\ &= 280 \div 2 \\ &= 140. \end{aligned}$$

Therefore, $560 \div 4 = \mathbf{140}$.

76. $$\begin{aligned} 2,500 \div 4 &= (2,500 \div 2) \div 2 \\ &= 1,250 \div 2 \\ &= 625. \end{aligned}$$

Therefore, $2,500 \div 4 = \mathbf{625}$.

77. $$\begin{aligned} 4,900 \div 4 &= (4,900 \div 2) \div 2 \\ &= 2,450 \div 2 \\ &= 1,225. \end{aligned}$$

Therefore, $4,900 \div 4 = \mathbf{1,225}$.

78. $$\begin{aligned} 2,108 \div 4 &= (2,108 \div 2) \div 2 \\ &= 1,054 \div 2 \\ &= 527. \end{aligned}$$

Therefore, $2,108 \div 4 = \mathbf{527}$.

79. Consider cutting a rope into 16 equal pieces. We first cut it into 2 equal pieces.

Then, each of those pieces can be cut into two equal pieces to give us a total of 4 equal pieces.

We repeat this step a third time, cutting each of the four equal pieces into two equal pieces to give us 8 equal pieces.

Finally, we cut each piece into two equal pieces a fourth time to get 16 equal pieces.

We have divided the length of the original rope into 16 equal smaller pieces by dividing its length by two 4 times.

Similarly, to divide a number by 16, we can divide it by two **4** times.

For example, $80 \div 16 = 80 \div 2 \div 2 \div 2 \div 2 = 5$.

— *or* —

Each time we divide a number by 2, we double the number of equal parts.

Dividing a number by 2 gives us 2 equal parts.

Dividing a number by 2 twice gives us $2 \times 2 = 4$ equal parts.

Dividing a number by 2 three times gives us $2\times2\times2=8$ equal parts.

Dividing a number by 2 four times, we get $2\times2\times2\times2=16$ equal parts.

So, to divide a number by 16, we can divide it by 2 **4 times.**

80. $325\div5=(325\times2)\div(5\times2)=650\div10=\textbf{65}$.

81. $445\div5=890\div10=\textbf{89}$.

82. $220\div5=440\div10=\textbf{44}$.

83. $185\div5=370\div10=\textbf{37}$.

84. $2,300\div5=4,600\div10=\textbf{460}$.

85. $315\div5=630\div10=\textbf{63}$.

86. $3,335\div5=6,670\div10=\textbf{667}$.

87. $1,745\div5=3,490\div10=\textbf{349}$.

88. 1,463 is 3 more than 1,460, which is a multiple of 5. So, $1,463\div5$ has remainder 3.

To find the quotient, we divide $1,460\div5$ by doubling the dividend and the divisor. $1,460\div5=2,920\div10=292$.

So, the quotient of $1,463\div5$ is **292**, and the remainder is **3**.

89. Doubling the dividend and divisor, we compute $270\div45=540\div90=\textbf{6}$.

90. $175\div35=350\div70=\textbf{5}$.

91. $1,650\div55=3,300\div110=\textbf{30}$.

92. $32,600\div50=65,200\div100=\textbf{652}$.

93. $465\div15=930\div30=\textbf{31}$.

94. $1,300\div65=2,600\div130=\textbf{20}$.

95. $31,500\div350=63,000\div700=\textbf{90}$.

96. $120,000\div150=240,000\div300=\textbf{800}$.

97. **Doubling any multiple of 5 gives us a number that is a multiple of 10.** As we found earlier in this chapter, dividing by multiples of ten is often easier than dividing by most other numbers. This is because we can remove the same number of zeros from the end of each number in a division problem without changing the quotient!

DIVISION
Division Pyramid   54-55

98. In this puzzle, the divisor is 2. We start at the top block, and continue to divide by 2 until we arrive at the bottom. The completed puzzle is shown below.

$248\div2=\boxed{124}$, and $124\div2=\boxed{62}$, and $62\div2=\boxed{31}$.

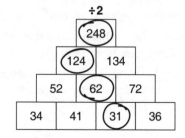

99. $832\div4=(832\div2)\div2=416\div2=\boxed{208}$.
  or $(800+32)\div4=(800\div4)+(32\div4)=200+8=\boxed{208}$.

$208\div4=(208\div2)\div2=104\div2=\boxed{52}$.
  or $(200+8)\div4=(200\div4)+(8\div4)=50+2=\boxed{52}$.

$52\div4=(52\div2)\div2=26\div2=\boxed{13}$.

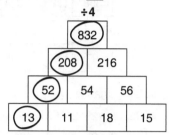

100. $848\div2=\boxed{424}$,
$424\div2=\boxed{212}$,
$212\div2=\boxed{106}$,
and $106\div2=\boxed{53}$.

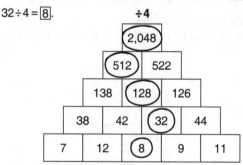

101. $2,048\div4=(2,048\div2)\div2=1,024\div2=\boxed{512}$.
  or $(2,000+48)\div4=(2,000\div4)+(48\div4)=500+12=\boxed{512}$.

$512\div4=(512\div2)\div2=256\div2=\boxed{128}$.

$128\div4=(128\div2)\div2=64\div2=\boxed{32}$.
  or $(120+8)\div4=(120\div4)+(8\div4)=30+2=\boxed{32}$.

$32\div4=\boxed{8}$.

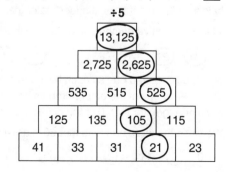

102. $13,125\div5=26,250\div10=\boxed{2,625}$.

$2,625\div5=5,250\div10=\boxed{525}$.

$525\div5=1,050\div10=\boxed{105}$.
  or $(500+25)\div5=(500\div5)+(25\div5)=100+5=\boxed{105}$.

$105\div5=210\div10=\boxed{21}$.
  or $(100+5)\div5=(100\div5)+(5\div5)=20+1=\boxed{21}$.

103. $1{,}584 \div 2 = \boxed{792}$,
$792 \div 2 = \boxed{396}$,
$396 \div 2 = \boxed{198}$,
and $198 \div 2 = \boxed{99}$.

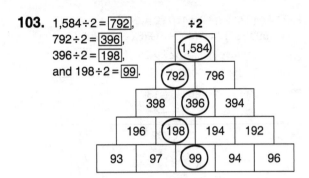

104. $10{,}496 \div 4 = (10{,}496 \div 2) \div 2 = 5{,}248 \div 2 = \boxed{2{,}624}$.

$2{,}624 \div 4 = (2{,}624 \div 2) \div 2 = 1{,}312 \div 2 = \boxed{656}$.

$656 \div 4 = (656 \div 2) \div 2 = 328 \div 2 = \boxed{164}$.

$164 \div 4 = (164 \div 2) \div 2 = 82 \div 2 = \boxed{41}$.

or $(160 + 4) \div 4 = (160 \div 4) + (4 \div 4) = 40 + 1 = \boxed{41}$.

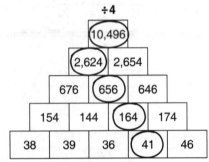

105. $41{,}250 \div 5 = 82{,}500 \div 10 = \boxed{8{,}250}$.

$8{,}250 \div 5 = 16{,}500 \div 10 = \boxed{1{,}650}$.

$1{,}650 \div 5 = 3{,}300 \div 10 = \boxed{330}$.

$330 \div 5 = 660 \div 10 = \boxed{66}$.

or $(300 + 30) \div 5 = (300 \div 5) + (30 \div 5) = 60 + 6 = \boxed{66}$.

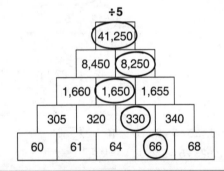

DIVISION
Divisibility   56–57

106. $81 \div 9$, $27 \div 9$, $63 \div 9$, $45 \div 9$, and $9 \div 9$ each have remainder 0. If we divide any of the other numbers below by 9, we get a remainder greater than 0.

We circle the five numbers that are divisible by 9:

(81)   (27)   78   (63)   57   (45)   (9)   3

107. $60 \div 1$, $60 \div 12$, and $60 \div 60$ each have remainder 0. If we divide 60 by any of the other numbers below, we get a remainder greater than 0 or the division is undefined.

We circle the three numbers that 60 is divisible by:

0   (1)   11   (12)   18   (60)   120

108. $96 = 8 \times 12$, so 96 is divisible by 8. The next-largest multiple of 8 is $8 \times 13 = 96 + 8 = 104$, which is a three-digit number. So, **96** is the largest two-digit number that is divisible by 8.

109. We work backwards, starting with the largest 2-digit number, 99.

$99 = 3 \times 33$, so 99 is divisible by 3.
98 is even, so 98 is divisible by 2.
$97 \div 2$ has remainder 1, and $97 \div 3$ has remainder 1.

So, **97** is the largest two-digit number that is not divisible by 2 or by 3.

110. There are two multiples of 6 between 40 and 50: 42 and 48. Since $42 = 6 \times 7$, we know 42 is divisible by both 6 and 7. However, $48 \div 7$ has remainder 6.

So **48** is the only number between 40 and 50 that is divisible by 6 but not by 7.

111. The two-digit numbers that are divisible by 10 are:

10, 20, 30, 40, 50, 60, 70, 80, and 90.

Among these nine numbers, four are divisible by 20:

20, 40, 60, and 80.

This leaves $9 - 4 = \mathbf{5}$ two-digit numbers that are divisible by 10 but not by 20.

112. We list multiples of 5 that are greater than 0:

5, 10, 15, 20, 25, 30, 35, 40, 45, 50, …

We also list multiples of 6 that are greater than 0:

6, 12, 18, 24, 30, 36, 42, 48, 54, 60, …

30 is the smallest number that appears on both lists. So, **30** is the smallest number besides 0 that is divisible by 5 and by 6.

113. $\boxed{2\,9\,A}$ is a three-digit multiple of 13 that is greater than $20 \times 13 = 260$. We add 13's to 260 to find a multiple of 13 with hundreds digit 2 and tens digit 9:

$$\overset{+13}{\curvearrowright} \quad \overset{+13}{\curvearrowright} \quad \overset{+13}{\curvearrowright}$$
$$260 \quad 273 \quad 286 \quad 299$$

The next-smallest multiple of 13 is $299 + 13 = 312$, so $\boxed{2\,9\,9}$ is the only number with hundreds digit 2 and tens digit 9 that is divisible by 13. Therefore, $A = \mathbf{9}$.

114. We know that $200 \times 4 = 800$ is a multiple of 4.

We add 4's to find the multiples of 4 with hundreds digit 8 and tens digit 1:

$201 \times 4 = 800 + 4 = 804$. $202 \times 4 = 804 + 4 = 808$.
$203 \times 4 = 808 + 4 = 812$. $204 \times 4 = 812 + 4 = 816$.

The next-smallest multiple of 4 is $205 \times 4 = 816 + 4 = 820$. So, the three-digit number can only be 812 or 816.

We divide both of these numbers by 7 to find that $812 \div 7$ has remainder 0 and $816 \div 7$ has remainder 4.

So, $\boxed{8\,1\,2}$ is the only three-digit number with hundreds digit 8 and tens digit 1 that is divisible by 4 and by 7. Therefore, $B = \mathbf{2}$.

115. We look for pairs of numbers whose product is 36, organizing our work as shown below.

36 = 1×36, so 36 is divisible by 1 and by 36.
36 = 2×18, so 36 is divisible by 2 and by 18.
36 = 3×12, so 36 is divisible by 3 and by 12.
36 = 4×9, so 36 is divisible by 4 and by 9.
36÷5 has remainder 1, so 36 is not divisible by 5.
36 = 6×6, so 36 is divisible by 6.

We have found the nine numbers 36 is divisible by:
1, 2, 3, 4, 6, 9, 12, 18, and 36.

DIVISION
Divisibility Rules   58-61

116. We are told that 156 is divisible by 12, and we know that 12 is divisible by 4. So, 156 is divisible by 4. The statement is **true**.

$$156 = 12 \times 13$$
$$= (4 \times 3) \times 13$$
$$= 4 \times (3 \times 13)$$
$$= 4 \times 39.$$

117. We are told that x is divisible by 15, and we know that 15 is divisible by 3. So, x is divisible by 3. The statement is **true**.

Since x is divisible by 15, x is a multiple of 15. We can write $x = 15 \times a$ for some number a. Then, since $15 = 3 \times 5$, we have

$$x = 15 \times a$$
$$= (3 \times 5) \times a$$
$$= 3 \times (5 \times a).$$

No matter what number a is, x is divisible by 3.

118. 22 is not divisible by 44. So, without more information, we cannot tell whether y is divisible by 44. Not every number that is divisible by 22 is also divisible by 44.

For example, 88 is divisible by 22 and by 44. However, 66 is divisible by 22 but not by 44.

So, the statement is **false**.

119. Some numbers that are divisible by 3 are divisible by 6, such as 12, 30, and 66.

However, there are also numbers that are divisible by 3 but not by 6, such as 3, 9, 15, 21, and 63.

The statement is **false**.

120. Since $21 = 7 \times 3$, we know that 21 is divisible by 7. So, a number that is divisible by 21 is divisible by 7. The statement is **true**.

121. Every number that is divisible by 24 is divisible by 4 and by 6. However, not every number that is divisible by 4 and by 6 is divisible by 24.

For example, 36 is divisible by 4 and by 6, but 36 is *not* divisible by 24. So, not every number that is divisible by 4 and by 6 is divisible by 24. The statement is **false**.

122. Since $14 = 2 \times 7$, we know that every multiple of 14 is a multiple of 2 and therefore even.

5,971 is an odd number, so it cannot possibly be divisible by 14.

123. If a number is divisible by 100, it is also divisible by all of the numbers that 100 is divisible by. To find the numbers that 100 is divisible by, we look for pairs of numbers whose product is 100. We organize our work as shown below.

100 = 1×100, so 100 is divisible by 1 and by 100.
100 = 2×50, so 100 is divisible by 2 and by 50.
100 is not divisible by 3.
100 = 4×25, so 100 is divisible by 4 and by 25.
100 = 5×20, so 100 is divisible by 5 and by 20.
100 is not divisible by 6, 7, 8, or 9.
100 = 10×10, so 100 is divisible by 10.

We found eight other numbers that Winnie's number is definitely divisible by: **1, 2, 4, 5, 10, 20, 25, and 50.**

124. We divide 5,100÷25 to find that **5,100÷25 = 204. Since 5,100÷25 has remainder 0, we know that 5,100 is divisible by 25.**

— or —

We see that 5,100 = 100×51, so 5,100 is divisible by 100. Any number divisible by 100 is also divisible by 25, since 100 is divisible by 25.

5,100 is divisible by 100, and 100 is divisible by 25. So, 5,100 is divisible by 25.

We can write $5,100 = 100 \times 51$
$$= (25 \times 4) \times 51$$
$$= 25 \times (4 \times 51)$$
$$= 25 \times 204.$$

125. All five of the answer choices are between 5,100 and 5,200. In the previous solution, we determined that 5,100 is divisible by 25, so 5,100 is a multiple of 25. We add 25's to 5,100 to find the next few multiples of 25:

5,100+25 = 5,125,
5,125+25 = 5,150,
5,150+25 = 5,175, and
5,175+25 = 5,200.

5,125 is the only number among the answer choices that is a multiple of 25 and therefore is divisible by 25.

5,105   5,115   (5,125)   5,135   5,145

126. We know that 1,234,567,800 is divisible by 100. So, 1,234,567,800 is divisible by 25. To find the next multiples of 25, we add 25's:

1,234,567,800+25 = 1,234,567,825.
1,234,567,825+25 = 1,234,567,850.
1,234,567,850+25 = 1,234,567,875.
1,234,567,875+25 = 1,234,567,900.

We notice that the multiples of 25 are multiples of 100, or are 25, 50, or 75 more than a multiple of 100. **1,234,567,890 is 90 more than a multiple of 100. Therefore, 1,234,567,890 is not a multiple of 25.**

127. We divide 678,900÷4 to find that **678,900÷4 = 169,725 with remainder 0. So, 678,900 is divisible by 4.**

— or —

We see that $678,900 = 100 \times 6,789$. So, $678,900$ is divisible by 100. Any number that is divisible by 100 is also divisible by 4, since 100 is divisible by 4. **678,900 is divisible by 100, and 100 is divisible by 4. So, 678,900 is divisible by 4.**

We could write $678,900 = 100 \times 6,789$
$$= (4 \times 25) \times 6,789$$
$$= 4 \times (25 \times 6,789).$$

128. Every number that is divisible by 100 is also divisible by 4. Since $700 = 7 \times 100$ is divisible by 100, we know that 700 is divisible by 4. To find the multiples of 4 that are greater than 700, we add 4's:

700, 704, 708, 712, 716, 720, 724, 728, 732, 736, 740, 744, 748, 752, ... are all multiples of 4.

720 is the one number among the five answer choices that is a multiple of 4 and therefore divisible by 4.

710　　(720)　　725　　734　　750

129. We know that $98,765,400$ is divisible by 100 and therefore divisible by 4.

We can add eight 4's to $98,765,400$ to get $98,765,400 + (8 \times 4) = 98,765,432$.

So, 98,765,432 is a multiple of 4 and therefore is divisible by 4.

130. A number is divisible by 25 if and only if it ends in 00, 25, 50, or 75. So, 10,0<u>25</u> and 1,4<u>00</u> are both divisible by 25.

9,855 and 5,485 do not end in 00, 25, 50, or 75. So, of these four numbers, only 10,025 and 1,400 are divisible by 25.

9,855　　5,485　　(10,025)　(1,400)

131. A number is divisible by 5 if and only if its units digit is 0 or 5. So, 65,80<u>0</u> and 1,39<u>5</u> and 6,48<u>0</u> are divisible by five.

A number is divisible by 2 if and only if its units digit is even: 0, 2, 4, 6, or 8.

The only number that is divisible by 5 but not by 2 is 1,395.

5,553　　65,800　　(1,395)　　6,480

132. A number is divisible by 4 if the number formed by its last two digits is divisible by 4 (00, 04, 08, ..., 92, or 96).

6,700 ends in 00, which is divisible by 4 (0 is divisible by every number except 0).
2,196 ends in 96, which is divisible by 4.
5,018 ends in 18, which is not divisible by 4.
5,434 ends in 34, which is not divisible by 4.
So, among the four numbers, two of the numbers are divisible by four: 6,700 and 2,196.

(6,700)　(2,196)　　5,018　　5,434

133. A number is divisible by 25 if the number formed by its last two digits is divisible by 25 (00, 25, 50, or 75).

19,075 is the smallest multiple of 25 that is greater than 19,056. Therefore, $19,075 - 19,056 = \mathbf{19}$ is the smallest number that you can add to 19,056 that will make a number that is divisible by 25.

134. We can look at the last two digits of the sums to find the pair whose sum ends in 00, 25, 50, or 75. We organize our work as shown below.

$9,802 + 1,488$ ends in 90.
$9,802 + 4,137$ ends in 39.
$9,802 + 5,135$ ends in 37.
$1,488 + 4,137$ ends in 25 (since $88 + 37 = 125$).
$1,488 + 5,135$ ends in 23 (since $88 + 35 = 123$).
$4,137 + 5,135$ ends in 72.

So, $1,488 + 4,137$ is the only sum that is divisible by 25.

9,802　(1,488)　(4,137)　5,135

135. A number is divisible by 4 if the number formed by its last two digits is divisible by 4.

There are 6 possible arrangements of the three squares: [4][5][62], [4][62][5], [5][4][62], [5][62][4], [62][5][4], and [62][4][5].

Of these, [5][62][4] is the only number whose last two digits form a number that is divisible by 4. So, **5,624** is divisible by 4.

136. Every multiple of 25 ends in either 0 or 5. We do not have a digit 0, so the 5 must be the ones digit in the multiple of 25: [ ][5].

185 is not divisible by 25 or by 4, so [18] cannot be placed before the [5]. So, [47] must be placed before the [5] to make [47][5], which is divisible by 25. Then, we have [18] and [4] left to make a multiple of 4. Of [18][4] and [4][18], only [18][4] is divisible by 4.

475 is divisible by 25, and **184** is divisible by 4.

137. Neither 75 nor 82 is divisible by 4. So, either [75] or [82] begins the three-digit number divisible by 4. The 3-digit multiple of 4 is either [75][ ] or [82][ ].

Multiples of 4 are even, so the units digit of the multiple of 4 must be [6]. Of [75][6] and [82][6], only **756** is divisible by 4.

Then, we have [82] and [5] left to make a multiple of 25. Of [82][5] and [5][82], only **825** is divisible by 25.

138. A number is divisible by 4 if the number formed by its last two digits is divisible by 4. The two-digit multiples of 4 with units digit 6 are 16, 36, 56, 76, and 96. So, A could be **1, 3, 5, 7, or 9.**

139. The number of muffins left over is equal to the remainder when 134 is divided by 14. We use long division to compute the remainder of $134 \div 14$:

$$
\begin{array}{r}
4 \\
5 \,\rlap{\Big]} 9 \\
14\,\overline{)\,134} \\
-70 \\
\hline
64 \\
-56 \\
\hline
8
\end{array}
$$

$134 \div 8$ has remainder 8, so there are **8** mini-muffins left after Joey shares equally with his chess team.

— *or* —

Since $14 \times 10 = 140$, we have $14 \times 9 = 140 - 14 = 126$. So, if Joey gives each of the 14 team members 9 mini-muffins, they will eat a total of $14 \times 9 = 126$ mini-muffins, leaving $134 - 126 = 8$ mini-muffins left over.

140. The side length of the regular dodecagon is $2,184 \div 12$ millimeters. We use long division to compute $2,184 \div 12$:

$$
\begin{array}{r}
2 \\
30 \\
50 \,\rlap{\Big]} 182 \\
100 \\
12\,\overline{)\,2,184} \\
-1,200 \\
\hline
984 \\
-600 \\
\hline
384 \\
-360 \\
\hline
24 \\
-24 \\
\hline
0
\end{array}
$$

$2,184 \div 12 = 182$, so the side length of the polygon is **182 millimeters**.

141. It will take $1,800 \div 450$ boxes to ship the order. We use long division to compute $1,800 \div 450$:

$$
\begin{array}{r}
2 \\
2 \,\rlap{\Big]} 4 \\
450\,\overline{)\,1,800} \\
-900 \\
\hline
900 \\
-900 \\
\hline
0
\end{array}
$$

It will take **4** boxes to ship the order of pencils.

— *or* —

We double the numerator and denominator:
$1,800 \div 450 = 3,600 \div 900 = 4$.

So, it will take **4** boxes to ship the order of pencils.

142. The area of right triangle ABC is half the area of a rectangle that has the same height and base, as shown below.

The area of triangle ABC is 4,720 square meters, so the area of the rectangle is $4,720 \times 2 = 9,440$ square meters. To find the base of the rectangle, we divide its area by its height: $9,440 \div 40$.

We can remove the zero from the end of each number to make the division a little easier. $9,440 \div 40 = 944 \div 4$.

$$
\begin{aligned}
9,440 \div 40 &= 944 \div 4 \\
&= (944 \div 2) \div 2 \\
&= 472 \div 2 \\
&= 236
\end{aligned}
$$

— *or* —

$$
\begin{array}{r}
6 \\
30 \,\rlap{\Big]} 236 \\
200 \\
4\,\overline{)\,944} \\
-800 \\
\hline
144 \\
-120 \\
\hline
24 \\
-24 \\
\hline
0
\end{array}
$$

$9,440 \div 40 = 236$. So, the length of BC is **236 meters**.

We check that a right triangle with a base of 236 meters and height 40 meters has area 4,720 square meters:

$236 \times 40 \div 2 = 9,440 \div 2 = 4,720$ square meters. ✓

143. When you divide Herbert's age by 25, the remainder is 1. So, Herbert's age is 1 more than a multiple of 25. Multiples of 25 end in 00, 25, 50, or 75. Numbers that are 1 more than a multiple of 25 end in 01, 26, 51, or 76. So, Herbert is either 801, 826, 851, or 876 years old.

When you divide Herbert's age by 4, the remainder is 2. So, Herbert's age is 2 more than a multiple of 4.

801 is 1 more than a multiple of 4 (800).
826 is 2 more than a multiple of 4 (824).
851 is 3 more than a multiple of 4 (848).
876 is a multiple of 4.

826 is the only number between 800 and 900 that is 1 more than a multiple of 25 and 2 more than a multiple of 4. So, Herbert is **826** years old.

144. The station wagon must carry Zack's weight. So, it can carry up to $1,800 - 176 = 1,624$ pounds of flour with Zack in the car. The flour comes in 35-pound sacks, so we divide 1,624 pounds by 35 to find the number of sacks Zack can transport.

$$
\begin{array}{r}
2 \rceil \\
4 \rceil\; 46 \\
40 \rfloor \\
35\,\overline{)\,1,624} \\
-1,400 \\
\hline
224 \\
-140 \\
\hline
84 \\
-70 \\
\hline
14
\end{array}
$$

$1,625 \div 35$ has quotient 46 and remainder 14. So, Zack can transport **46** sacks of flour without exceeding the weight limit. Note that he will still have room for 14 more pounds in the car.

145. Since the school buses can hold no more than 25 monsters, including a driver and one additional adult, each bus can hold at most $25 - 2 = 23$ students.

So, we divide $785 \div 23$ to find the number of school buses needed to take 785 students on a field trip.

$$
\begin{array}{r}
4 \rceil \\
10 \rceil\; 34 \\
20 \rfloor \\
23\,\overline{)\,785} \\
-460 \\
\hline
325 \\
-230 \\
\hline
95 \\
-92 \\
\hline
3
\end{array}
$$

So, we could fill 34 buses with 23 little monsters each, with 3 students left over. We cannot leave any little monsters behind, so we need one more bus.

All together, $34 + 1 = $ **35** buses are needed to take 785 students on a field trip.

146. We multiply 43×225 then divide by 42 to find the remainder. $43 \times 225 = 9,675$. Using long division, we compute that $9,675 \div 42$ has quotient 230 and remainder **15**.

— *or* —

We use what we learned in the Division chapter of Beast Academy 3C.

To find the remainder when 43×225 is divided by 42, we first find the remainder when each of 43 and 225 is divided by 42.

$43 \div 42$ has remainder 1.
$225 \div 42$ has remainder 15.

Then, we multiply the remainders.
$(43 \times 225) \div 42$ has the same remainder as $(1 \times 15) \div 42$.

$1 \times 15 = 15$, and $15 \div 42$ has quotient 0 and remainder 15. So, $(43 \times 225) \div 42$ has remainder **15**.

147. In any division problem, the remainder must always be less than the divisor. Otherwise, we could subtract at least one more of the divisor to get a smaller remainder. Since Amy divides her number by 11, we know that the remainder must be 10 or less.

Then, since we know Amy's remainder is greater than the quotient, Amy's quotient must be 9 or less.

If Amy divides a number by 11, and gets quotient 9 with remainder 10, then she subtracted nine 11's from the number and got a remainder of 10. So, her original number must have been $(11 \times 9) + 10 = 99 + 10 = 109$.

If Amy's quotient is less than 9, then the original number must be less than $11 \times 9 = 99$, which is not a three-digit number. So, Amy's favorite three-digit number must be **109**.

A note about rows and columns:

Many of the problems in this chapter are puzzles that are completed on a grid. We can refer to an item in a grid by the box's row and column. Rows are counted from top to bottom, and columns are counted from left to right as shown below.

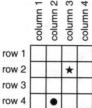

For example, the star on the grid above is in row 2, column 3 (or second row, third column). The circle is in row 4, column 2 (or fourth row, second column).

True/False *page 65-66*

For problems 1-4, we begin by creating a diagram to organize what we know. Arrows point from older to younger, and numbers represent age differences.

Fring is 5 years older than Kim, who is older than Wicket.

Elmore is 4 years older than Zoe.

We use the final statement that Kim is older than Zoe to combine the two diagrams above into one:

1. Fring is older than Kim, who is older than Zoe. So, "Fring is older than Zoe" is **true**.

2. Fring is older than Kim who is older than Wicket, so Fring is older than Wicket. "Wicket is older than Fring" is **false**.

3. We do not know *how much* older Kim is than either Zoe or Wicket.

For example, Kim may be 20 years older than Zoe but 1 year older than Wicket, which makes Wicket older than Elmore.

Or, Kim could be 1 year older than Zoe and 20 years older than Wicket, which makes Elmore older than Wicket.

So, we **can't tell** whether Elmore is older than Wicket.

4. Using the previous diagram, we see that Fring is 5 years older than Kim, who is older than Zoe. So, Fring is more than 5 years older than Zoe. Since Elmore is only 4 years older than Zoe, we know that Fring is older than Elmore. The statement is **true**.

For problems 5-13, we begin by creating a diagram to organize what we know. Arrows point from taller to shorter.

Ella is taller than Dave, who is taller than Carl.

Ben is taller than Anna, who is taller than Frank.

We use the statements that Dave is taller than Ben, and Carl is taller than Anna, to combine the diagrams above into one.

5. Ella is taller than Dave, who is taller than Carl. So, "Ella is taller than Carl" is **true**.

6. Dave is taller than Carl, who is taller than Anna. So, "Dave is taller than Anna" is **true**.

7. Carl is taller than Anna, who is taller than Frank. So, Carl is taller than Frank. "Frank is taller than Carl" is **false**.

8. Dave is taller than Carl, who is taller than Anna, who is taller than Frank. So, "Dave is taller than Frank" is **true**.

9. We know that Carl and Ben are both shorter than Dave and taller than Anna. However, we do not have any clues that allow us to compare Carl's height to Ben's height. So, we **can't tell** whether Carl is taller than Ben.

10. Ella is taller than Dave, who is taller than Ben, who is taller than Anna. So, Ella is taller than Anna, and "Anna is taller than Ella" is **false**.

11. Using the diagram above, we see that Ella is taller than Carl, and that Carl is taller than Frank. So, if all three stood from tallest to shortest, **Carl** would stand in the middle.

12. Using the diagram above, we see that Ella is tallest, and that Frank is shortest. So, **Ella will stand first, and Frank will stand last**.

13. Using the diagram above, we see that Ella and Dave stand first and second, while Anna and Frank stand fifth and sixth. However, since we cannot tell whether Carl is taller than Ben, or Ben is taller than Carl, **we cannot tell who stands third and who stands fourth**.

14. We begin with the clue "When 36 is divided by Sam's age, the remainder is 1." Both 36÷7 and 36÷5 have remainder 1, but 36÷10 has remainder 6. So, Sam is not 10. Then, "Ann is younger than Sam," tells us that Sam cannot be 5. That means **Sam is 7**, and since Ann is younger than Sam, **Ann is 5**. This leaves 10 for Lou, so **Lou is 10**.

	5	7	10
Sam	✘	✓	✘
Ann	✓	✘	✘
Lou	✘	✘	✓

15. The clue "none of our names matches the color of our fur" allows us to cross out red fur for Mr. Red, green fur for Mr. Green, and blue fur for Mr. Blue.

	red	grn	blue
Mr. Red	✘		
Mr. Green		✘	
Mr. Blue			✘

The other clue is hidden. Notice that Mr. Red makes the first statement, and the monster with blue fur replies. This lets us know that Mr. Red is not the monster with blue fur. So, Mr. Red must have green fur.

This leaves blue for Mr. Green and red for Mr. Blue. We complete the chart as shown.

	red	grn	blue
Mr. Red	✘	✓	✘
Mr. Green		✘	✓
Mr. Blue		✘	✘

	red	grn	blue
Mr. Red	✘	✓	✘
Mr. Green	✘	✘	✓
Mr. Blue	✓	✘	✘

So, **Mr. Red's fur is green, Mr. Green's fur is blue, and Mr. Blue's fur is red.**

16. The statement "Jun finishes two places ahead of his younger brother, Tosh" tells us that Jun did not finish 3rd or 4th, and Tosh did not finish 1st or 2nd.

Next, "Boys finish first and last" lets us know that Kim did not finish 1st or 4th. We mark our chart as shown.

	1st	2nd	3rd	4th
Tosh	✘	✘		
Jun			✘	✘
Van				
Kim	✘			✘

Finally, we are told that the youngest runner wins the race. We know that Jun is not the youngest (since Tosh is his younger brother), so Jun did not finish first.

	1st	2nd	3rd	4th
Tosh	✘	✘		
Jun	✘		✘	✘
Van				
Kim	✘			✘

So, Jun must have come in 2nd place. This allows us to complete the chart as shown:

	1st	2nd	3rd	4th
Tosh	✘	✘		
Jun	✘	✓	✘	✘
Van		✘		
Kim	✘	✘		✘

	1st	2nd	3rd	4th
Tosh	✘	✘		
Jun	✘	✓	✘	✘
Van	✓	✘		
Kim	✘	✘	✓	✘

	1st	2nd	3rd	4th
Tosh	✘	✘	✘	
Jun	✘	✓	✘	✘
Van	✓	✘	✘	✘
Kim	✘	✘	✓	✘

	1st	2nd	3rd	4th
Tosh	✘	✘	✘	✓
Jun	✘	✓	✘	✘
Van	✓	✘	✘	✘
Kim	✘	✘	✓	✘

So, **Van finished 1st, Jun finished 2nd, Kim finished 3rd, and Tosh finished 4th.**

17. First, "No girl is the same age as the number of letters in her name" lets us eliminate 4 for Lisa, 5 for Ellie, 6 for Sophia, 7 for Madison, and 8 for Samantha.

	4	5	6	7	8
Lisa	✘				
Ellie		✘			
Sophia			✘		
Madison				✘	
Samantha					✘

The next clue tells us that Ellie is not 4, Lisa is not 5, Madison is not 6, Samantha is not 7, and Sophia is not 8.

	4	5	6	7	8
Lisa	✘	✘			
Ellie	✘	✘			
Sophia			✘		✘
Madison			✘	✘	
Samantha				✘	✘

Sophia is older than Ellie. Since Ellie can only be 6, 7, or 8 years old, Sophia cannot be 4, 5, or 6. This means that Sophia is 7, and Ellie is 6.

	4	5	6	7	8
Lisa	✗	✗	✗	✗	
Ellie	✗	✗	✓	✗	✗
Sophia	✗	✗	✗	✓	✗
Madison			✗	✗	
Samantha			✗	✗	✗

This leaves 8 as the only possible age for Lisa. Finally, Samantha is older than Madison, so Samantha is 5, and Madison is 4. We complete the chart as shown.

	4	5	6	7	8
Lisa	✗	✗	✗	✗	✓
Ellie	✗	✗	✓	✗	✗
Sophia	✗	✗	✗	✓	✗
Madison	✓	✗	✗	✗	✗
Samantha	✗	✓	✗	✗	✗

Lisa is 8, Ellie is 6, Sophia is 7, Madison is 4, and Samantha is 5.

18. The clue, "Janice parks her truck across from the white car" tells us that Janice has a truck, the car is white, and Janice does not have the white vehicle. We mark this on our chart as shown:

	truck	car	motorcycle	red	white	black
Tommy	✗					
Amy	✗					
Janice	✓	✗	✗		✗	
red		✗				
white	✗	✓	✗			
black		✗				

Next we learn that the girl with the red vehicle had *both tires* replaced. The phrase "both tires" tells us that this vehicle has two tires: it's a motorcycle. So, the motorcycle is red, and is owned by a girl (not Tommy). This means that Amy has the motorcycle and Tommy has the car. We complete the chart as shown.

	truck	car	motorcycle	red	white	black
Tommy	✗	✓	✗			
Amy	✗	✗	✓			
Janice	✓	✗	✗		✗	
red	✗	✗	✓			
white	✗	✓	✗			
black	✓	✗	✗			

So, **Tommy has a white car, Amy has a red motorcycle, and Janice has a black truck.**

Notice that we did not need the top-right section of our chart to complete the problem. We could fill in the missing entries, but it is not necessary for this problem.

19. First, we learn that one of the birthdays is on April 4th. Fred and Ted were born on even-numbered days, so neither was born on the 9th. This means that Ned must have his birthday on the 9th. We mark this in our chart as shown.

	January	April	November	4th	9th	18th
Fred					✗	
Ned				✗	✓	✗
Ted					✗	
4th	✗	✓	✗			
9th		✗				
18th		✗				

Next, we are told that Fred is the oldest. Since all three monsters were born in the same year, the monster born in the earliest month is the oldest. So, Fred was born in January.

	January	April	November	4th	9th	18th
Fred	✓	✗	✗		✗	
Ned	✗			✗	✓	✗
Ted	✗				✗	
4th	✗	✓	✗			
9th		✗				
18th		✗				

Then, we finish the section on the right. We know that the monster born in January was not born on the 4th, so Fred's birthday is not on the 4th. This leaves the 18th for Fred and the 4th for Ted.

	January	April	November	4th	9th	18th
Fred	✓	✗	✗	✗	✗	✓
Ned	✗			✗	✓	✗
Ted	✗			✓	✗	✗
4th	✗	✓	✗			
9th		✗				
18th		✗				

Finally, we know that the monster born in April was born on the 4th. So, Ted was born on April 4th. This leaves November for Ned.

	January	April	November	4th	9th	18th
Fred	✓	✗	✗	✗	✗	✓
Ned	✗	✗	✓	✗	✓	✗
Ted	✗	✓	✗	✓	✗	✗
4th	✗	✓	✗			
9th		✗				
18th		✗				

Fred's birthday is January 18th, Ned's birthday is November 9th, and Ted's birthday is April 4th.

LOGIC
Minesweeper
72-73

20. The 5 is surrounded by exactly five empty squares. So, each of these squares must contain a mine. We draw these mines in the grid.

2		4	
●	●		
5	●		
●	●	2	

Then, each of the 2's on the grid touches two mines. So, we can mark each of the empty squares surrounding a 2 with an X.

2	×	4	
●	●		
5	●	×	×
●	●	2	×

Finally, the 4 touches only one mine so far. So, we draw a mine in each of the three remaining empty squares that surround the 4.

2	×	4	●
●	●	●	●
5	●	×	×
●	●	2	×

21. The 2 in the bottom-right corner is surrounded by exactly two empty squares. So, we draw a mine in each of these squares.

1		1	
2		2	●
		●	2

Then, the 2 in the third column is already touching two mines, so we X the empty squares that surround that 2.

1		1	
	×	×	×
2	×	2	●
	×	●	2

Finally, the 2 in the first column needs a mine in each of the two empty squares that surround it. This puts a mine next to the 1 in the top-left corner. So, the mine for the 1 in the third column must be in the top-right corner.

1	×	1	●
●	×	×	×
2	×	2	●
●	×	●	2

22. The 5 is surrounded by exactly five empty squares. So, each of these squares must contain a mine. We draw these mines in the grid.

		3	
2			
●	●	●	4
●	5	●	

The 2 touches two mines, so we X the remaining empty squares that surround the 2.

×	×	3	
2	×		
●	●	●	4
●	5	●	

Finally, the 3 needs a mine in each of the empty squares that surround it. The 4 is already surrounded by four mines, so we can X the bottom-right square.

×	×	3	●
2	×	●	●
●	●	●	4
●	5	●	×

23. The 4 is surrounded by exactly 4 empty squares. So, each of these squares must contain a mine.

●	●		
4	6		3
●	●		
	2		1

The 2 touches two mines, so we X the remaining empty squares that surround the 2.

●	●		
4	6		3
●	●	×	
×	2	×	1

Finally, the 6 needs two more mines, and the 1 needs a mine. Placing these mines in the available empty squares gives three mines to the 3, so we X the top-right corner.

●	●	●	×
4	6	●	3
●	●	×	●
×	2	×	1

24. The 2 in the bottom-left corner touches exactly 2 empty squares. So, we draw a mine in each of these squares. Then, the 2 above the bottom-left corner is already touching 2 mines. So, we place an X in the remaining empty square that surrounds it. This leaves one place for a mine next to the 1.

1	●		
2	×	5	
2	●		
2	●	2	

The 2 in the third column already touches two mines, so we X the remaining squares that surround it.

1	●		
2	×	5	
2	●	×	×
2	●	2	×

Finally, the 5 needs three additional mines. So, we fill the three empty squares that surround it with mines.

1	●	●	●
2	×	5	●
2	●	×	×
2	●	2	×

25. There are four empty squares that surround the 3 in the fourth column. Three must be filled with mines, so only one is empty. The 1 in the bottom-right corner lets us know that at least one of the two shaded squares shown must be empty.

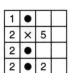

So, we know that both of the remaining squares that touch the 3 in the fourth column must be filled with mines. We fill these two squares with mines. The 2 in the first row touches two mines, so we fill the remaining empty squares that surround it with X's.

Next, the 3 in the first column is surrounded by exactly 3 empty squares. We draw mines in each of these three squares.

Finally, the 2 in the fourth row touches two mines, so we fill the remaining empty squares that surround it with X's. This leaves only one square for the mine that touches the 1 in the bottom-right corner.

26. There are four empty squares that surround the 1 in the third column. Only one can contain a mine. So, both of the unshaded squares around the 3 must contain a mine. The third mine will be in a shaded square.

Now, the 1 in the first column, third row touches one mine, so we fill the remaining empty squares that surround it with X's. Similarly, the 1 in the fourth column touches one mine, so we fill the remaining squares that surround it with X's.

Finally, there is only one empty square touching the 1 at the top-left corner of the puzzle. That square must contain a mine. That mine is in a square that also touches the 1 in the first row, third column, so we fill the remaining squares around the 1 with X's. We also check that the 3 touches exactly 3 squares with mines.

27. There are eight empty squares that surround the 7 in the second column. The 1 in the fourth column lets us know that only one of the two shaded squares can be empty, and the other must contain a mine. We place mines in the six other empty squares around the 7, and we place X's in the three other empty squares around the 1.

The 2 in the fourth column touches one mine and one empty square. So, that empty square must contain a mine.

The 1 in the fourth column touches one mine, so we fill the remaining empty square around it with X.

Finally, the 3 in the fourth row touches two mines and one empty square. So, that empty square must contain a mine.

28. There are two empty squares that surround the 2 at the top-left corner of the puzzle, and two empty squares that surround the 2 in the bottom-right corner of the puzzle. Each of these squares must contain a mine.

Two of the three squares surrounding the 2 at the bottom-left corner of the puzzle must contain a mine. So, at least one of the two shaded squares must contain a mine. There are already two mines in the squares surrounding the 3, so one of the shaded squares must be empty. We place an X in the other two empty squares around the 3.

Next, since there must be only one mine in one of the two shaded squares, the 2 in the bottom-left corner must have a mine to its right. Additionally, there is only one empty square that touches the 1. So, that square must contain a mine.

Finally, there are four mines in the squares surrounding the 4, and we fill the remaining empty square that touches it with an X. This leaves one empty square touching the bottom-left 2. So, that square must contain a mine.

29. In the first and second arrangements, we see three different shapes. So, each of the three cards must have one of three different shapes on the back: a circle, a triangle, or a square.

In the first arrangement, the 4 appears with the triangle and square cards. This leaves the **circle** as the shape on the other side of the 4 card.

30. Since there is a 1 card that appears in the first arrangement but not the second, Anton must have flipped the 1 card over to its shape side.

The only shape showing in the second arrangement is a triangle. Therefore, the shape on the other side of the 1 is a **triangle**.

31. In the first arrangement, we see two triangles. In the second arrangement, we see one triangle, one circle, and one square. So, among these four cards, two have a triangle on one side, one has a circle, and one has a square.

In the second arrangement, we see one triangle, one circle, and one square. So, the fourth card (with a 9 on it) must have the second triangle on it. Therefore, the shape on the other side of the 9 is a **triangle**.

32. In the first and second arrangements, we see four different shapes. So, each of the four cards must have one of four different shapes on the back: a square, a triangle, a circle, or a star.

We see two of the shapes in the first arrangement with two numbers, and we see the other two shapes in the second arrangement with two numbers. So, Willa must have flipped over all four cards.

Therefore, the numbers on the cards are 1, 1, 2, and 3. **Three** of the four cards have an odd number on one side.

For each puzzle below, we offer one possible approach to solve the puzzle. You may have taken different steps to arrive at the same solution.

33. The bottom-right box contains a 1, a 2, and a 3. So, the missing entry is a 4.

Then, the fourth row is missing a 2 and a 4. The second column already contains a 4. So, the 4 in the fourth row goes in the first column and the 2 goes in the second column.

The third column is missing a 3 and a 4. The second row already contains a 4, so the 4 in the third column goes in the first row and the 3 goes in the second row.

We use the above strategies to complete the Sudoku as shown below:

34. The second row needs a 4.

Then, the third row needs a 1 and a 2. We cannot place the 1 in the first column, or the 2 in the third column. So, we place the 1 in the third column and the 2 in the first column.

The top-left box is missing a 2 and a 3. We cannot place the 3 in the second column, so the 3 goes in the first column, and the 2 goes in the second column.

We complete the Sudoku as shown:

35. We use our strategies from the previous problems to complete the Sudoku as shown:

36. The number in the shaded square cannot be a 1, since there is already a 1 in the first column. It cannot be a 2, since there is already a 2 in the fourth row. It cannot be a 3, since there is already a 3 in the bottom-left box. So, it must be a **4**.

37. One of the four squares in the top-right box must contain a 2. The third column already contains a 2, so we must place the 2 in the fourth column, in the first row. The shaded square must be a **2**.

38. The bottom three rows and the first three columns each contain a 2. So, the fourth 2 must be placed in the first row in the fourth column, as shown.

39. The top-right box must contain a 3. The fourth column already contains a 3. So, we place the 3 in the second row in the third column, as shown.

Only the first row does not contain a 3. Only the second column does not contain a 3. So, the last 3 must be placed in the first row in the second column.

40. The bottom-left box must contain a 3. There is already a 3 in the fourth row, and there is already a 3 in the first column. So, the shaded square must be a 3.

Only the first row does not contain a 3. Only the third column does not contain a 3. So, the last 3 must be placed in the first row in the third column.

41. The bottom-left box needs a 2. There is already a 2 in the third row, so the 2 must be placed in the fourth row.

Then, the final 2 must be placed in the first row in the second column.

The top-left box needs a 4. There is already a 4 in the second row, so the 4 goes in the first row in the first column.

Then, the final 4 must be placed in the third row in the fourth column.

42. We fill in additional entries that will allow us to fill in the shaded square. The bottom-left box needs a 2. There is already a 2 in the third row, so the 2 must be placed in the fourth row.

Similarly, the top-right box needs a 2. There is already a 2 in the third column, so the 2 must be placed in the fourth column.

Then, the final 2 must be placed in the shaded square.

43. We fill in additional entries that will allow us to fill in the shaded square. The bottom-right box needs a 1. There is already a 1 in the fourth row, so the 1 must be placed in the third row.

The top-right box needs a 1. There is already a 1 in the third column, so the 1 must be placed in the fourth column.

Then, the final 1 must be placed in the shaded square.

LOGIC
Liars & Truth-tellers   78-79

44. If Bib is telling the truth when he says that Loaf is a liar, then Loaf is a **liar**.

45. If Bib is lying when he says that Loaf is a liar, then Loaf is a **truth-teller**.

46. Loaf says, "We're both liars!" A truth-teller would never say, "We're both liars," so Loaf cannot be a truth-teller. So, **Case 2** is impossible.

If Bib is telling the truth, then Bib is a truth-teller. Then, Loaf must be a liar and is lying when he says, "We are both liars!" Case 1 works!

47. We learned above that Case 2 is impossible, and Case 1 works. So, **Bib is a truth-teller, and Loaf is a liar**.

48. Geoff and Iggy make contradictory statements (their statements are opposites). So, if Geoff is telling the truth, Iggy is a **liar**. Huck says that one is lying and one is telling the truth, so Huck's statement is **true**.

49. Geoff and Iggy make contradictory statements. So, if Geoff is lying, then Iggy is a **truth-teller**. Huck says that one is lying and one is telling the truth, so Huck's statement is **true**.

50. In Case 1 above, we assumed that Geoff was telling the truth, and he stated that Huck is a liar. However, we determined that Huck's statement was true, so Huck is a truth-teller! Huck can't be both, so we get a contradiction in **Case 1**.

If Geoff is a liar, he is lying when he says, "Huck is a liar," and Iggy is telling the truth when he says, "Huck is a truth-teller." Then, Huck's statement is true and Huck is a truth-teller. Case 2 works!

51. We've determined that Huck is telling the truth. So, Huck must be a **truth-teller**.

52. Since Huck is a truth-teller, Geoff is lying when he says that Huck is a liar. So, Geoff is a **liar**.

53. Since Huck is a truth-teller, Iggy is telling the truth when he says that Huck is a truth-teller. So, Iggy is a **truth-teller**.

54. If Hurb were a truth-teller, he would answer Alex's question, "Yes." So, **Hurb is a liar**. Since Hurb lied when he said, "No," we know that there is at least one truth-teller. So, **Gurk is a truth-teller**.

55. If Alex asks a liar if he is a truth-teller, he will lie and say "yes." Similarly, if Alex asks a truth-teller if he is a truth-teller, a truth-teller will truthfully say "yes." It doesn't matter if Oomlot is a liar or a truth-teller, he will always say "yes." So, "urp" means **yes**.

56. If Mo is lying when he says that he and Jo are in the same tribe, then they are in opposite tribes. In this case, Mo is a liar, and Jo is a truth-teller.
If Mo is telling the truth when he says that he and Jo are in the same tribe, then they are in the same tribe. In this case, Mo is a truth-teller, and Jo is a truth-teller.

Either way, **Jo is a truth-teller**.

57. Each of the 4 monsters says something different, and each monster contradicts the other three. So, either exactly one monster is telling the truth and the other three are lying, or all of the monster are lying.

If all four students are lying, then Gus's statement, "We're all liars," is true, and we have a contradiction.

If exactly one monster is telling the truth and the other three are lying, then Dorn is telling the truth when he says, "Exactly three of us are liars," and all three of the other monsters' statements are lies. This works, so **3** monsters are liars.

58. Consider the possibility that Jaggle is telling the truth when he says, "Exactly one of us is a truth-teller." In this case, Jaggle is the truth-teller, and the other two monsters must both be liars. However, if Kip and Lyra are both liars, Kip cannot make the true statement, "Lyra and I are in the same tribe."

So, Jaggle must be a liar, and his statement is a lie: there is *not* exactly one truth-teller.

Since Kip and Lyra cannot both be liars, we consider the possibility that Kip's statement is a lie. Then, Lyra is a truth-teller and we have exactly one truth-teller in the group. However, above, we determined that Jaggle is a liar and that there is *not* exactly one truth-teller.

Finally, if Kip's statement is true, then Lyra is also a truth-teller and Jaggle is a liar. This works! So, **Jaggle is a liar, Kip is a truth-teller, and Lyra is a truth-teller**.

59. Consider the possibility that Al is a truth-teller. In this case, Bo is a liar, Cade is a liar (since Bo lied), Dina is a truth-teller, Eli is a liar, Frey is a truth-teller, and Al is a truth-teller (as we assumed in the beginning). There are no contradictions, and we have 3 truth-tellers (Al, Dina, and Frey).

Then, consider the possibility that Al is a liar. In this case, Bo is a truth-teller, Cade is a truth-teller, Dina is a liar, Eli is a truth-teller, Frey is a liar, and Al is a liar (as we assumed in the beginning). There are no contradictions, and we have 3 truth-tellers (Bo, Cade, and Eli).

In both cases, there are **3** truth-tellers.

60. If Ak is a truth-teller, then Lief and Quiggy are in the same tribe. However, if Ak is a liar, then Lief and Quiggy are in different tribes.

This gives us four possibilities to consider, as outlined in the table below.

	Ak	Lief	Quiggy
1.	T	T	T
2.	T	L	L
3.	L	T	L
4.	L	L	T

We want to determine when Quiggy would answer "yes" to Alex's question, "Are Ak and Lief in the same tribe?" So, for each case, we write down Quiggy's response.

In the first case, where all three are truth-tellers, Quiggy says "yes."

In the second case, Ak and Lief are in different tribes, but Quiggy is a liar. So, Quiggy says "yes."

In the third case, Ak and Lief are in different tribes, but Quiggy is a liar. So, Quiggy says "yes."

Finally, in the fourth case, Ak and Lief are in the same tribe and Quiggy is a truth-teller. So, Quiggy says "yes."

	Ak	Lief	Quiggy	Quiggy Says
1.	T	T	T	"Yes"
2.	T	L	L	"Yes"
3.	L	T	L	"Yes"
4.	L	L	T	"Yes"

In every possible case, Quiggy says "yes." Therefore, we cannot tell whether Quiggy is a liar or a truth-teller.

61. If the monster who says "I am a liar" is a liar, then the statement is true. However, monsters on the island who are liars *always* lie.

If the monster who says "I am a liar" is a truth-teller, then the statement is a lie. However, monsters on the island who are truth-tellers *always* tell the truth.

This is called a paradox. **Neither a monster who always lies nor a monster who always tells the truth could make the statement, "I am a liar."**

So, the monster does not live on the island.

For each puzzle below, we offer one possible approach to solve the puzzle. You may have taken different steps to arrive at the same solution.

62. The sum of the eight squares that make up the first two columns is 20. The sum of the numbers in seven of these squares is 17, as labeled. So, the number in the remaining shaded square must be 20 − 17 = 3. We write a 3 in the shaded square.

63. The two numbers in the shaded cage have a sum of 4.
To get a sum of 4 using two digits from 1 through 4, we can add 2 + 2 or 1 + 3. We cannot use two 2's, because we can only place one 2 in the fourth column. So, we must use a 1 and a 3. There is already a 3 in the first row, so the 3 is placed in the second row, and the 1 is placed in the first row.

64. The two numbers in the shaded cage have a sum of 7.
To get a sum of 7 using two digits from 1 through 4, we must add 3 + 4. There is already a 3 in the fourth column, so the 3 is placed in the third column, and the 4 is placed in the fourth column.

65. The fourth column needs a 2 and has one empty square.

Then, the two-square cage whose sum is 6 needs a 4.

The remaining squares can be filled using standard Sudoku strategies, as shown below.

66. To begin, we fill in the single-square cage whose sum is 2.

The cage with a sum of 3 can only be filled with a 1 and a 2. Since the third column already has a 2, we place the 2 in the fourth column, and the 1 in the third column.

Next, the third row needs a 3. We place the 3 in the only empty square in the third row. Then, we place a 1 in the same cage to give a sum of 4.

The four entries in the first row sum to 10. The entries in the first three columns of the first row have a sum of 7, so the top-right square must be filled with $10-7=3$.

We use the above Sum-doku and standard Sudoku strategies to complete the puzzle as shown below.

The sum of the four numbers in the first row is 10. The cage with a sum of 13 contains all four numbers in the first row, plus a fifth number. So, the fifth number is $13-10=3$.

We complete the puzzle with the steps shown below.

67. To begin, we fill in the single-square cage whose sum is 2.

The cage with a sum of 3 can only be filled with a 1 and a 2. Since the second row already has a 2, we place the 2 in the first row, and the 1 in the second row.

The cage in the third column with a sum of 6 can only be filled with a 2 and a 4. Since the second row already has a 2, we place the 2 in the third row and the 4 in the second row.

The cage in the fourth row with a sum of 6 can only be filled with a 2 and a 4. Since the first column already has a 2, we place the 2 in the second column and the 4 in the first column.

We complete the puzzle with the steps shown below.

68. To begin, we fill in the single-square cage whose sum is 1.

The cage with a sum of 3 can only be filled with a 1 and a 2. Since the third row already has a 1, we place the 2 in the third row and the 1 in the fourth row.

Next, the four entries in the first column sum to 10. The entries in the bottom three rows of the first column have a sum of 7, so the top-left square must be filled with $10-7=3$.

69. To begin, we fill in the single-square cage whose sum is 2. The four entries in the first row sum to 10. So, the top-right square must be $10-9=1$.

Then, the two remaining entries in the cage whose sum is 5 sum to $5-1=4$. These two squares can only be filled with a 1 and a 3. There is already a 1 in the fourth column, so we place the 1 in the third column and the 3 in the fourth column.

The cage with a sum of 7 can only be filled with a 3 and a 4. There is already a 3 in the fourth column, so we place the 3 in the third column and the 4 in the fourth column.

We complete the puzzle with the steps shown below.

70. The four entries in the first column sum to 10. The top three of these entries sum to 6, so the bottom-left square must be filled with a $10-6=4$.

Similarly, the four entries in the first row sum to 10, so the top-left corner must be filled with a $10-9=1$.

The cage with a sum of 7 can only be filled with a 3 and a 4. The fourth row already has a 4, so the 4 goes in the third row and the 3 goes in the fourth row.

Then, the cage in the second column with a sum of 6 can only be filled with a 4 and a 2. Since the third row already has a 4, we place the 4 in the second row and the 2 in the third row.

We complete the puzzle with the steps shown below.

The four squares in the fourth row of the cage labeled 17 sum to 10. The same cage has a 3 in the third row. Together, these five entries sum to 10+3 = 13. So, the missing entry must be 17 − 13 = 4.

We complete the puzzle with the steps shown below.

71. The cage whose sum is 11 can only be filled with 4, 4, and 3. Since we cannot place two 4's in the same row or column, we place the three numbers as shown.

Then, the cage whose sum is 7 can only be filled with a 3 and a 4. The third row already has a 4, so we place the 4 in the fourth row and the 3 in the third row.

Next, the cage whose sum is 5 can be filled with 1, 2, 2 or 1, 1, 3. However, since there is already a 3 in each of the third and fourth columns, we must use 1, 2, 2. Since we cannot place two 2's in the same row or column, we place the three numbers as shown.

We complete the puzzle with the steps shown below.

72. The cage whose sum is 4 can only be filled with 1, 1, and 2. Since we cannot place two 1's in the same row or column, we place the three numbers as shown.

Then, the cage whose sum is 6 can only be filled with a 2 and a 4. The second row already has a 2, so we place the 2 in the first row and the 4 in the second row.

The bottom two entries in the fourth column are a 1 and a 3. The third row already has a 1, so we place the 1 in the fourth row and the 3 in the third row. We can also complete the second row by placing a 3 in the first column.

73. The cage with the sum of 10 contains 6 numbers. 10 is a very small sum for 6 numbers, so we look to make the numbers as small as possible. The number in the third row can be a 1. The smallest possible sum of the two numbers in the second row is 1+2 = 3. The smallest possible sum of the three numbers in the top row of this cage is 1+2+3 = 6. So, 6+3+1 = 10 is the smallest possible sum.

Therefore, we place a 1 in the third row of the cage.

Then, the 1 and the 2 in the second row can only be placed as shown.

Then, we must arrange a 1, 2, and 3 in the top row of the cage. The 1 can only be placed in the second column. Then, the 2 can only be placed in the third column. The 3 fills the fourth column.

We complete the puzzle with the steps shown below.

74. To begin, we fill in the single-square cage whose sum is 4.

The two-square cage with a sum of 6 can only be filled with a 4 and a 2. Since there is already a 4 in the second column, we place the 4 in the third column and the 2 in the second column.

The four entries in the fourth column sum to 10. The bottom three of these entries sum to 6, so the top-right square must be filled with a 10−6 = 4.

Then, the first column needs a 4, which we can only place in the fourth row, as shown.

Next, we look at the three-square cage whose sum is 7. There are three ways to add three of 1, 2, 3, or 4 to make 7: 1+2+4 = 7, 2+2+3 = 7, or 1+3+3 = 7.

All the 4's in this puzzle have already been placed, so we cannot fill the three squares in the cage with 1, 2, and 4.

The second column already contains a 2, and we cannot put two 2's in the same column. So, we cannot fill the three squares in the cage with 2, 2, and 3.

So, the three squares contain 1, 3, and 3. Since we cannot put two 3's in the same row or column, we arrange the 1, 3, and 3 in the squares as shown.

We complete the puzzle with the steps shown below.

75. The ∟ pentomino needs a 4. There is already a 4 in the first column. So, the only place to put a 4 in the ∟ pentomino is in the second column.

The ⊤ pentomino needs a 2. There is already 2 in the second row. So, the only place to put a 2 in the ⊤ pentomino is in the third row.

The first column needs a 3 and a 5. Since the third row already has a 3, we place the 3 in the fourth row and the 5 in the third row.

The third row needs a 1 and a 4. Since the fifth column already has a 4, we place the 4 in the fourth column and the 1 in the fifth column.

Then, the ⊔ pentomino has a 1, 2, 4, and 5 and only needs a 3. We place the 3 in the bottom-right square.

We complete the puzzle with the steps shown below.

76. The ⊏⊐ pentomino needs a 2. There is already a 2 in the fourth row, and there is already a 2 in the first column. So, the only place to put a 2 in the ⊏⊐ pentomino is in the fourth row, second column.

Then, the ⌐ pentomino needs a 1. The only place to put a 1 in the ⌐ pentomino is in the bottom-right square.

The ⌐ pentomino now needs a 3 and a 4. There is already a 3 in the third column, so we place the 3 in the fifth column and the 4 in the third column.

Then, the ⊏⊐ pentomino needs a 3, a 4, and a 5. The 3 must fill the only square on the fifth row. Then, since the fourth column already has a 5, we place the 5 in the second column and the 4 in the fourth column.

We complete the puzzle with the steps shown below.

77. The ⊔ pentomino needs a 1. The only place to put a 1 in the ⊔ pentomino is in row 5, column 2.

Then, since there are four 1's in the puzzle already, the fifth 1 must be placed in the row 2, column 5.

The fifth column needs a 4 and a 2. Since the fifth row already has a 4, we place the 4 in the fourth row and the 2 in the fifth row.

Then, the ⌐ pentomino needs a 4. The only place to put a 4 in the ⌐ pentomino is in the third row.

Now, we place the two remaining 4's. We need a 4 in the second row. There is already a 4 in the ⌐ pentomino, and there is already a 4 in the first column. So, we place a 4 in the second row, second column. Then, the 4 in the first row must be placed in the third column.

Next, the ⌐ pentomino needs a 3. The third row already has a 3, so the 3 in the ⌐ pentomino must be placed in the second row.

We complete the puzzle with the steps shown below.

78. The ⌐ pentomino needs a 5. There is already a 5 in the fifth column, so we place the 5 in the ⌐ pentomino in the fourth column.

The ⌐ pentomino needs a 5. The only place to put a 5 in the ⌐ pentomino is in the second row, first column.

The fifth 5 must be placed in the third row, second column.

The ⌐ pentomino needs a 2. Since there is already a 2 in the first row, we place the 2 in the second row, third column.

The ♫ pentomino needs a 4. The third row already has a 4, so we place the 4 in the ♫ pentomino in row 2, column 4.

The third row needs a 2. There is already a 2 in the ♫ pentomino, so the 2 must be placed in row 3, column 5.

We complete the puzzle with the steps shown below.

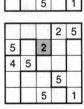
LOGIC
word Problems   86-89

79. **a.** There are two odd numbers and two even numbers on the sticky notes. Alex will only know his number is even if he sees both of the odd numbers on the heads of the other students. So, Alex sees **1** and **3** on the heads of Lizzie and Winnie.

b. Since Lizzie and Winnie have 1 and 3, all of the remaining numbers are even. So, the number in Professor Grok's pocket is **even**.

80. **a.** In order to know that her own number is greater than 2, Lizzie must know that she does not have either 1 or 2 on her head. So, she must see **1 and 2** on the heads of Alex and Winnie.

b. Winnie knows from Lizzie's answer that Lizzie sees the numbers 1 and 2. Since Winnie says that the number on her own head is 1, she must see the number **2** on Alex's head.

81. **a.** The largest number is 4. If Winnie had seen a 4 on Alex's head or on Lizzie's head, she would have known which monster had the biggest number. So, the **4** cannot be on Alex's or Lizzie's head.

b. Lizzie says that Alex has the biggest number, so we know that the 4 is not on Winnie's head. From Winnie's previous statement, Lizzie knows that the 4 is not on her head or Alex's (as we found in part (a).) So, the **4** must be in Grok's pocket.

c. We know that the 4 is in Grok's pocket. Lizzie knows this as well, and says that Alex's number is the largest. So, Alex must have the largest remaining number on his head, the **3**.

82. a. If Winnie sees the 1 or the 4 on Alex's head, she knows whether her own number is smaller or larger than Alex's. So, Alex cannot have a **1** or a **4**.

b. From part (a), we know that Alex has either the 2 or the 3. Consider the possibility that Alex has the 3.

If Winnie had seen the 3 on Alex and the 4 on Lizzie, then Winnie would have known her own number is smaller than Alex's (since the only numbers left are 1 and 2). So, if Alex has the 3, Lizzie can't have the 4.

However, Lizzie says that she has the 4. So, Alex does not have the 3. Since Alex does not have the 1, 3, or 4, Alex must have the **2**.

c. For this part, we consider the question, "How did Lizzie know that she had the 4 on her own head?" From part (b), we know that Alex has the 2. Seeing the 2 on Alex, Lizzie knows that her own number is not a 1 (if Winnie had seen a 1 on Lizzie and a 2 on Alex, Winnie would have known her own number is bigger than Alex's). So, Lizzie knows that her own number is either the 3 or the 4.

For Lizzie to know that she has the 4 (not the 3), she must see the 3 on Winnie's head.

So, Alex has the 2, Winnie has the 3, Lizzie has the 4, and the **1** is in Professor Grok's pocket.

83. a. Alex could have drawn two silver coins, two gold coins, or one of each. So, we have **silver & silver, silver & gold** (which is the same as gold & silver) and **gold & gold**.

b. If Alex had drawn two gold coins, he would have known that Grogg had two silver coins (since there were only a total of two gold coins in the satchel). So, we eliminate **gold & gold** from the choices in part (a).

c. From part (b) above, we know that Alex has either two silver coins, or one gold coin and one silver coin. For Grogg to know that Alex has one gold and one silver coin, he must be able to eliminate the possibility that Alex has two silver coins. For Grogg to eliminate this possibility, Grogg must have two silver coins. Grogg has **silver & silver**.

84. Lizzie does not know what type of coin is in the satchel. This tells us (and Alex) that Lizzie does not have two gold coins. Hearing this, Alex still does not know what type of coin is left in the satchel. So, we know that Alex also does not have two gold coins.

If Alex has two silver coins and knows that Lizzie does not have two gold coins, then Alex also knows that Lizzie must have a gold coin and a silver coin (she cannot have two silver coins, or two gold coins).

So, if Alex has two silver coins, he knows that the coin in the satchel is gold.

If Alex has one gold coin and one silver coin, he cannot tell whether Lizzie has two silver coins, or one gold coin and one silver coin, and therefore cannot tell what type of coin is in the satchel.

The fact that Alex doesn't know what type of coin is left in the satchel tells us that Alex must have **one** of each coin: silver & gold.

85. The sum of two even numbers is even. The sum of two odd numbers is even. The sum of one odd number and one even number is odd. For Grogg to know that Lizzie's sum is even, Grogg must know that Lizzie does not have one odd number and one even number.

The only way Grogg can eliminate this possibility is if he has all of the odd numbers or all of the even numbers. Of the five numbers, three are odd and two are even. Since Grogg picked only two numbers, Grogg cannot have all of the odd numbers. However, if Grogg has both of the even numbers, he knows that Lizzie's numbers are both odd. So, Grogg must have both even numbers: **the 2 and the 4**.

86. Consider the sum of every possible pair of numbers:

$$1+2=3 \quad\quad 2+3=5 \quad\quad 3+4=7 \quad\quad 4+5=9$$
$$1+3=4 \quad\quad 2+4=6 \quad\quad 3+5=8$$
$$1+4=5 \quad\quad 2+5=7$$
$$1+5=6$$

If the sum of Winnie's numbers is 3 or 4, she knows that her sum is less than Grogg's (if she has $1+3=4$, the smallest sum Grogg can have is $2+4=6$).

If the sum of Winnie's numbers is 5 (1+4 or 2+3), then Grogg can have a sum that is equal to (2+3 or 1+4), but not less than Winnie's. So, if Winnie's sum is 5, then her statement, "It may be equal, but it's definitely not greater (than Grogg's)" makes sense.

If Winnie's sum is 6 (1+5 or 2+4), then Grogg's sum could be less (2+3 or 1+3), and Winnie's statement is not true.

Similarly, Winnie's sum cannot be greater than 6. So, the sum of Winnie's numbers is **5**.

87. Winnie doesn't know whether the number in the bag is odd or even. So, we know (and Lizzie knows) that Winnie does not have two even numbers.

Next, Lizzie does not know whether the token in the bag is odd or even until Winnie speaks. So, Lizzie does not have two even numbers.

After Winnie speaks and Lizzie learns that Winnie does not have two even numbers, Lizzie is able to tell whether the coin in the bag is odd or even.

Consider the possibility that Lizzie has one odd and one even number. In this case, Lizzie has no way of knowing whether Winnie has two odd numbers, or one odd and one even. For example, if Lizzie has 1 and 2, Winnie may have 3 and 4 (in which case the number in the bag, 5, is odd) or 3 and 5 (in which case the number in the bag, 4, is even).

However, if Lizzie has two odd numbers, Winnie cannot have two odd numbers (since there are only three odd numbers). So, if Lizzie has two odd numbers, she knows that Winnie has one odd number and one even number, and that the coin in the bag is **even**.

88. The empty hexagon on the left touches a 2 and a 3. The smallest number it does not touch is a 1.

The empty hexagon on the right touches a 1 and a 2. The smallest number it does not touch is a 3.

89. The empty hexagon on the left touches a 2 and a 3. The smallest number it does not touch is a 1.

The empty top-right hexagon touches a 1, a 2, and a 3. The smallest number it does not touch is a 4.

90. The 2 on the right must touch a 1. So, we place a 1 in the bottom-center hexagon.

Then, the empty top-left hexagon touches a 1, a 2, and a 3. The smallest number it does not touch is a 4. So, the top-left hexagon is a 4.

91. The 2 must be touching a 1. We cannot place a 1 in the hexagon to the left of the 2, because that hexagon also touches a 1. So, the 1 goes in the top-right hexagon.

The empty bottom-center hexagon touches a 1 and a 2, so it must be at least a 3. If we place a 3 in the bottom-center hexagon, the top-left hexagon is a 2 and the puzzle is complete.

 ✓

Notice that if we place a 4 in the bottom-center hexagon, the smallest number that the top-left hexagon does not touch is still a 2. But, the 4 is not touching a 3, so this placement does not work.

 ✗

92. The 2 in the bottom-left hexagon needs to touch a 1. So, the top-left hexagon is a 1.

Then, the top-right hexagon cannot then be a 1, so the smallest number the bottom-right hexagon does not touch is a 1.

The top-right hexagon touches a 1 and a 3. The smallest number it does not touch is a 2. So, the top-right hexagon is a 2.

 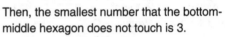

93. The 4 must touch a 1, a 2, and a 3. We look for a hexagon for the 3. The 3 cannot be placed in either of the empty hexagons that touch the 3 in the top-right corner. We also cannot place the 3 in the bottom-left hexagon, because the 3 needs to touch both a 1 and a 2. So, the 3 must be placed in the top-left hexagon.

Then, the smallest number that the bottom-left hexagon does not touch is 1.

Next, the 3 in the top-left hexagon needs to be touching a 2. So, the top-middle hexagon is a 2.

Finally, the smallest number that the bottom-right hexagon does not touch is a 1.

94. The 3 must touch both a 1 and a 2. The 1 cannot touch the 1 that is already there, and the 2 cannot touch the 2 that is already there. So, we place the 1 and 2 as shown.

Then, the smallest number that the bottom-middle hexagon does not touch is 3.

95. The 2 must touch a 1. So, we place a 1 in the only empty hexagon that the 2 touches.

Then, the 4 must touch a 3. We cannot place the 3 in the bottom-left hexagon, because the 3 needs to touch both a 1 and a 2. So, the 3 goes in the middle row on the left.

We fill the two remaining empty hexagons with the smallest numbers that they do not touch.

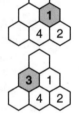

96. The 2 must touch a 1. We cannot place the 1 in any hexagon that touches the 1 in the top-right hexagon, so we place the 1 as shown in the bottom-left hexagon.

Then, the 4 needs to touch a 2. The 2 cannot touch the 2 that is already there, so we place the 2 in the other empty hexagon as shown.

Then, the 4 must touch a 3. We fill the 3 in as shown. To complete the puzzle, we fill the top-left hexagon with the smallest number it does not touch, 4.

97. The 3 must touch a 2. We cannot place a 2 in any of the hexagons that touch the existing 2. So, we place a 2 as shown in the top-right hexagon.

The 2 on the left must touch a 1. We cannot place a 1 in either of the hexagons that touch the 1 in the bottom-right hexagon, so we place a 1 as shown in the top-left hexagon.

The center hexagon touches a 1, a 2, and a 3. So, the center hexagon must be at least a 4. If we try making the center hexagon a 5, it must touch a 4 in the bottom-left hexagon. However, we cannot make the bottom-left hexagon a 4, because the 4 will not touch a 3.

We place the 4 in the center as shown, and fill in the bottom-left hexagon with the smallest number it does not touch.

98. The 4 must touch a 2. We cannot place a 2 in either of the hexagons that touch the existing 2, so we place a 2 in the leftmost hexagon that touches the 4.

The 4 must touch a 1. We cannot place a 1 in the hexagon that touches the existing 1, so we place a 1 in the rightmost hexagon that touches the 4.

Then, the 4 must touch a 3, so we place a 3 in the remaining empty hexagon that touches the 4.

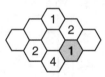

The empty upper-left hexagon touches a 1, 2, and 3, so it must be at least a 4. The leftmost hexagon does not touch a 1, so 1 is the smallest number it does not touch. We place a 1 in the leftmost hexagon.

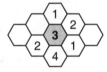

We fill the two remaining empty hexagons with the smallest numbers that they do not touch.

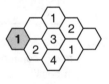

99. The 4 must touch a 1. We cannot place a 1 in either of the hexagons that touch the existing 1, so we place a 1 in the leftmost hexagon that touches the 4.

The 5 must touch a 4. We cannot place a 4 in a hexagon that touches the existing 4. We also must place the 4 so that it can touch a 1, 2, and 3. The only hexagon where this is possible is in the middle of the bottom row.

Then, the 4 in the bottom-center hexagon must touch a 3. We must place the 3 so that it can touch a 1 and a 2. So, the 3 cannot be placed to the left of the 4. It must be placed as shown.

Both of the 4's must touch 2's, so we place 2's in the remaining empty hexagons that touch the 4's.

The 2 in the bottom-left hexagon must touch a 1, so we place a 1 in the available hexagon.

We fill the remaining empty hexagon with the smallest number it does not touch.

100. There is only one place to attach a tent to the tree in the bottom-right corner. This leaves only one place to attach a tent to each of the remaining trees, as shown.

101. There is only one place to attach a tent to the tree in the top-left corner. This leaves only one place to attach a tent to the tree in the second column. Then, we attach a tent to the remaining tree as shown.

102. We attach the tents as shown in the steps below.

103. There are three places to attach a tent to the tree in the third column. Attaching the tent above the tree in the third column makes it impossible to attach a tent to the tree in the fourth column. Attaching a tent to the left of the tree in the third column makes it impossible to attach a tent to the tree in the first column. So, we attach the tent to the right of the tree in the third column as shown.

Next, there is only one place to attach a tent to the tree in the fourth column.

Then, the tent attached to the tree in the second column must not block the attachment of a tent to the tree in the first column. So, the remaining tents are placed as shown below.

104. There are two places to attach a tent to the tree in the second row, second column. We cannot attach the tent to the right of the tree as shown below, because this makes it impossible to attach a tent to the tree in the fourth column.

So, we attach a tent to the left of the tree, as shown. Then, we attach the remaining tents as shown below.

105. There are four places to attach a tent to the tree in the second column. However, three of these make it impossible to attach a tent to one of the trees in the first column, as shown below.

So, we attach the tent to the right of the tree in the second column, as shown below. Then, we attach the remaining tents as shown.

106. We attach the tents as shown in the steps below.

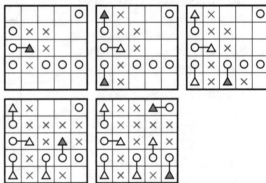

107. We attach the tents as shown in the steps below.

108. We attach the tents as shown in the steps below.

109. There are three places to attach the tent to the tree in row 4, column 3. Attaching the tent to its left makes it impossible to attach a tent to the tree in the bottom-left corner. Similarly, attaching the tent to its right makes it impossible to attach a tent to the tree in the bottom-right corner. So, we attach the tent below the tree as shown.

Then, we attach the remaining tents as shown.

110. There are three places to attach the tent to the tree in row 3, column 2. Attaching the tent above the tree makes it impossible to attach a tent to the tree in the top-left corner. Similarly, attaching the tent below the tree makes it impossible to attach a tent to the tree in the bottom-left corner. So, we attach the tent to the left of the tree as shown.

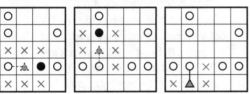

Then, we attach the remaining tents as shown.

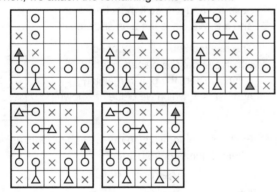

111. There are three places to attach the tent to the tree in row 4, column 2. Attaching the tent to the right of the tree makes it impossible to attach a tent to the tree in column 4. Similarly, attaching the tent above the tree makes it impossible to attach a tent to the tree in row 2, column 2. So, we attach the tent below the tree as shown.

Then, we attach the remaining tents as shown.

112. First, we look for ways to make each product using two numbers from 1 to 6:

$5 = 1 \times 5$ $18 = 3 \times 6$ $6 = 1 \times 6$ or 2×3 $30 = 5 \times 6$

The row marked with a 30 needs a 5 and a 6. Since the column marked with a 5 needs a 5, we place a 5 in the bottom-left square. Since the column marked with an 18 needs a 6, we place a 6 in the bottom-center square.

Since the 6 is in the third row, the row marked with a 6 cannot have a 1 and a 6, so it must have a 2 and a 3. Since the column marked with an 18 needs a 3, we put the 3 in the top-center square.

The column marked with a 5 needs a 1. We cannot place the 1 in the first row, so we place the 1 in the first column, second row.

The row marked with a 6 needs a 2. The 2 must be placed in the top-right square.

Finally, the only number we have not placed is the 4. We need a second number in row 2, column 3, so the 4 goes in the third column, second row.

113. First, we look for ways to make each product using two different numbers from 1 to 6:

$15 = 3 \times 5$ $2 = 1 \times 2$ $3 = 1 \times 3$ $12 = 3 \times 4$ or 2×6

The row marked with a 3 needs a 1 and a 3. Since the column marked with a 15 needs a 3, we place the 3 in the top-left square. Since the column marked with a 2 needs a 1, we place the 1 in the top-right square.

Since the 3 is in the first row, the row marked with a 12 cannot have a 3 and a 4, so it must have a 2 and a 6. Since the column marked with a 2 needs a 2, we place the 2 in the bottom-right square. Since 15 is not divisible by 6, we place the 6 in the bottom-center square.

The first column needs a 5. The 5 can only be placed in the second row. Finally, the only number we have not placed is the 4. We need a second number in row 2, column 2, so the 4 goes in the center square.

114. First, we look for ways to make each product using two different numbers from 1 to 6:

12 = 3×4 or 2×6   6 = 1×6 or 2×3   20 = 4×5

The row marked with a 20 needs a 5 and a 4. Neither 12 nor 6 is divisible by 5, so we place the 5 in the top-center square. Since 6 is not divisible by 4, but 12 is divisible by 4, we place the 4 in the top-left square.

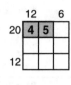

The column marked with a 12 needs a 3. Then, since the 4 has already been used, the row marked 12 cannot have a 4 and a 3. Instead, it must have a 2 and a 6. So, the 3 cannot be placed in the third row. We place the 3 as shown.

Since the 3 is in the first column, the column marked with a 6 cannot have a 2 and a 3. Instead, it must have a 1 and a 6. Since the third row also needs a 6, we place the 6 in the bottom-right square.

The row marked with a 12 needs a 2. The 2 can only be placed in the second column. The third column needs a 1. The 1 can only be placed in the second row.

— *or* —

We begin this problem by trying to sort out which products will be used. We record the possible products on our puzzle as shown below.

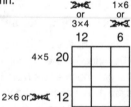

Since the first row's product can only be 20 = 4×5, neither the 4 nor the 5 can be in any other row. So, we must use 12 = 2×6 in the third row.

Since both 2 and 6 are in the third row, the column labeled 12 cannot also use both 2 and 6. So, we must use 12 = 3×4 in the first column. Then, neither 3 nor the 4 can be in any other column. So, we must use 6 = 1×6 in the third column.

Then, since each of 1-6 must appear once in the puzzle, we use the above products to determine the products in the unlabeled row and the unlabeled column.

1, 3, 4, and 6 appear in the first and third columns, so the product of the second column must be 2×5. Similarly,

2, 4, 5, and 6 appear in the first and third rows, so the product of the second row must be 1×3.

Now, each number is listed in its row and column, so we complete the puzzle as shown.

115. First, we look for ways to make each product using two different numbers from 1 to 8:

7 = 1×7   40 = 5×8   6 = 1×6 or 2×3
3 = 1×3   12 = 2×6 or 3×4   35 = 5×7

The column marked with a 40 needs a 5 and an 8. None of 3, 12, or 35 are divisible by 8, so the 8 is placed as shown. The row marked with a 35 needs a 5, so the 5 is placed as shown.

The column marked with a 7 needs a 1 and a 7. The row marked with a 3 needs a 1, so the 1 is placed in the top-left square. The row marked with a 35 needs a 7, so the 7 is placed in the bottom-left square.

Since the 1 is in the first column, the column marked with a 6 cannot have a 1 and a 6. So, it must have a 2 and a 3. The first row needs a 3, so we place the 3 in the top-right square. Then, since the 3 is in the first row, the row marked with a 12 cannot have a 3 and a 4, so it must have a 2 and a 6. We place the 2 as shown.

The row marked with a 12 needs a 6, which can only be placed in the third column. Then, the only remaining number is 4, which we place as shown.

116. First, we look for ways to make each product using two different numbers from 1 to 8:

32 = 4×8   18 = 3×6   2 = 1×2
4 = 1×4   16 = 2×8   21 = 3×7

The row marked with a 4 needs a 1 and a 4. Since the column marked with a 32 needs a 4, we place the 4 in the top-left square. Since the column marked with a 2 needs a 1, we place the 1 in the top-right square.

The row marked with a 21 needs a 3 and a 7. Since none of 32, 18, or 2 are divisible by 7, we place the 7 in the column whose product is not labeled. The column marked with an 18 needs a 3, so we place the 3 as shown.

	32	18		2
4	4			1
16				
21		3	7	

The row marked with a 16 needs a 2 and an 8. The column marked with a 32 needs an 8, and the column marked with a 2 needs a 2. So, we place the 8 and the 2 as shown.

	32	18		2
4	4			1
16	8			2
21		3	7	

The remaining numbers, 6 and 5, must be placed in the fourth row. The column marked with an 18 needs a 6, so we place the 6 as shown. The third column only has one number, so the 5 goes in the third column.

	32	18		2
4	4			1
16	8			2
21		3	7	
		6	5	

117. First, we look for ways to make each product using two different numbers from 1 to 8:

$2 = 1 \times 2$ $20 = 4 \times 5$ $24 = 3 \times 8$ or 4×6
$8 = 1 \times 8$ or 2×4 $10 = 2 \times 5$

The row marked with a 10 needs a 2 and a 5. Since the column marked with a 2 needs a 2 and the column marked with a 20 needs a 5, we place the 2 and the 5 as shown.

	2	20		24
8				
10	2	5		
24				

Since the 2 is in the row marked with a 10, the row marked with an 8 cannot have a 2 and a 4. So, it must have a 1 and an 8. The column marked with a 2 needs a 1, so we place the 1 in the top-left corner.

	2	20		24
8	1			
10	2	5		
24				

The 7 must be placed somewhere. None of the numbers marking the rows and columns is a multiple of 7. So, we place the 7 in the unmarked row and column as shown.

	2	20		24
8	1			
			7	
10	2	5		
24				

The row marked with an 8 has a 1 and needs an 8. So, the row marked with a 24 cannot have an 8 and a 3. Therefore, it must have a 4 and a 6. The column marked with a 20 needs a 4, so we place the 4 as shown.

	2	20		24
8	1			
			7	
10	2	5		
24		4		

The column marked with a 20 has a 4, so the column marked with a 24 cannot have a 4 and a 6. Therefore, it must have a 3 and an 8. The row marked with an 8 needs an 8, so we place the 8 in the top-right corner.

	2	20		24
8	1			8
			7	
10	2	5		
24		4		

The remaining numbers to place are a 3 and a 6. The column marked with a 24 needs a 3, which can only be placed in the unmarked row. The row marked with a 24 needs a 6, which can only be placed in the unmarked column.

	2	20		24
8	1			8
			7	3
10	2	5		
24		4	6	

118. First, we look for ways to make each product using two different numbers from 1 to 8:

$18 = 3 \times 6$ $20 = 4 \times 5$ $56 = 7 \times 8$
$14 = 2 \times 7$ $12 = 2 \times 6$ or 3×4 $8 = 1 \times 8$ or 2×4

The row marked 14 needs a 2 and a 7. Since the column marked with a 56 needs a 7, we place the 7 in the top-right square. Then, since no marked column needs a 2, we place the 2 in the top-left square.

	18	20		56
14	2			7
12				
8				

Since the 2 has already been placed in the first row, the row marked 12 needs a 3 and a 4. Since the column marked 18 needs a 3, we place a 3 in the second column. Then, since the column marked 20 needs a 4, we place a 4 in the third column.

	18	20		56
14	2			7
12		3	4	
8				

The row marked with an 8 needs a 1 and an 8. Since the column marked 56 needs an 8, we place an 8 in the fourth column. Then, since no marked column needs a 1, we place the 1 in the bottom-left square.

	18	20		56
14	2			7
12		3	4	
8	1			8

Finally, the column marked 18 needs a 6, and the column marked 20 needs a 5. The 5 and the 6 can only be placed in the third row.

	18	20		56
14	2			7
12		3	4	
		6	5	
8	1			8

119. First, we look for ways to make each product using two different numbers from 1 to 8:

$8 = 1 \times 8$ or 2×4 $24 = 3 \times 8$ or 4×6 $15 = 3 \times 5$
$56 = 7 \times 8$ $12 = 2 \times 6$ or 3×4 $6 = 1 \times 6$ or 2×3

Since so many of the rows and columns have two possible products, we begin this problem by trying to sort out which products will be used. We record the possible products on our puzzle as shown below.

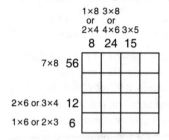

Since the third column's product can only be $15 = 3 \times 5$, neither the 3 nor the 5 can be in any other column. So, we must use $24 = 4 \times 6$ in the second column. Then, since the 4 is in the second column, we must use $8 = 1 \times 8$ in the first column.

For the products of the rows, consider the possibility that we use 2×3 for the 6 in the fourth row. If we have a 2 and a 3 in the fourth row, we cannot use 2×6 or 3×4 in the third row, which leaves us with no way to make 12. So, we must use $6 = 1 \times 6$ for the fourth row. Then, since the 6 is in the fourth row, we must use $12 = 3 \times 4$ in the third row.

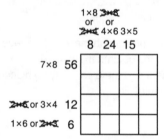

Each of the numbers from 1-8 must appear once in the puzzle. From these products, we see that the product of the unlabeled fourth column must be 2×7, and the product of the unlabeled second row must be 2×5.

Now, each number is listed in its row and column, so we complete the puzzle as shown.

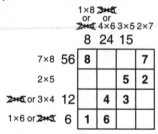

120. First, we look for ways to make each product using two different numbers from 1 to 8:

$8 = 1 \times 8$ or 2×4 $24 = 3 \times 8$ or 4×6 $35 = 5 \times 7$
$28 = 4 \times 7$ $12 = 2 \times 6$ or 3×4

Since so many of the rows and columns have two possible products, we begin this problem by trying to sort out which products will be used.

We record the possible products on our puzzle as shown below.

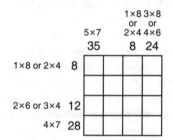

Since the fourth row's product can only be $28 = 4 \times 7$, neither the 4 nor the 7 can be in any other row. So, we must use $8 = 1 \times 8$ in the first row and $12 = 2 \times 6$ in the third row.

Since both 1 and 8 are in the first row, both 1 and 8 cannot be in the third column. So, for the products in the columns, we must use $8 = 2 \times 4$ in the third column. Then, neither 2 nor 4 can be in any other column. So, we must use $24 = 3 \times 8$ in the fourth column.

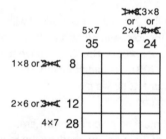

Each of the numbers from 1-8 must appear once in the puzzle. From these products, we see that the product of the unlabeled second column must be 1×6, and the product of the unlabeled second row must be 3×5.

Now, each number is listed in its row and column, so we complete the puzzle as shown.

	35	1×6	2×4	24
1×8 or 2×4 8		1		8
3×5	5			3
2×6 or 3×4 12		6	2	
4×7 28	7		4	

For additional books, printables, and more, visit
www.BeastAcademy.com

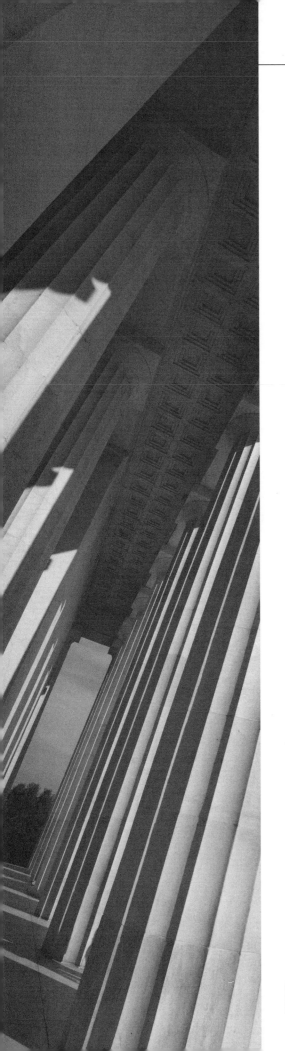

Government Alive!
Power, Politics, and You

NATIONAL CONSTITUTION CENTER

TCi™

Director of Product Development: Liz Russell

Managing Editor: Laura Alavosus

Project Editor: Mali Apple

Copyeditor: Tara Joffe

Editorial Associates: Anna Embree, Sarah Sudano

Production Manager: Lynn Sanchez

Art Director: John F. Kelly

Senior Graphic Designer: Christy Uyeno

Graphic Designers: Paul Rebello, Sarah Wildfang, Don Taka

Photo Editor: Margee Robinson

Art Editor: Eric Houts

Audio Director: Katy Haun

TCi™ Teachers' Curriculum Institute
P.O. Box 50996
Palo Alto, CA 94303

ISBN 978-1-934534-02-1

1 2 3 4 5 6 7 8 9 10 -EB- 12 11 10 09 08 07

Acknowledgements

Program Director

Bert Bower

Program Author

Diane Hart

Senior Writer

Brent Goff

Contributing Writers

Melissa Biegert

David Fasulo

Linda Scher

Creative Development Manager

Kelly Shafsky

Curriculum Developers

Nicole Boylan

Julie Cremin

Erin Fry

Amy George

Steve Seely

Program Consultant

Sharon Pope
Houston, Texas

Teacher and Content Consultants

Karl Grubaugh
Granite Bay High School
Granite Bay, California

Cathy Hix
Swanson Middle School
Arlington, Virginia

Deidre Jackson
Taylor High School
Houston, Texas

Eli Lesser
National Constitution Center
Constitution High School
Philadelphia, Pennsylvania

Greg Nakata
Glendora High School
Glendora, California

Ron Pike
Lincoln High School
San Jose, California

Ken Shears
Ponderosa High School
Shingle Springs, California

Steve Watts
Davidson High School
Hilliard, Ohio

Nathan Welbourne
Taylor High School
Houston, Texas

Scholars

Dr. Paul Barressi
Southern New Hampshire University

Dr. Dave Campbell
Notre Dame University, Indiana

Dr. Jim Gimpel
University of Maryland

Dr. George Gordon
Illinois State University
Illinois Wesleyan University

Dr. Darla Mallein
Emporia State University, Kansas

Dr. Patrice McMahon
University of Nebraska

Dr. Richard Niemi
University of Rochester, New York

Dr. Tari Renner
Illinois Wesleyan University

Dr. Michael Smith
Emporia State University, Kansas

Dr. Beth Theiss-Morse
University of Nebraska

Music Consultant

Melanie Pinkert
Music Faculty
Montgomery College, Maryland

Cartographer

Mapping Specialists
Madison, Wisconsin

Internet Consultant

Clinton Couse
Cedar Valley Community School
Edmonds School District
Edmonds, Washington

Researcher

Carla Valetich
Pittsboro, North Carolina

NATIONAL CONSTITUTION CENTER

525 Arch Street | Independence Mall
Philadelphia | PA 19106 | T 215 409 6600 | F 215 409 6650
www.constitutioncenter.org

Dear Educator,

We are pleased to introduce *Government Alive! Power, Politics, and You*, a collaboration between TCI and the National Constitution Center. We are excited to work with TCI on this dynamic new program, which will connect government to high school students' everyday lives. By creating opportunities to practice the rights and responsibilities of citizenship, *Government Alive! Power, Politics, and You* will prepare high school students to become active and informed citizens.

The National Constitution Center is a museum, an education center, and a forum for deliberation on constitutional issues. The Constitution Center is located in Philadelphia on America's "most historic mile," where America's founders met, deliberated, and created the system of government we still live under today. It is the only museum in the world dedicated to increasing public understanding of the United States Constitution and the ideas and values it represents. The museum dramatically tells the story of the U.S. Constitution from Revolutionary times to the present through more than 100 interactive multimedia exhibits, film, photographs, text, sculpture, and artifacts, and it features a powerful, award-winning theatrical performance, *Freedom Rising*. The Constitution Center also houses the Annenberg Center for Education and Outreach, the national hub for constitutional education.

Through this collaboration, *Government Alive! Power, Politics, and You* will provide a unique combination of hands-on lessons and online resources for students to explore. The resources and expertise of the National Constitution Center are made available to students and teachers as they access breaking news on current constitutional issues, gain the tools to analyze and assess information on civic matters, and utilize our extensive online exhibits to further examine issues being addressed in the *Government Alive!* program. Every day at the National Constitution Center thousands of visitors are encouraged—and we trust inspired—to make the choice of becoming more engaged and active citizens. We believe that *Government Alive!* and its innovative use of the Center's online resources can encourage your students to make the same decision.

Sincerely,

Joseph M. Torsella
President & CEO

Unit 1   Power, Authority, and Government

Chapter 1   The Nature of Power, Politics, and Government   3

Why should you care about power, politics, and government?

EXPERIENTIAL EXERCISE

Chapter 2   Comparing Forms of Government   13

How should political and economic power be distributed in a society?

RESPONSE GROUP

Unit 2   Foundations of American Government

Chapter 3   The Roots of American Democracy   27

What ideas gave birth to the world's first modern democratic nation?

EXPERIENTIAL EXERCISE

Chapter 4   The United States Constitution   37

How and why did the framers distribute power in the Constitution?

SOCIAL STUDIES SKILL BUILDER

Chapter 5   The Bill of Rights and Civil Liberties   49

How are your rights defined and protected under the Constitution?

PROBLEM SOLVING GROUPWORK

Chapter 6   Federalism: National, State, and Local Powers   61

How does power flow through our federal system of government?

RESPONSE GROUP

Contents

Unit 3   **Political Participation and Behavior**

Chapter 7   **Citizen Participation in a Democracy**   **75**

How can you make a difference in a democracy?
Visual Discovery

Chapter 8   **Parties, Interest Groups, and Public Policy**   **85**

*Political parties and interest groups: How do they
influence our political decisions?*
Experiential Exercise

Chapter 9   **Public Opinion and the Media**   **97**

*To what extent do the media influence your
political views?*
Experiential Exercise

Chapter 10 **Political Campaigns and Elections**   **107**

Elections and voting: Why should they matter to you?
Experiential Exercise

Unit 4   **The Legislative Branch**

Chapter 11 **Lawmakers and Legislatures**   **123**

What makes an effective legislator?
Social Studies Skill Builder

Chapter 12 **Congressional Lawmaking**   **135**

How do laws really get made?
Experiential Exercise

Unit 5   **The Executive Branch**

Chapter 13 **Chief Executives and Bureaucracies**   **151**

*What qualities do modern presidents need to fulfill
their many roles?*
Problem Solving Groupwork

Chapter 14 The Federal Budget   **163**

*Does the federal government budget and spend
your tax dollars wisely?*
SOCIAL STUDIES SKILL BUILDER

Unit 6   The Judicial Branch

Chapter 15 Courts, Judges, and the Law   **175**

*How is the U.S. judicial system organized to
ensure justice?*
RESPONSE GROUP

Chapter 16 The Criminal Justice System   **187**

*From doing the crime to doing time: How just is
our criminal justice system?*
WRITING FOR UNDERSTANDING

Unit 7   The United States and the World

Chapter 17 Creating American Foreign Policy   **203**

*How should the United States conduct foreign
policy?*
RESPONSE GROUP

Chapter 18 Confronting Global Issues   **213**

*How effectively do international organizations
respond to global issues?*
EXPERIENTIAL EXERCISE

Resources

Pacing Guides   **223**

Analysis of Skills by Chapter   **224**

Correlation to National Standards   **229**

Notes   **233**

Credits   **234**

How to Use This Program:
Government Alive! Power, Politics, and You

Teaching with the TCI Approach means shifting to a student-centered, activity-based classroom. To meet this exciting challenge, this introduction to the Lesson Guide for *Government Alive! Power, Politics, and You* will give you the basics you need to start teaching this program with confidence right away.

The TCI Approach   x

Multiple Intelligences Teaching Strategies   xii

Program Components   xiv

Chapter Essentials   xvi

Organizing a TCI Classroom   xviii

Creating a Cooperative, Tolerant Classroom   xix

Using the Interactive Student Notebook   xx

Building Active Citizenship   xxii

Assessing Learning   xxiv

Enhancing Instruction with the DTR   xxvi

Finding Additional Resources Online   xxvii

Growing Professionally   xxviii

The TCI Approach

Why is the TCI Approach so effective at igniting students' passion for learning? The TCI Approach consists of a series of instructional practices that allow students of all abilities to experience key social studies concepts. It is characterized by eight features.

Theory- and Research-Based Active Instruction

Lessons and activities are based on five well-established theories.

Understanding by Design   Grant Wiggins and Jay McTighe maintain that teaching for deep understanding must begin with planning the big ideas students should learn. That's why you will see an Essential Question at the start of every chapter in *Government Alive! Power, Politics, and You.*

Nonlinguistic Representation   Research by Robert Marzano and colleagues demonstrates that teaching with nonlinguistic activities helps improve comprehension. Use of graphic organizers and movement are both key to TCI lessons.

Multiple Intelligences   Howard Gardner believes that all students are intelligent—just not in the same ways. TCI activities address Gardner's seven intelligences: verbal-linguistic, logical-mathematical, visual-spatial, body-kinesthetic, musical-rhythmic, interpersonal, and intrapersonal.

Cooperative Interaction   Elizabeth Cohen's research shows that cooperative groupwork leads to learning gains and higher student achievement. Working in small groups is a cornerstone of TCI activities.

Spiral Curriculum   Jerome Bruner championed the idea of the spiral curriculum, in which students learn progressively—understanding more difficult concepts through a process of step-by-step discovery. TCI questioning strategies spiral from simple recall to higher-order thinking skills such as analysis and evaluation.

Standards-Based Content

Dynamic lessons that integrate hands-on learning and content reading build mastery of state and national civic and government standards.

Preview Assignment

A short, engaging assignment at the start of each lesson helps you preview key concepts and tap students' prior knowledge and personal experience.

Multiple Intelligences Teaching Strategies

TCI activities incorporate six multiple intelligences teaching strategies:

- Visual Discovery
- Social Studies Skill Builder
- Experiential Exercise
- Writing for Understanding
- Response Group
- Problem Solving Groupwork

These six strategies are explained in detail on the following pages.

Considerate Text

Carefully structured reading materials enable students at all levels to understand what they read. Uncluttered pages present content in digestible "chunks." Engaging images reinforce content, while consistent vocabulary development improves student comprehension.

Graphically Organized Reading Notes

Comprehensive graphic organizers help students record key ideas and make meaning out of what they read. By using graphic organizers that display the underlying logic of and interconnections among concepts, students improve their comprehension and retention of content.

Processing Assignment

An end-of-lesson assignment, involving multiple intelligences and higher-order thinking skills, challenges students to apply what they have learned in a variety of creative ways.

Multiple Intelligences Assessments

Carefully designed tests encourage students to use their various intelligences to demonstrate their understanding of key concepts while also preparing them for standardized tests.

Multiple Intelligences Teaching Strategies

The TCI Approach uses the six teaching strategies described here to bring learning alive. All six appear in the *Government Alive! Power, Politics, and You* Lesson Guide with detailed, step-by-step instructions. Support materials for the chapter activities appear in the Lesson Masters, Transparencies, and Placards and on the *Sounds of Government* audio CD and Digital Teacher Resources (DTR) CD-ROM.

Visual Discovery

In Visual Discovery activities, students view, touch, interpret, and bring to life compelling images as they discover key social studies concepts. Seeing and interacting with an image in combination with reading and recording notes on the content helps students remember salient ideas.

Here are some tips for Visual Discovery activities:

- Arrange your classroom so that projected images will be large and clear.
- Ask carefully sequenced questions that lead to discovery.
- Challenge students to read about each image and apply what they learn.
- Have students interact with each image to demonstrate learning.

Social Studies Skill Builder

In Social Studies Skill Builders, students work in pairs or small groups on fast-paced, skill-oriented tasks such as mapping, graphing, identifying perspective, and interpreting political cartoons to enhance their understanding of chapter content.

Here are some tips for Social Studies Skill Builders:

- Teach each skill through modeling and guided practice.
- Prepare students to work in pairs or small groups.
- Set clear expectations, allow students to practice each skill repeatedly, and give immediate feedback.
- Debrief the activity to help students make connections to key social studies concepts.

Experiential Exercise

In Experiential Exercises, participating in short, memorable experiences helps students grasp social studies concepts. Through the use of movement and introspection, students capture a moment or feeling that is central to understanding a particular concept or historical event.

Here are some tips for Experiential Exercises:

- Prepare students for a safe, successful experience by arranging the classroom appropriately, communicating clear behavioral and learning expectations, anticipating student reactions, and recognizing teachable moments.

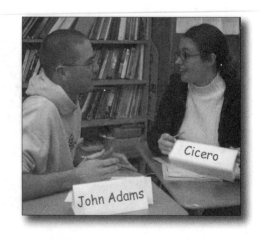

- Bring authenticity to the experience by assuming an appropriate persona, hamming it up, and using simple props, costumes, music, and sound effects.
- Allow students to express their feelings immediately after the experience.
- Ask carefully sequenced questions to help students make connections between their experience and key concepts or events.

Writing for Understanding

Writing for Understanding activities give students a rich experience—such as viewing powerful images, role-playing, discussing complex issues, or acting out key events—to write about. Students develop ideas and form opinions during the experience, before beginning to write. The experience becomes a springboard for writing, challenging students to clarify ideas, organize information, and express what they have learned.

Here are some tips for Writing for Understanding activities:

- Have students record their ideas, thoughts, and feelings in prewriting activities.
- Guide students through the writing process.

Response Group

In Response Group activities, students work in small groups with thought-provoking resources to discuss critical thinking questions among themselves. A presenter then shares each group's findings with the class.

Here are some tips for Response Group activities:

- Create mixed-ability groups and a suitable classroom arrangement.
- Prepare students to answer provocative critical thinking questions.
- Allow groups time to prepare their responses.
- Facilitate a lively class discussion.

Problem Solving Groupwork

In Problem Solving Groupwork activities, students work in heterogeneous groups to create projects that require multiple abilities so that every student can contribute. Within a group, each student takes a defined role. After completing their task, groups present their projects to the class.

Here are some tips for Problem Solving Groupwork activities:

- Review ground rules for working cooperatively in groups.
- Give group members clearly defined roles and requirements.
- Give groups autonomy and time to prepare high-quality projects.
- After groups present their work, debrief each presentation for deeper meaning and historical accuracy.

Program Components

The components of *Government Alive! Power, Politics, and You* work together to maximize your time and creativity. Everything you need to provide insightful and stimulating classroom experiences is included in the program. There are also plenty of opportunities to add your own resources.

Student Edition

United States government presented through Essential Questions that help students focus their learning around important issues and active citizenship. In the Student Edition you will find

- 18 chapters that make government understandable and relevant to students

- considerate text that is uncluttered and easy to navigate

- powerful graphic elements that spark student interest and foster comprehension

- vocabulary treatment that covers both key content and social studies terms

- optional reading at the end of each chapter that explores current issues

Lesson Guide

"Command central" for the program, with detailed, step-by-step instructions for each chapter as well as the following resources to help you plan your lesson:

- a materials list and estimated timing

- a guide to the Reading Notes

- options for providing quicker or deeper coverage of the content

- suggestions for using online resources and multimedia with students

- recommendations for differentiating instruction for English language learners, students reading and writing below grade level, special education students, and advanced learners

- answers for assessments

Lesson Masters

Reproducible pages for classroom support. Follow the materials list in the Lesson Guide to know how many photocopies to prepare before class for

- Notebook Guides and Notebook Handouts for each chapter

- Student Handouts and Information Masters for each activity

- chapter assessments

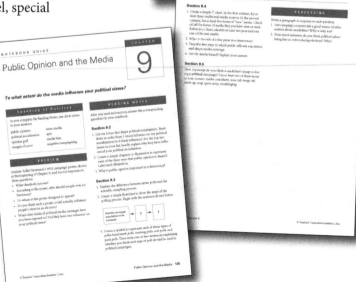

Transparencies and Placards

Visual support for chapter activities, including

- photographs
- maps, graphs, diagrams, charts, and tables
- primary sources

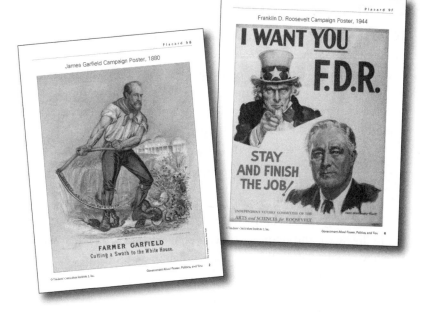

Sounds of Government Audio CD

Audio tracks that play essential roles in several lessons, including

- historic speeches and other recordings
- summaries of court cases
- dramatizations
- music
- background sound effects

Doing Democracy: A Toolkit for Civic Action

Practical templates for teachers to use with students to facilitate active participation in civic affairs, with step-by-step instructions on these and many other topics:

- registering to vote
- evaluating candidates for political office
- presenting an issue at a school board meeting
- sponsoring a ballot initiative

insert reduced cover of the Doing Democracy Toolkit

Still waiting for cover

Digital Teacher Resources

CD-ROM to facilitate lesson planning and provide multisensory dimensions to classroom activities. On the CD-ROM, you will find

- Lesson Guides
- Lesson Masters
- Transparencies, Placards, and chapter opener images
- *Sounds of Government* audio tracks
- the Assessment Creator
- *Doing Democracy: A Toolkit for Civic Action*

Chapter Essentials

While students look forward to the wide variety of activities they will experience in a TCI classroom, they also reap the benefits of TCI's consistent organization of learning in the chapters. Following sound pedagogical practices, each lesson begins with a Preview assignment to spark interest and connect to prior learning, progresses to visually engaging Reading Notes, and concludes with a Processing assignment that asks students to apply what they have learned.

Preview

The Preview assignment is a short, engaging task that foreshadows upcoming content. The goal is to ignite interest, activate prior knowledge, tap a wide range of intelligences, and prepare students to tackle new concepts. Students read the Preview assignment in the chapter's Notebook Guide and complete it in their interactive student notebooks.

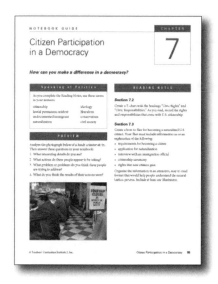

Types of Preview assignments include

- comparing personal experience with key concepts
- predicting
- responding to images
- responding to hypothetical or "what if" scenarios
- responding to statistics
- analyzing historic documents

Reading Notes

One of the most powerful ways to improve students' comprehension and retention is to have them complete graphically organized Reading Notes for each chapter. Using this format helps students see the underlying logic of and interconnections among events, facts, and concepts. When students record information in engaging, visual ways, they are better able to recall social studies content months and even years later. Students read directions for the Reading Notes in the chapter's Notebook Guide and complete them in their interactive student notebooks.

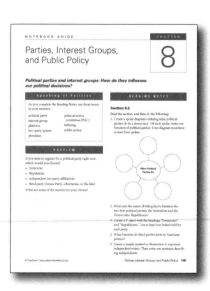

Types of graphically organized Reading Notes include

- Venn diagrams
- spoke diagrams
- matrices
- annotated images
- illustrated timelines
- T-charts
- illustrated dictionary entries
- political cartoons

- annotated analogies
- how-to flyers
- flowcharts
- cause-and-effect diagrams
- annotated graphs
- rankings
- report cards

Processing

Processing assignments are wrap-up activities that challenge students to synthesize the information in a chapter in a demonstration of their understanding of it. The intent is to allow students to actively apply what they have learned so that you—and they—can assess their comprehension. Students read directions for the chapter's Processing assignment in the Notebook Guide and complete it in their interactive student notebooks.

Products of Processing assignments include

- journal entries
- opinion surveys
- letters to the editor
- news story analyses
- public service flyers
- persuasive essays
- blog postings
- action plans
- flowcharts
- proposal papers
- annotated report cards

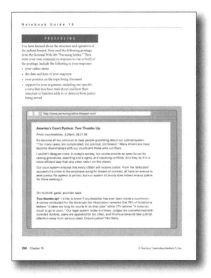

Organizing a TCI Classroom

Most of the *Government Alive! Power, Politics, and You* activities require students to move into small groups of two, three, or four. With a brief training exercise, you can teach them how to do so quickly without wasting valuable time.

Moving Your Classroom Furniture

Tell students that they will be working in small groups of different sizes throughout the year. They must know how to move into each grouping quickly and efficiently with all their materials. When working in pairs, they should place their desks either side by side or face to face, with the edges touching. For groups of three or more, the front corners of the desks must touch.

With these expectations clear, allow students to practice moving into groups. Randomly assign students to groups and indicate where they should meet. Then say "Go!" and time them. If necessary, allow the class to discuss what went wrong and brainstorm ideas for getting into groups more efficiently. Have students repeat the process until they can do it in "record time."

Be prepared for students to think this exercise is silly. However, if you spend twenty minutes at the beginning of the school year teaching this skill, you will save hours of instructional time. Your goal should be for students to be able to form various group configurations in less than one minute, without your needing to touch any student furniture.

Organizing Your Teacher Resources

Government Alive! Power, Politics, and You comes with all the materials you need to excite your students about local, state, and national government and students' roles both as citizens now and as future voters. It will be up to you, however, to gather the materials for each chapter and organize them in a way that makes it fast and easy to conduct activities year after year. Here are some tips to save you time and make running your classroom much easier:

1. Begin preparation for each activity by gathering everything on the materials list, such as Placards, Transparencies, and the audio CD. Consider opening the Lesson Guide and Lesson Masters on the appropriate Digital Teacher Resources CD-ROM and printing out all pages of both.

2. Make all the copies you will need of classroom masters, such as Notebook Guides, Student Handouts, and Information Masters.

3. When you finish each activity, place all the printed materials in a clear, resealable plastic bag (an ideal size is 10 by 12 in. and 4 mm thick) with the Lesson Guide on top as a "label." This will keep the many individual activity pieces together and will ensure that next year's preparation takes virtually no time.

Creating a Cooperative, Tolerant Classroom

The interactive, experiential, and stimulating learning at the heart of the TCI Approach can happen only when students feel comfortable sharing ideas, taking risks, working cooperatively, tolerating differences, and disagreeing honestly and respectfully with you and their classmates. Thus you need to take purposeful steps to develop a "safe" community in your classroom.

Here are some tips for creating a cooperative, tolerant classroom:

- Greet your students at the door every day to make a personal connection with them as they enter your classroom.

- Explain your expectations for classroom behavior, using specific examples. You may also involve students in shaping class rules.

- Stage an icebreaker at the beginning of the year to help students feel more comfortable with their new classmates. For example, make a list of descriptions (likes to dance, speaks another language, and the like), give each student a copy, and ask the class to get the autograph of one person who fits each profile.

- Convince students that learning to work effectively with others will benefit them throughout their lives.

- Teach students how to move efficiently into groups of various sizes.

- Use role-playing activities to teach students cooperative skills.

- Form mixed-ability groups.

- Allow newly formed groups to engage in team-building activities to promote group cohesion.

- Allow students to engage in groupwork activities without unnecessary interventions by you.

Using the Interactive Student Notebook

In the interactive student notebook, all parts of the integrated lesson come together as students create a dynamic repository for their learning. For each chapter, students receive a two-page Notebook Guide that explains how to complete Preview assignments, Reading Notes, and Processing assignments. Students enter their work into a spiral notebook or three-ring binder.

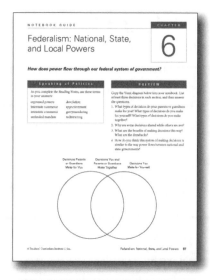

Interactive Student Notebook Guidelines for Students

One of the most important steps for helping students to create successful notebooks is establishing clear guidelines. Decide ahead of time what you expect your students to produce in their notebooks, and clearly communicate your expectations on a single sheet of paper that students can glue into the inside front cover of their notebooks. Here are example guidelines that you might adapt for your own students.

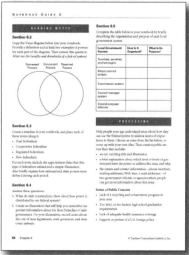

Purpose Your interactive student notebook will help you to become a creative, independent thinker and writer. You will use your notebook in class for class notes, writing assignments, activity notes, extra credit assignments, and other assignments that ask you to express your ideas and process information presented in class.

Materials You will need a spiral notebook (college ruled, at least 100 pages) or three-ring binder, colored pencils, glue stick, tape, scissors, highlighters, and a zipper pouch.

Notebook Guides These sheets will explain exactly how to complete all chapter Preview, Reading Notes, and Processing assignments.

Grading To earn an A– or higher grade, you must keep a complete, neat notebook, produce quality work, and consistently take the time to extend your learning beyond classroom assignments. Notebooks will be checked for completeness periodically—usually every three to four weeks, except during the first few weeks of class, when they will be checked more regularly. You must keep an updated assignment sheet listing all class assignments, due dates, and point values. Also include columns for recording self-assessment points and teacher-assessment points.

Absence If you are absent, check the class assignment sheet the teacher has placed in the large envelope in the front of the class. It will list all assignments that are due.

Managing Assessment of Interactive Student Notebooks

If you teach four or five classes a day, you could have 150 or more student notebooks to monitor. Because so much of students' work appears in these notebooks, you will need an efficient and accurate system for assessing them.

Informal Assessment   Monitor student notebooks aggressively in the first few weeks of the course. Look at notebooks as you walk around, making positive comments and helpful suggestions. Here are some additional ideas:

- While students work on another assignment, conduct a quick review of the previous night's homework, giving students checks or special stamps to denote completed assignments.
- Provide a model of outstanding work for an assignment or set of class notes.
- Allow students to use their notebooks on a quiz or test. This will come as a pleasant surprise and reward for students with well-organized notebooks.

Formal Assessment   At the beginning of the year, clearly explain the criteria on which notebooks will be assessed, such as quality and completeness of assignments, visual appearance, neatness, higher-order thinking, and organization. Here are some additional ideas for assessing student work:

- Create a simple rubric that identifies the criteria you feel are most important.
- Stagger notebook collection so that you correct only one class set at a time.
- Grade selectively. Don't feel compelled to grade every notebook entry.
- Create an evaluation sheet like the one below to support your expectations of student work.

Notebook Assignment	Due Date	Possible Points	Student Assessment	Teacher Assessment
Chapter 9 Preview	11/8	5	3	4
Chapter 9 Reading Notes	11/9	20	19	17
Chapter 9 Processing	11/10	10	8	10
Chapter 10 Reading Notes	11/15	20	18	19
Chapter 10 Processing	11/16	10	9	8
Totals		65	57	58
Student Comments: I'm not used to these kinds of assignments, but I'm trying my best.				
Teacher Comments: Your work is solid. Think about creating some of your excellent visuals for extra credit.				

Building Active Citizenship

Government Alive! Power, Politics, and You challenges students to think like active citizens. Throughout each chapter, students are encouraged and supported to "do" democracy through thought-provoking Essential Questions and exploration of current issues. In addition to engaging activities, *Government Alive! Power, Politics, and You* includes the following resources and tools to help foster a lifelong commitment to active citizenship.

Partnership with the National Constitution Center

The National Constitution Center in Philadelphia, Pennsylvania, is a museum and education center dedicated to increasing public understanding of the U.S. Constitution and the ideas and values it represents. The center's Web site includes breaking news of current constitutional issues, information on elections and candidates, a Citizen Action Center with pros and cons on controversial topics, and instant e-mail connections to the media and to all elected officials at local, state, and federal levels.

TCI's partnership with the National Constitution Center provides focused access to these resources for students and teachers by linking individual chapters in *Government Alive! Power, Politics, and You* to the center's Web site. Under the Enhancing Learning section of most chapters in the Lesson Guide, you will be directed to the National Constitution Center's site for a wealth of resources related to the focus or content of that chapter.

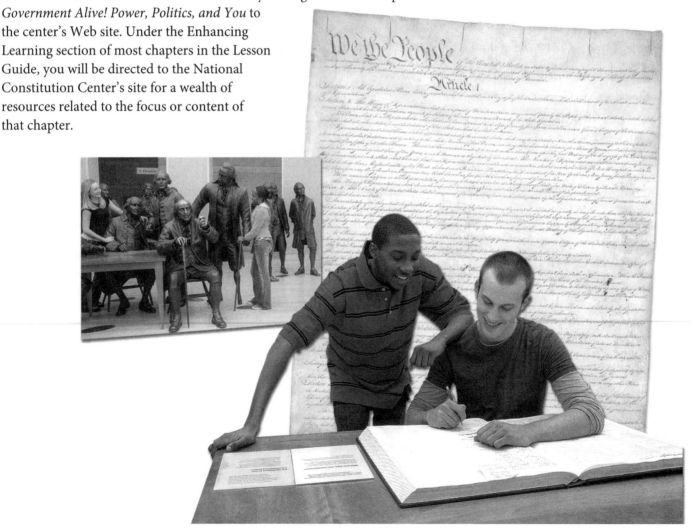

Doing Democracy: A Toolkit for Civic Action

As students' knowledge of civics grows, they need hands-on support to put that knowledge into action. The *Doing Democracy* toolkit offers flexible, easy-to-use resources to help students practice the skills and develop the confidence they need to become active, engaged, and informed citizens.

The *Doing Democracy* toolkit is divided into six sections that encompass the civic knowledge, skills, and dispositions that are essential elements of active citizenship in a democratic society.

- Gathering, Analyzing, and Assessing Information
- Researching and Communicating Positions
- Understanding and Respecting Diverse Points of View
- Influencing Policy by Engaging with Public Officials
- Participating in Elections
- Working Cooperatively to Take Action in the Community

The "tools" in each section are reproducible two-page handouts. The first page introduces the student to the "doing democracy" activity—describing its purpose and explaining how to do it. The second page serves as a guide for action to help students navigate through the activity. These guides include note-taking templates, step-by-step directions, sample writing formats, and planning documents.

In the Lesson Guide, you will find suggestions for which *Doing Democracy* tools to use and when to use them. You might choose to assign "doing democracy" activities that students can carry out relatively easily working as individuals or in small groups and then move on to more demanding projects for the whole class.

The *Doing Democracy* toolkit also includes a survey for measuring your students' levels of civic engagement at the beginning and end of your government course.

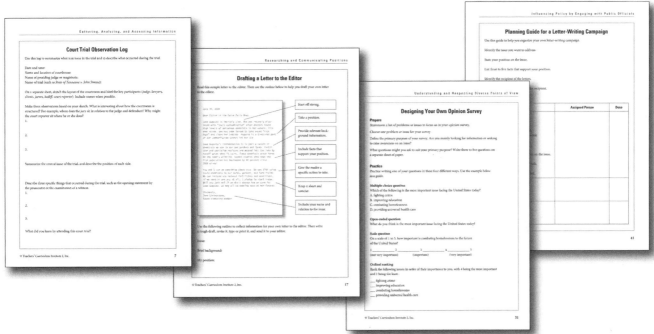

Assessing Learning

Effective assessment requires many approaches—individual and group, informal and formal—to create a well-rounded understanding of student performance. Here are some tips for evaluating student work.

Informal Assessment

Assessment of day-to-day activities benefits both you and your students. You send the message that every activity is important. And by identifying what works and what doesn't, you are able to adjust your instructional plans. Try these methods:

- Make your expectations known in advance so students will know how they will be rated.
- Note a student's answers to questions, both oral and written.
- Evaluate participation in act-it-outs and class discussions.
- Look for a student's level of cooperation in a pair or small group.
- Ask students to assess their own work.
- Skim notebooks as students work in class.

Groupwork Assessment

Evaluating groupwork presents a lot of questions: Should you rate the product or the process? The individual or the group? The amount of effort or the quality of the result? Here are five steps that will help you assess groupwork equitably:

1. Set clear criteria for evaluation.
2. Make both individuals and groups accountable.
3. Record notes as groups work and while they present their final products.
4. Have students complete self-assessments to evaluate their individual contributions as well as the group's performance.
5. Determine group and individual grades.

Formal Assessment

In addition to classroom observations and evaluation of student notebooks, you will need formal measurements of how much your students have learned. Research has shown that the TCI Approach improves student comprehension and retention. (For research results, visit www.teachtci.com.)

Government Alive! Power, Politics, and You provides an assessment at the end of each chapter. You will find reproducible test pages in the Lesson Masters and answers in the Lesson Guide.

Each chapter assessment has two parts. The first part, "Mastering the Content," consists of ten multiple-choice questions. Students will find it helpful to review their Reading Notes in their interactive student notebooks as preparation for these questions.

The second part, "Exploring the Essential Question," requires higher-order thinking skills as students respond to prompts that ask them to analyze a variety of primary sources and sets of data. These open-response questions are scaffolded to help students move from concrete analysis to synthesis and evaluation.

You will find digital versions of the assessments on the Digital Teacher Resources CD-ROM. You can use each test as is, randomize the order of questions, edit questions, or add your own questions. See the following pages for more information on these assessments.

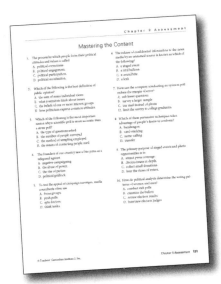

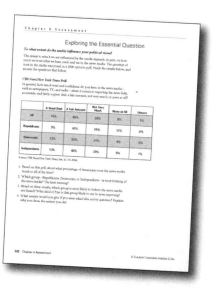

Enhancing Instruction with the DTR

With the Digital Teacher Resources CD-ROM (DTR), you can maximize your time both before and during class.

Lesson Planning

There is no need to lug all the components of the program home with you—just bring the DTR. With it, you can

- view and print Lesson Guide and Lesson Master pages
- preview audio tracks
- view transparencies, mark them with text, boxes, and arrows, and save them for presentation in class
- create and customize assessments

Creating Assessments

With the DTR, you can create your own assessments. Choose from a bank of questions, modify any of those questions, and add your own questions.

Visual Discovery with the Transparency Tool

One of the cornerstones of the TCI Approach is the power of using visuals as a teaching tool. With transparencies on the DTR, you can easily zoom in and out to help enhance students' understanding of an image.

Another way to use the DTR to its maximum advantage is to create transparency overlays with your own annotations. This is an easy and effective way to boost visual learning. You can mark transparencies with arrows, lines, circles, boxes, and text and save your work, without permanently changing the original.

Annotated Transparency

African American men protest segregation policies.

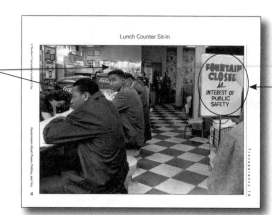

Sign indicates the lunch counter has been closed due to "public safety" concerns.

Finding Additional Resources Online

Support for *Government Alive! Power, Politics, and You* extends beyond the box of print and audiovisual materials to a wealth of resources on the Internet. Visit **www.teachtci.com** and explore these ways to enhance your teaching.

Online Resources   Click on the Students tab and select *Government Alive!* Choose from Internet Connections (links to chapter-related content), Enrichment Essays and Activities (additional content to support state standards), and Celebrating the Life and Contributions of César Chávez and Martin Luther King Jr.

Community Resources   Click on the Teachers tab for an array of community and professional resources. Visit our discussion groups and get ideas for your own classroom, engage in professional exchanges with teachers from around the country, and share your own best practices. Or get inspired by reading powerful TCI stories of teachers and administrators nationwide.

Standards Correlations   Click on the Program tab and select *Government Alive!* Choose Correlations and select your state. Download a PDF document for a correlation of *Government Alive! Power, Politics, and You* to your state standards.

Growing Professionally

There is much, much more to learn about igniting students' interest in history and creating insightful and memorable classroom experiences. For more detailed explanations, teaching tips, reproducible pages, and sample lessons, please read *Bring Learning Alive!* This book covers every aspect of TCI's methodology for the secondary social studies classroom. Please visit **www.teachtci.com** or call Customer Service at **1-800-497-6138** for more information or to order.

TCI Academy Training

After you have taught a few TCI lessons and seen your students' active interest in learning history, you may find that they have reignited your passion for teaching. Help your colleagues remember why they went into teaching by bringing a TCI Academy training to your school or district.

Trainings are built around immersion lessons, in which teachers become students to experience the power of the active, student-centered instruction. TCI Academy trainers are classroom teachers themselves and debrief activities to provide immediate feedback. You can mix and match TCI Academy sessions to build a course that best meets your needs. Please visit **www.tciacademy** or call us at **1-800-840-2698** to get started.

Power, Authority, and Government

1 The Nature of Power, Politics, and Government 3

Why should you care about power, politics, and government?

Experiential Exercise

2 Comparing Forms of Government 13

How should political and economic power be distributed in a society?

Response Group

The Nature of Power, Politics, and Government

Why should you care about power, politics, and government?

Overview

Students examine the concept of power and how it influences politics and shapes government authority.

Preview Students complete a "personal power assessment" to evaluate power in their own lives.

Activity In an Experiential Exercise, students participate in a trading game to explore how people gain and exercise power.

Processing Students analyze quotations that express various views about power to determine which they believe are most true about power, politics, and their own lives.

Objectives

In the course of reading this chapter and participating in the classroom activity, students will

- analyze the relationship between power and authority.
- describe the purpose and role of government.
- explain how political behavior is a natural function of society.
- evaluate differing assumptions held by people across time and place regarding power and authority.

Materials

Government Alive! Power, Politics, and You

Lesson Masters

- Notebook Guide 1 (1 per student)
- Notebook Handout 1 (1 per student)
- Student Handout 1 (1 copy, cut apart)
- Information Master 1 (1 transparency)

index cards (5 pink, 10 yellow, 20 blue, 25 white; substitute other colors if necessary)

Preview

Suggested time: 20 minutes

1 **Have students complete Preview 1.** Distribute *Notebook Guide 1* and have students complete a "personal power assessment" to evaluate power in their own lives. (**Note:** This assignment encourages students to examine their assumptions about power at the beginning of this course. Consider having them revisit this assignment at the end of the course to see whether their assumptions have changed.)

2 **Have students share their responses in pairs or with the class.**

3 **Explain the connection between the Preview and Chapter 1.** Tell students that their assessments reveal some of the assumptions they hold about power in their own lives. In this chapter, they will learn why they should care about power and how it connects with the study of politics and government. Throughout this course, they will learn about power in the American system of politics and government as well as the power they have to influence and participate in that system.

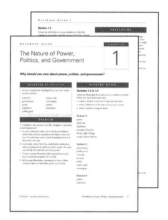

Notebook Guide 1

Reading

Speaking of Politics Encourage students to use the following terms as they complete their Reading Notes for the chapter: *authority, government, power, legitimacy, public good, nation-state, sovereignty, politics,* and *institution.*

1 **Introduce the Essential Question and have students read Section 1.1 of the chapter.** Then ask them to consider possible answers to the Essential Question: *Why should you care about power, politics, and government?*

2 **After the Experiential Exercise, students will read and complete the Reading Notes for Sections 1.2 to 1.5.** Consider the alternate reading and note-taking strategy in the first option under "Quicker Coverage."

Experiential Exercise

Suggested time: 45 minutes

1 **Understand the intent of the *Chip* game.** In this game, students trade colored chips. After each round of the game, the student with the highest point value is allowed to make a rule to govern the next round. Typically this student will make a rule to stay in power so that he or she can continue making the rules in future rounds. After two or more rounds, other students will pool their chips together to "overthrow" this student so they can make the rules.

2 **Prepare for the game.** Prepare the "chips" by cutting the index cards (see the materials list for quantities) in half and mixing them up in a large container or bag. Cut the six hint cards from *Student Handout 1: Hint Cards*. (**Note:** The number of chips is designed for a class of 32 students. For more or fewer than 32 students, increase or reduce the number of each color of chip by one for every one student.)

Student Handout 1

3 **Introduce the game.** Explain that students will be playing a game in which they trade colored chips. Project the top half of *Information Master 1: The Chip Game,* and review the rules with the class. (**Note:** Do not reveal the point values at this time.)

Information Master 1

4 **Distribute the chips.** Randomly distribute the chips to students so that the distribution is uneven in both color and amount. To make sure that only one student will have the most points at the end of the first round of trading, give three or four pink chips to one student.

5 **Conduct the first round of trading.** Give students approximately two minutes to trade chips. Expect some confusion, as students do not know the point values of their chips and have not been given any guidance on how to trade. Encourage them to move around and trade with one another in whatever way they think makes sense. (**Note:** Consider playing music while students trade and having students cease trading and sit down when you stop the music.)

6 **Have students calculate their point values.** Reveal the point values on *Information Master 1.* Expect students to be surprised and frustrated when they realize the point values of their chips. Determine who has the most points.

7 **Have the student with the most points make a rule for Round 2.** Give this student Hint Card 1 from *Student Handout 1,* and ask him or her to create a rule for the next round of trading. The only limitation is that the rule cannot end all trading. Write the new rule where everyone can see it, reminding the class that this rule will apply only to the next round of trading.

8 **Follow Steps 5 to 7 to conduct at least two more rounds of trading.** Make these adjustments:

- At the beginning of Round 2, give Hint Card 2 to a student. This card encourages the student to build an alliance with the student who is making the rules.

- At the beginning of Round 3, give Hint Cards 3 and 4 to two other students. These cards suggest that students group together to overthrow the student who is making the rules.

- After each round, cross out the previous rule and record the new one.

- End the game when a group of students has succeeded in overthrowing the student making the rules. Allow this group to make their own rule, and then announce that the game is over. If students do not group together by the middle of Round 4, give Hint Cards 5 and 6 to two additional students.

9 **Debrief the game.** Help students to connect their experience to the concept of power. Ask,

- What happened to you during the game?

- What happened in the class during the game?

- What do you think the game was about?

- Based on this experience, how would you define power?

- Why might power be related to a course on American politics and government?

Power, Politics, and You

Have students read the "Power, Politics, and You" section of the chapter, and facilitate a discussion by asking the questions below. Consider having students discuss the questions in pairs or small groups first.

- According to Alvin Toffler, what are the three kinds of power? Give an example of each.

- Which of these three is the highest-quality power?

- Why should you care about knowledge as a kind of power?

Processing

Suggested time: 20 minutes

Distribute *Notebook Handout 1: Quotations About Power,* and have students follow the directions on Notebook Guide 1 to complete Processing 1 in their notebooks. In the assignment, students will analyze quotations expressing different views about power and determine which they believe are most true about power, politics, and their own lives.

Notebook Handout 1

Quicker Coverage

Break Up the Reading Divide students into expert groups of three, and assign each group to read and complete the Reading Notes for one of Sections 1.2 to 1.4. Then give expert groups a few minutes to discuss the definitions and clarify any information they may have found confusing. Ask students to then number off within their expert groups. Form new jigsaw groups by having all number 1s meet, all number 2s meet, and all number 3s meet. In each jigsaw group, have students share the information from their reading section. Finally, have all students read and complete the Reading Notes for Section 1.5.

Simplify the Game Reduce the time necessary to play *Chip* by distributing Hint Cards 3 through 6 at the end of Round 2. Students will likely overthrow the student in power by the end of Round 3.

Deeper Coverage

Expand the Processing Enhance the Processing by having students work in groups to rate the quotations, answer the questions, and then share their responses.

- Post a copy of each quotation on the walls around the classroom.

- Appoint one presenter in each group.

- For Question 1, have presenters stand in front of the quotation their group chose and share the reasons they chose that quotation. Encourage other students to ask questions and bring in other examples.

- Repeat for Questions 2 and 3, appointing new presenters for each question.

Also consider having groups share their ratings of each quotation by creating a human spectrum. Or allow groups time to discuss which of the quotations is least true about power, politics, and their lives.

Assessment

Masters for the chapter assessment appear in the *Lesson Masters*.

Mastering the Content

1. B	2. C	3. B	4. D	5. A
6. B	7. D	8. A	9. D	10. C

Exploring the Essential Question

1. persuasion, sometimes rewards

2. formal authority, coercion

3. Possible answers:

   formal authority: conduct class, make assignments, maintain order, give out grades

   persuasion: motivate students to do homework, inspire students to do outside reading

   expertise: explain content, answer questions

   rewards: give out extra points, offer extra credit assignments

   coercion: enforce school rules, expel students who misbehave, withhold grades until work is completed

4. Possible answer: I could use the power of persuasion to try to build a base of popular support by talking to people and writing letters to the newspaper. I could find out who has the formal authority to decide about the bike path (city council? parks department?) and follow procedures to place it on the agenda. I could find sources of expertise on costs and benefits, knowing that my arguments will carry more weight if supported by data.

English Language Learners

Simplify the Processing For the Processing assignment, provide a rewrite of the quotations on *Notebook Handout 1,* such as these:

- *Quotation 1:* We are now better at making scientific advancements than at making good decisions. People in charge of using these advancements are making poor decisions.

- *Quotation 2:* People with power usually use it poorly, and people with total power abuse it.

- *Quotation 3:* Power doesn't make people bad; fear does. People who have power act badly because they don't want to lose it. People who are afraid of people in power also act badly.

- *Quotation 4:* People use force to gain political power.

- *Quotation 5:* The determination and courage of free men and women are stronger than any weapon.

- *Quotation 6:* Good has always won out in history. There have been terrible leaders who seemed would have power forever, but they always failed in the end.

- *Quotation 7:* The world will know peace when people care more about each other than having power.

- *Quotation 8:* The rich and powerful have destroyed the country. If you think this is a problem, you should do something about it.

- *Quotation 9:* Powerful people make the country great, but the people who question power are just as important.

Learners Reading and Writing Below Grade Level

Clarify the Processing Vocabulary Before students complete the Processing assignment, review the quotations on *Notebook Handout 1* with the class. Underline key vocabulary and write definitions above the terms. Then have students work in groups to rewrite the quotations in their own words.

Learners with Special Education Needs

Simplify the Preview Quantify the directions for the Preview assessment. Require that students identify only four individuals, institutions, and circumstances that have power over them and four that they have power over. Offer an example of each to get students started.

Pair Students for the Game Have students work in pairs throughout the *Chip* game so they can consult with one another when trading. Also, simplify the point values so it will be easier for students to add the values of their chips; for example: pink, 10; yellow, 5; blue, 2; white, 1.

Advanced Learners

Bring in Current Events After they complete the Processing assignment, have students identify a current event that illustrates one of the quotations from *Notebook Handout 1*. Have them locate a representative news article, photograph, or other resource to share with the class.

Assign Power Essays Have students write a multiparagraph essay on the concept of power. The essay should analyze various definitions of power and offer the student's own definition of power, including a historical or present-day example to support that definition.

Internet Connections

For related research materials on the concepts of power, politics, and government, refer students to Online Resources at www.teachtci.com.

Multimedia

Please follow school and district guidelines for showing films in the classroom.

Blood Diamond (R) This 2006 film by Edward Zwick is set during the tumultuous 1990s civil war in Sierra Leone. It is the story of two very different men who come together with a common goal: to find a rare diamond. One man is a diamond smuggler who works to finance terrorists. The other is a local fisherman who needs the diamond to save his family. The film shows what can happen when a country is torn apart by a deadly power struggle between government soldiers and rebel forces.

Downfall (R) This German film, nominated for an Oscar in 2005 as Best Foreign Language Film, re-creates the last days of Adolf Hitler. In April 1945, Germany faces inevitable defeat, with the Russians closing in from the East and the Allies from the West. The film takes place in Hitler's bunker, where viewers watch the personal experience of a leader as he loses power. Some of his officials abandon him, while others pledge to fight with him to his death. The film is in German with English subtitles.

Gandhi (PG) This 1982 biography of Mohandas Gandhi, directed by Richard Attenborough, begins with his experience as a young lawyer in South Africa, where he feels the pain of racism as he is treated as a second-class citizen. With new awareness, he returns to India with a pledge to liberate Indians from British colonial rule. Though others think he is crazy, he lives like a peasant to truly understand India. He organizes a campaign of civil disobedience and successfully unites the country to win independence. This film garnered eight Oscars, including one for Ben Kingsley as Best Actor.

Walkout This 2006 HBO film relates the true story of Mexican American students who organized to protest educational conditions and bias in their schools. The students staged a series of protests and walkouts in five East Los Angeles high schools in 1968. It is a compelling story of the power of students to change the world around them, while realistically portraying the challenges such a commitment involves.

Below are possible definitions for the dictionary entries. Symbols and sentences will vary.

Section 1.2

power: The ability to cause others to behave as they might not otherwise choose to do. The power to rule can be gained or lost in many ways. Power can be used for positive or negative purposes.

authority: The legal right to give orders and enforce rules. In government, political scientists speak of formal authority, or power that has been defined in a legal or other official way.

legitimacy: Being accepted as an authority, often applied to laws or those in power. Legitimacy rises and falls depending on the willingness of those being led to follow those leading.

mandate of heaven: A doctrine of legitimacy introduced by the Zhou of China. The Chinese ruler was the "son of heaven" and had authority over "all under heaven." He retained this right only as long as he ruled his subjects in a moral manner.

divine right of kings: A doctrine of legitimacy used by European monarchs in the 1500s. Monarchs represented God on Earth. Because their right to rule was God-given, they had absolute power to govern as they saw fit.

social-contract theory: A theory of legitimacy that emerged from European philosophers who said that a government existed because of an unwritten contract between the ruler and the ruled. A ruler who breaks this contract by abusing power loses legitimacy and should be removed from power.

Section 1.3

government: Institutions and officials organized to establish and carry out public policy. Government serves many purposes, such as maintaining public order, protecting life and property, and providing public goods.

public good: A product or service that is available for all people to consume, whether they pay for it or not. Today's governments provide a variety of public goods to their citizens.

coercion: The ways in which a government uses its power to force citizens to behave in certain ways. Governments use the threat of punishment to maintain public order. They also require involuntary services of citizens, such as jury duty.

revenue: Governments need money to provide security and pay for public goods. They generally get it from the people they govern, as through taxes.

polity: A government ruled by a virtuous and well-educated middle class. Aristotle believed that a polity would suit most societies, as opposed to rule by one or a few.

nation-state: An independent state, especially one in which the people share a common culture. In a nation-state, people have a sense of belonging to one country, even if they have different ethnic backgrounds.

sovereignty: The right to exercise supreme authority over a geographic region, a group of people, or oneself.

Section 1.4

politics: The process and method of making decisions for groups. Although generally applied to governments, politics is observed in all human interactions. Political activity has a purpose and involves collective action.

institution: An established organization, especially one providing a public service, and the rules that guide it. Institutions shape political activity through written and unwritten rules.

Section 1.5

Horse trading

Description: Hard bargaining with the objective of achieving a win-win situation, in which both players walk away happy. The basic strategy is to give up something in exchange for something of equal or greater value.

Example: In the Missouri Compromise, the Northern states allowed Missouri to enter as a slave state, while the Southern states agreed to a ban on slavery in most of Louisiana Territory and the admission of Maine as a free state.

Walkout

Description: Instead of giving something to the opposition, players walk out and refuse to return until the opposition agrees to give them something they want.

Example: César Chávez organized a strike of California grape pickers and encouraged Americans to boycott table grapes as a sign of support, bringing national attention to the struggle of farmworkers.

Power Struggle

Description: Clever politicians try to win by outfoxing or overpowering their opponents. This game was first described by 16th-century political philosopher Niccolò Machiavelli.

Example: During the Cuban missile crisis, President John F. Kennedy employed both force and cunning against the Soviet Union. He ordered a naval blockade and planned for an invasion. At the same time, he successfully negotiated with the Soviet Union to remove its missiles from Cuba.

Demolition Derby

Description: The goal is complete destruction of one's opponents. Players try to eliminate all real and perceived enemies. The key players are those who command the means of force using a variety of strategies, from fear to murder.

Example: After the Third Punic War, the Roman army demolished Carthage, burning the city to the ground and selling survivors into slavery.

Civil Disobedience

Description: Players forsake violence, instead being people of conscience whose goal is to end some social or political evil. Their strategy is to publicly shame the opposition by deliberately disobeying what they think is an unjust law.

Example: Mohandas Gandhi organized massive campaigns to protest the injustices of British colonial rule. Arrested many times, he used his imprisonment to remind the world that taking action against an unjust government is the highest duty of a citizen.

Comparing Forms of Government

How should political and economic power be distributed in a society?

Overview

Students investigate the advantages and disadvantages of various forms of governments and economic systems.

Preview Students debate the benefits and drawbacks of having various groups of people at their school make the rules.

Activity In a Response Group activity, students take on the role of representatives at a constitutional convention that is charged with creating a stable government and an economic system for a fictitious, newly independent country.

Processing Students suggest government and economic systems based on a new country's various priorities.

Objectives

In the course of reading this chapter and participating in the classroom activity, students will

- analyze the origins and development of governments over time and classify various political systems.

- analyze the advantages and disadvantages of various political systems and compare the ways in which power is distributed in systems of shared power.

- compare and contrast constitutional democracies with authoritarian regimes; presidential and parliamentary governments; and federal, confederal, and unitary systems of government.

- classify and evaluate various economic systems and identify the role of government in each.

Materials

Government Alive!
Power, Politics, and You

Transparency 2

Lesson Masters

- Notebook Guide 2
  (1 per student)
- Student Handouts 2A
  and 2C (1 of each per
  group)
- Student Handout 2B
  (1 version for each
  group)

Preview

Suggested time: 10 minutes

1 **Have students complete Preview 2.** Distribute *Notebook Guide 2,* and have students answer the Preview questions in their notebooks.

2 **Have students share their responses in pairs or with the class.** Then ask,

- Which group do you think should be allowed to make the rules? Why?

- Are there groups you think should not be allowed to make the rules? Why?

- Which group usually makes the rules at your school? Why do you think that is? What are the advantages of this system? The disadvantages?

- In general, what advantages does the group that is in power have? How are the groups that are not in power at a disadvantage?

3 **Explain the connection between the Preview and Chapter 2.** Tell students that they will now learn about various forms of government, systems for distributing power in a government, and economic systems. Similar to determining who should make the rules for running a school, there are advantages and disadvantages to different forms of government, ways of organizing government, and economic systems.

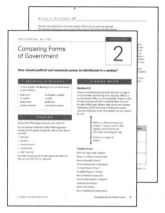

Notebook Guide 2

Reading

Speaking of Politics Encourage students to use the following terms as they complete their Reading Notes for the chapter: *democracy, monarchy, dictatorship, market economy, traditional economy, republic, parliament,* and *command economy.*

1 **Introduce the Essential Question and have students read Section 2.1.** Afterward, ask students to consider possible answers to the Essential Question: *How should political and economic power be distributed in a society?*

2 **Before conducting the activity, have students read Sections 2.2 to 2.5 and complete the Reading Notes.** Consider the alternate reading and note-taking strategy in the first option under "Quicker Coverage."

Response Group

Suggested time: 90 minutes

1 **Place students in eight groups of equal size and introduce the activity.** Explain that students will take on the role of representatives at a constitutional convention that is charged with creating a stable government and an economic system for a fictitious country that has just achieved independence. Each group will represent a different interest group within that society. Some groups will have similar interests, while others will have conflicting interests. Groups must work together to establish a new form of government, create a system of organization for that government, and choose an economic system for their newly independent country.

2 **Have groups review** *Student Handout 2A: Background Information on Nucountry* **to learn about the country.** Then ask, *What issues is Nucountry facing as it gains its independence?*

3 **Assign and have groups learn about their interest groups.**

- Assign each student group to one of the eight interest groups by distributing the appropriate version of *Student Handout 2B: Interest Groups at the Constitutional Convention* to each group.

- After students read about their interest group, have them record on Student Handout 2B their group's characteristics and primary concerns about the future of Nucountry.

- Have each group use colored markers to create a sign with the name of their interest group and a simple slogan that illustrates what is important to them. Have them post their signs on the wall near them.

- Have each group give a brief verbal summary of their interest group's characteristics, as well as their main concerns about the future of Nucountry.

- Ask the class, *What potential challenges might Nucountry face in making decisions about the type of government and economic system it will use?*

4 **Project** *Transparency 2: Demographic Information on Nucountry* **and distribute** *Student Handout 2C: Demographic Information on Nucountry* **to each group.** Explain that this information will help interest groups determine their goals for Nucountry. Have groups examine the maps and the graph one at a time and discuss the questions about each on Student Handout 2C. You may want to hold a discussion about the answers to each set of questions before moving on to the next map or graph.

5 **Have groups prepare for the constitutional convention.** Have groups complete the matrix on Student Handout 2B by listing their preferred options and compromise choices for form of government, system of government, and economic system. They will find a list of choices for each topic in their Reading Notes for Sections 2.3, 2.4, and 2.5.

6 **Give groups time to form alliances.** Have each group send *one* ambassador to meet with other groups to negotiate, form alliances, and gain support for their listed preferences. You may want to limit the time spent on this step to 10 minutes or less.

7 **Explain the format of the constitutional convention.** Explain that during the first round of the convention, each group will have 30 seconds to explain what form of government they believe Nucountry should have and why. After each group's presenter has shared the group's ideas, the floor will be open for additional debate. Consider limiting debate to five minutes or less. Explain the following Response Group guidelines that students should follow during the discussion:

- Each person must stand when speaking.

- Each person will begin his or her statement with "*(Name of presenter), my group agrees/disagrees with your group because . . .*" or a similarly polite opening.

Student Handout 2A

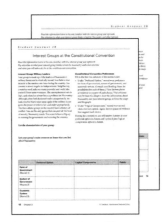

Student Handout 2B

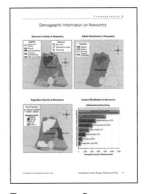

Transparency 2

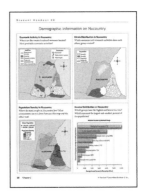

Student Handout 2C

Comparing Forms of Government **15**

- Every argument must be backed by relevant historical and political facts and ideas pertaining to Nucountry.

- Each presenter will choose the next presenter.

8 **Conduct Round 1 of the constitutional convention.** Acting as president of the convention, call the convention to order. You may want to use a gavel and a black robe or other props. Have each group choose its first presenter. Begin Round 1 by having each group present its choice for form of government. Keep Transparency 2 projected so students can use the maps or graph to illustrate their points. You may want to use a scored discussion to award groups points for arguments that are supported by evidence from the chapter, information about Nucountry and the interest groups, maps, or the graph.

9 **Have groups vote.** Tell students that a majority vote will be taken in which each group casts one vote. Hold the vote, and announce the new form of government for Nucountry. You may want to use a secret ballot and make a dramatic announcement to heighten anticipation. Then have students record the decision and assign themselves points appropriately (3 points if their preferred option was chosen, 1 point if their logical compromise option was chosen) in the "Points" column of the matrix on Student Handout 2B.

10 **Conduct Rounds 2 and 3 of the constitutional convention.** Repeat Steps 8 and 9 to have groups debate and hold a vote for Nucountry's system of government (Round 2) and economic system (Round 3).

11 **Critique the final decisions.** Have students consider the three decisions they made. Ask,

- Who will have power in Nucountry? Who will not have power?

- Why will this government and economic system work? What problems might arise?

- In the activity, what factors influenced the creation of the government and economic systems?

- What are some of the advantages and disadvantages of each type of government? Of each system of organizing government? Of each economic system?

- How might this constitutional convention be similar to what a country would go through in forming a government and economic system today? How might it be different?

Power, Politics, and You

Have students read the "Power, Politics, and You" section of the chapter, and facilitate a class discussion by asking the questions below. Consider having students discuss the questions in pairs or small groups first.

- The authors of this article point out the trend of democracy stagnation. What factors account for this, and why is each a problem?
- How do the current methods of suppressing political dissenters around the world differ from past methods of repression?
- Do you think that this is an issue that we, as Americans, should be concerned about? Why or why not?

Processing

Suggested time: 20 minutes

1 **Have students complete the Processing activity on Notebook Guide 2.** Students will suggest government and economic systems based on varying priorities a country might have.

2 **Debrief the activity.** Have students share their recommended combination and their reasoning for each priority in pairs or with the class.

Quicker Coverage

Break Up the Reading Follow these steps:

- Have students read Section 2.2 and complete the Reading Notes for that section individually, either at home or in class.
- Have each student within a group take responsibility for reading and completing the Reading Notes for one section. For Section 2.3, divide the terms equally between two students. Assign one student to each of Sections 2.4 and 2.5. Adjust accordingly for groups of fewer than four students.
- During the activity, have each student be responsible for leading the discussion relevant to the section of text he or she read (Section 2.3, form of government; Section 2.4, system of government; or Section 2.5, economic system). That student should also present during the appropriate round of the convention.

Simplify the Reading Notes Have students complete the reading and the Reading Notes for Section 2.2. Then give each group a copy of the Guide to Reading Notes for Sections 2.3, 2.4, and 2.5 to use as a reference during the activity.

Simplify the Activity Have groups complete only Rounds 1 and 3 of the activity.

Deeper Coverage

Investigate Recent Democracies As an alternative Processing assignment, have students investigate the constitutions of a recent democracy, such as Afghanistan or Iraq. Require them to find passages in the country's constitution that show the form of government, system of government, and economic system.

Assessment

Masters for the chapter assessment appear in the *Lesson Masters.*

Mastering the Content

1. B	2. B	3. C	4. C	5. D
6. A	7. A	8. D	9. C	10. A

Exploring the Essential Question

1. presidential democracy

2. parliamentary democracy

3. They all have parliamentary democracies, suggesting that they modeled their governments on that of the former colonial ruler.

4. Possible answers:

   - They believed that a presidential system would be more stable than a parliamentary one.

   - They had lived under a single-party system for many years and knew the disadvantages of that form of government.

   - They had experienced dictators in the past and knew that they could abuse their power.

   - They wanted to be more like other countries with a democratic form of government.

   - They believed that a presidential system would keep any one branch of government from gaining too much power.

   - They believed that a president would be more responsive to people's needs than a prime minister.

English Language Learners

Simplify Student Handout 2A To help students who may have difficulty identifying critical information within a large amount of text, give them this overview of Student Handout 2A to refer to during the activity:

- *Size:* 50,000 square miles (slightly larger than New York state)
- *Population:* 21 million
- *Geographic regions:* northern—dry climate and low population; southeastern—fertile land and two major rivers; and southwestern—fertile land and valuable natural resources.
- *Ethnic groups:* 85% Nupeeple—live mostly in the southeast and tend to be farmers or work in business or factories; 10% Apeeple—live mostly in the southwest and control valuable natural resources; 5% Upeeple—live mostly in the north and have a traditional nomadic lifestyle.
- *History:* Occupied for more than 100 years by neighboring country Ayland; currently achieving independence and holding a constitutional convention to establish new government and economic systems.

Summarize Group Presentations To assist students with the oral presentation of their group's viewpoint during the convention, provide a talking-points summary for each group, such as the one below.

Military Leaders

Major issue: Security of Nucountry.

Reasons: Powerful neighboring country, high crime rate, high unemployment rate that might lead to more crime.

Solution: A military dictatorship will provide stability and keep the country safe.

Modify the Processing Use one or both of these suggestions:

- Provide a definition of the key priorities (*efficiency, freedom, prosperity, equality,* and *security*) before creating the government and economic system combinations that would achieve these goals.
- Allow students to choose the three priorities they understand the best, and have them create the government and economic system combinations for those three priorities.

Learners Reading and Writing Below Grade Level

Support Vocabulary Development Provide support for key vocabulary throughout the program by implementing these vocabulary development strategies:

- **Word Wall** In a prominent area of the classroom, set up a space to post key vocabulary and definitions. Review the vocabulary at the beginning and end of the chapter. Have students use the terms in sentences.

- **Personal Glossary** Have students create a personal glossary of key vocabulary in their notebooks. Each entry might include a definition in the student's own words, a sentence using the word, and a simple illustration.

- **Flashcards** Have students create flashcards with definitions and illustrations for some or all of the words in their glossaries. These flashcards can be organized by chapter for easy review and stored in resealable bags.

Pair Students for the Reading Have pairs within each group complete the reading together using the WRAP (Whisper-Read Alternating Paragraphs) method. Model the volume at which you want them to read—loud enough for their partners to hear, quietly enough that no one else can hear. Then have partners complete the Reading Notes together.

Learners with Special Education Needs

Give Students Their Own Maps To help students process the maps and graph on Student Handout 2C, distribute a copy of the handout to each student rather than to each group.

Simplify the Reading Notes Consider reducing the requirements for the Reading Notes.

- Section 2.2: Require students to place only the following events on their timelines: *first city-states arise in Sumer, Athens formed direct democracy, Roman Republic formed, feudalism began in Europe, rise of absolute monarchies, Glorious Revolution in England, American Revolution.*

- Sections 2.3 to 2.5: On a separate handout, create a table that includes the definitions for each term. Require that students find one or two pros and cons for each term.

Advanced Learners

Determine Vote-Counting Method Before convening the constitutional convention, have groups determine how votes will be counted. Hold a brief class discussion about how a country might vote during a constitutional convention. Have students identify some possible advantages and disadvantages with a majority vote, a two-thirds vote, and a unanimous vote. Ask groups what methods of voting they think should be used to determine the type of government. Take a majority vote to decide how votes will be counted for *all* rounds of the convention.

Add Realism to the Activity During the convention, report "breaking news" events that may influence the debate, such as an earthquake with a high death toll, the assassination of a political figure, the discovery of a new resource (preferably in the northern region of the country), or threats from Ayland. Make sure to make the events not so drastic that students overreact and choose extremism, but drastic enough that students will consider the events as they debate. After the activity, discuss the role that these events played in students' decisions and, if reasonable for your class, draw historical analogies.

Internet Connections

For related research materials on the advantages and disadvantages of various forms of governments and economic systems, refer students to Online Resources at www.teachtci.com.

Following are possible answers to the Reading Notes questions.

Section 2.2

3000 B.C.E.   First city-states arise in Sumer: The government settles disputes and coordinates the harvesting and trading of crops.

2330s B.C.E.   Sargon of Akkad formed empire: Sargon rules with absolute power.

509 B.C.E.   Roman Republic formed: Romans expel monarchy and form a republic in which the people elect representatives to make public decisions.

400s B.C.E.   Athens formed direct democracy: All free, adult males share equally in governing.

31 B.C.E.   Roman Empire formed: Power held by emperors for life.

700s C.E.   Feudalism began in Europe: Nobles serve as vassals to lords.

1300s C.E.   Rise of absolute monarchies: In most of Europe, monarchs control all aspects of government.

1688 C.E.   Glorious Revolution in England: The first constitutional monarchy is established, limiting the power of the monarch.

1775 C.E.   American Revolution: American colonists revolt against the British and set up the first modern constitutional democracy.

1789 C.E.   French Revolution: The French overthrow the monarchy, resulting in a repressive dictatorship that sets the stage for the totalitarian regimes of the 20th century.

1900s C.E.   Rise of totalitarian dictatorships: Russian Revolution leads to communist dictatorship; fascist dictatorship established in Italy; Nazi dictatorship established in Germany.

Section 2.3

Term	Definition	Pros	Cons
Monarchy	a system of government in which a single ruler exercises supreme power based on heredity or divine right	• efficient way of carrying out decisions and policies • clear line of succession • loyalty to monarch as unifying power	• quality of leadership can vary dramatically from one generation to the next • job of running modern nation-state has become too big for any but the most exceptional monarchs to do well
Dictatorship	a system of government in which a single person or group exercises supreme power based on its control of the military and police	• power centralized in the hands of a single military or political leader who can get things done efficiently • control of the military and police allows dictator to maintain peace and order	• power can be used to abuse citizens who oppose the dictator • dictators face serious legitimacy problems
Theocracy	a system of government headed by religious leaders	• single, state-supported religion encourages political and social unity • ensures that political decisions are in line with the people's moral values and beliefs	• difficult to enforce religious unity • religious minorities often marginalized or even persecuted
Single-party state	a system of government in which only one political party is allowed by the constitution to govern and power is exercised by the leading members of the party	• easier to pass laws by avoiding the political wrangling common in multi-party states	• the views of the party elite may differ from the interests of the people as a whole, leading to social unrest • people with differing political views are often shut out of the political process
Direct democracy	a system of government in which public decisions are made directly by citizens meeting together in an assembly or voting by ballot	• each citizen has an equal say in public affairs • decisions have widespread support	• very time-consuming for citizens
Parliamentary democracy	a system of government in which voters elect lawmakers to represent them in the nation's parliament; the leaders of the executive branch come from the ruling party in parliament	• members of the legislative majority usually vote with the prime minister on key issues, making it easier to get legislation passed	• no clear-cut separation between the executive and legislative, so no real check on the prime minister's powers • prime minister can be forced to resign, leading to instability
Presidential democracy	a system of government in which voters elect lawmakers to represent them in the legislature and a president to lead the government as head of the executive branch	• president may be more responsive to the public than to party concerns • separation of executive and legislative powers allows each branch to watch over the other to prevent abuses of power • fixed terms of office creates stability	• no easy way to remove an unpopular president from power • gridlock may result when a president is not from the party that controls the legislature

Section 2.4

Term	Definition	Pros	Cons
Unitary system	a system of government in which power is centralized in the national government; regional governments only exercise powers given by national government	• promotes national unity • all parts of the country follow the same laws and policies	• broad public policies may not fit the needs of the entire country or population • central government officials cannot know the needs of every locality
Federal system	a system of government in which power is divided between national and regional governments	• works well for large, diverse countries • gives regional governments flexibility in meeting diverse needs	• patchwork of conflicting or competing laws from region to region • may foster conflict between central and regional governments
Confederal system	a system of government in which power resides in the regions, which are independent states; the central government gets power from regional governments	• allows regional governments to unite for some purposes without giving up the power to run their own affairs • gives regional governments flexibility to meet local needs • prevents rise of an authoritarian central government	• central government may be too weak to meet the needs of the nation as a whole • may lead to conflict between regions

Section 2.5

Term	Definition	Pros	Cons
Traditional economy	an economic system in which decisions about what goods and services to produce and how are made on the basis of tradition	• tradition and community values keep the economy running smoothly • people can provide for themselves	• very low standard of living • limited access to goods and services
Market economy	an economic system that relies mainly on markets to determine what goods and services to produce and how	• efficient at meeting people's needs, based on demand • competition keeps prices from rising too high • business investment helps the economy grow	• instability; periods of growth usually alternate with recessions • unequal distribution of wealth
Command economy	an economic system that relies mainly on the central government to determine what goods and services to produce and how	• can ensure full employment • can control prices and bring stability to the economy • distributes income more equally	• workers have little incentive to work hard or to produce quality goods • government planners are less efficient than the market at making economic decisions

UNIT **2**

Foundations of American Government

3 **The Roots of American Democracy   27**
What ideas gave birth to the world's first modern democratic nation?

Experiential Exercise

4 **The United States Constitution   37**
How and why did the framers distribute power in the Constitution?

Social Studies Skill Builder

5 **The Bill of Rights and Civil Liberties   49**
How are your rights defined and protected under the Constitution?

Problem Solving Groupwork

6 **Federalism: National, State, and Local Powers   61**
How does power flow through our federal system of government?

Response Group

The Roots of American Democracy

What ideas gave birth to the world's first modern democratic nation?

Overview

Students trace the evolution of democratic government in the United States by analyzing the political philosophies, documents, and historical figures that shaped its development.

Preview Students compare ancient Greek and Roman buildings with those in Washington, D.C., to predict how ancient ideas influenced the United States.

Activity In an Experiential Exercise, students "walk through" the National Statuary Hall in the U.S. Capitol to interview historical figures about key ideas that influenced democratic government in the United States.

Processing Students compose journal entries on the writing and ratification of the Constitution from the perspective of delegates to the Constitutional Convention.

Objectives

In the course of reading this chapter and participating in the classroom activity, students will

- evaluate the historical ideas and political philosophies that shaped the development of the U.S. government.

- summarize key political principles expressed in the foundational documents of the United States.

- examine the debates and events that led to the writing and ratification of the Constitution.

- analyze the ideas expressed in the Constitution from the perspective of a delegate to the Constitutional Convention.

Materials

Government Alive! Power, Politics, and You

Transparencies 3A and 3B

Lesson Masters

- Notebook Guide 3 (1 per student)
- Notebook Handout 3 (1 for every 4 students, cut apart)
- Student Handout 3A (1 per pair)
- Student Handouts 3B and 3C (1 biography and corresponding mask per pair)
- Student Handout 3D (1 per student)

Preview

Suggested time: 15 minutes

1 **Have students complete the first part of Preview 3.** Distribute *Notebook Guide 3* and project *Transparency 3A: Greece, Rome, or Home Challenge.* Students will compare images of ancient Greek and Roman buildings with those in Washington, D.C., to predict how ancient ideas influenced the United States.

2 **Reveal the locations of the buildings.** Dramatically reveal the answers, one at a time:

   A. United States: Supreme Court building

   B. ancient: Parthenon in Athens, Greece

   C. United States: Department of the Treasury building

   D. ancient: Pantheon in Rome, Italy

   E. United States: Jefferson Memorial

   F. United States: Capitol building

3 **Ask students to answer the Preview questions.** Have them share their responses in pairs or with the class.

4 **Explain the connection between the Preview and Chapter 3.** Explain that the ideas of the ancient Greeks and Romans are just a few of the many ideas that shaped democratic government in the United States. Over time, varying concepts emerged about the way government should be organized, how much power a government should have, and what role the people should play in government. Students will learn about the key documents, political philosophies, historical figures, and important events that contributed ideas and influenced the development of democratic government in the United States.

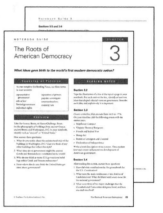

Notebook Guide 3

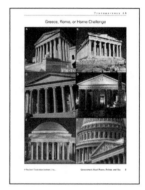

Transparency 3A

Reading

Speaking of Politics Encourage students to use the following terms as they complete their Reading Notes for the chapter: *representative government, rule of law, limited government, individual rights, separation of powers, popular sovereignty, constitutionalism,* and *majority rule.*

1 **Introduce the Essential Question and have students read Section 3.1.** Then ask,

   • What events did the two bicentennial celebrations in the United States mark?

   • Of what did the bicentennial events remind Americans? Why were these events so powerful?

   • What ideas might have given birth to the world's first modern democratic nation?

2 *Following* **the Experiential Exercise, have students read and complete the Reading Notes for Sections 3.2 to 3.6.** For Section 3.2, students will need an illustration cut from *Notebook Handout 3: Roots of U.S. Government.*

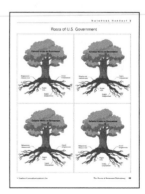

Notebook Handout 3

Consider the alternative reading and note-taking strategy in the first option under "Quicker Coverage." Or consider having students complete the Reading Notes for Sections 3.2 and 3.3 before the activity and for the remaining sections following the activity.

Student Handout 3A

Experiential Exercise

Suggested time: 90–120 minutes

1 **Place students in pairs and introduce the activity.** Explain that students will pretend to be statues of historical figures temporarily on display in the U.S. Capitol's National Statuary Hall. These statues represent important individuals who influenced the development of democratic government in the United States. Pairs will first prepare to bring to life their assigned historical figures. Then they will split up for the interviews. One student will be interviewed as a statue, while the other will interview the other statues. Students will then switch tasks.

2 **Assign pairs to one of the eight historical figures.** Give each pair of students *Student Handout 3A: Preparing for the Interviews.* Also assign each pair one of the following historical figures by distributing the appropriate page of *Student Handout 3B: Biographies of Historical Figures* and a corresponding mask from *Student Handout 3C: Masks of Historical Figures* to each pair. Depending on the class size, you may need to assign the same figure to more than one pair.

Student Handout 3B

- Pericles, ancient Athenian leader
- Cicero, ancient Roman senator
- Archbishop Stephen Langton, witness to the sealing of the Magna Carta
- John Somers, member of the 1689 English Parliament
- John Locke, English philosopher
- Baron de Montesquieu, French philosopher
- John Adams, American founding father
- Thomas Jefferson, American founding father

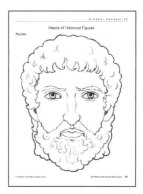
Student Handout 3C

3 **Allow most of a class period for pairs to prepare for the interviews.** You might provide additional support by distributing the appropriate handouts from the "Contacting and Interviewing Experts" section of the *Doing Democracy* toolkit and briefly reviewing how to use them.

4 **Arrange the classroom for the interviews.** Have pairs designate who will be the statue first and who will conduct the interviews. Have statues stand around the edges of the room. If more than one student is playing a particular role, tell interviewers to interview that historical figure only once.

5 **Set the scene for the interviews.** Project *Transparency 3B: National Statuary Hall.* Tell interviewers that they have entered the U.S. Capitol's National Statuary Hall. This hall showcases a collection of statues donated by the 50 states. Each state donated two statues to honor individuals who have made significant contributions to the United States. Tell students that in a "special

Transparency 3B

exhibit," statues have temporarily been added to honor individuals who influenced the development of democratic government in the United States.

6 **Conduct the interviews.** Distribute *Student Handout 3D: Interviews of Historical Figures*. Have interviewers complete the handout as they meet each statue. For efficient interviews, follow these steps:

- Assign each interviewer to a different statue.
- Direct the statues to come to life by announcing, "Unfreeze."
- Allow approximately three minutes for the interview.
- When the time limit is up, direct statues to stop talking by announcing, "Freeze," and instruct the interviewers to move to the next statue.
- Continue until interviewers have completed Student Handout 3D.
- Have pairs switch tasks, and repeat the procedure.

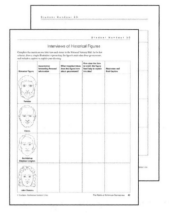

Student Handout 3D

7 **Review the answers.** Have students review the answers to Student Handout 3D in their pairs or with the class.

8 **Debrief the activity.** Ask,

- Where did ideas about our government come from?
- Which of the ideas do you think was the most unique or interesting? Why?
- Which of the ideas do you think had the most influence on the development of democratic government in the United States?

Power, Politics, and You

Have students read the "Power, Politics, and You" section of the chapter, and facilitate a class discussion by asking the questions below. Consider having students discuss the questions in pairs or small groups first.

- Why is there "cause for satisfaction" with the U.S. Constitution?
- Why are the challenges to national unity under the Constitution far greater today than in the past?
- What can you do to keep our republic alive and well?

Processing

Suggested time: 30 minutes

Have students complete the processing assignment on Notebook Guide 3. Students will compose journal entries on the writing and ratification of the Constitution from the perspective of a delegate to the Constitutional Convention. Consider having them share their journal entries in pairs or with the class. You might ask them to write from the perspective of actual delegates. To find biographies of convention delegates, visit the National Constitution Center connections at www.teachtci.com.

Quicker Coverage

Break Up the Reading Divide students into groups of four, and assign each group one of Sections 3.2 to 3.6. Tell groups they will become experts on their assigned section and present the answers to the corresponding Reading Notes to the class. After students read and complete the Reading Notes, have each group transfer their answers onto a blank transparency. Tell groups to determine who will explain each component of the Reading Notes and to find interesting examples, facts, or statistics from the text to incorporate into their presentations. Depending on the number of groups, you may want to divide each of Sections 3.2 to 3.4 in half.

Conduct Fewer Interviews Have the first set of interviewers visit only four of the eight statues. After students switch tasks, have the second set of interviewers visit the remaining statues. Then have pairs share their interview notes.

Deeper Coverage

Get Involved in Constitution Day Have students learn about their school's or community's plans to celebrate Constitution Day, September 17. They might attend a faculty or public meeting or speak with a school or local official. They then might volunteer to help. Provide support by distributing the "Attending a Public Meeting" handout from the *Doing Democracy* toolkit, making sure students understand how to use it. To find Constitution Day resources, visit the National Constitution Center connections at www.teachtci.com.

Assessment

Masters for the chapter assessment appear in the *Lesson Masters*.

Mastering the Content

1. C	2. D	3. C	4. A	5. A
6. B	7. A	8. B	9. C	10. B

Exploring the Essential Question

1. Hobbes and Locke saw a social contract as an agreement between the ruler and the ruled in which the ruled give up some of their freedom in exchange for security and order provided by the ruler. Hobbes thought people would enter into such a contract to escape the misery and insecurity of living in a state of nature, or a world without laws and government. Locke thought people would enter a social contract to secure their natural rights to life, liberty, and property.

2. Possible answers: Mayflower Compact, Massachusetts Body of Liberties, English Bill of Rights, U.S. Constitution. Each is an agreement by people to create a more orderly society by defining the rights and powers of the rulers and the ruled.

3. The key idea from Locke and Rousseau that appears in the Declaration of Independence is their belief that if a government fails to protect the people's rights, it has broken the social contract and the people have the right to abolish it.

4. The key idea from Montesquieu that helped shape the Constitution is his belief that governments should be divided into three branches—executive, legislative, and judicial—with separate functions so that no branch gains too much power.

English Language Learners

Guide the Interview Preparation Help students prepare for the interviews by highlighting key sections on Student Handout 3B that correspond to the two interview questions on Student Handout 3A. Have students write a list of talking points on a note card that they can use during the interviews. Then have them practice their interview answers out loud with their partners.

Offer Vocabulary for the Processing Give students a list of vocabulary or other terms to use in their journal entries for the Processing assignment. For example:

- Which ideas most influenced you in the development of the Constitution? *representative government, rule of law, limited government, separation of powers, popular sovereignty, constitutionalism, majority rule*

- What were the greatest challenges in developing the Constitution? *representation, slavery, commerce, executive*

- Do you think the states should ratify the Constitution? *strong national government, bill of rights*

Learners Reading and Writing Below Grade Level

Offer an Outline for the Processing Have students use the questions in the Processing assignment to create an outline such as the following for the three journal entries.

I. Ideas That Influenced the Constitution

   A. Idea 1

   B. Idea 2

II. Challenges in Developing the Constitution

   A. Challenge 1

      1. Problem

      2. Resolution

   B. Challenge 2

      1. Problem

      2. Resolution

III. Ratifying the Constitution

   A. Should the states ratify?

   B. Why or why not?

Learners with Special Education Needs

Aid Comprehension of Visual and Oral Information Provide support during the Experiential Exercise to help students comprehend the visual and oral information. Consider these suggestions:

- Place students in groups of four to allow them to interview and be interviewed in pairs.
- Assign students the roles of historical figures with whom they are familiar.
- Highlight key information on Student Handout 3B to help students find the appropriate information when preparing for their interviews.
- Limit the number of statues being interviewed to four. Then provide notes for the remaining statues.

Advanced Learners

Add Historical Figures to the Activity Add historical figures, such as those below, to the Experiential Exercise. Have pairs research the appropriate information to prepare for the interviews.

- King David, second king of Israel
- Thomas Aquinas, medieval Christian philosopher
- Thomas Hobbes, English philosopher
- Jean-Jacques Rousseau, French philosopher
- William Bradford, governor of Plymouth Colony
- Benjamin Franklin, American founding father

National Constitution Center

Have students find biographies of delegates to the Constitutional Convention by visiting the National Constitution Center connections at www.teachtci.com. For the Processing assignment, you might ask students to write from the perspective of actual delegates.

Internet Connections

For related research materials on the roots of democracy, refer students to Online Resources at www.teachtci.com.

Multimedia

Please follow school and district guidelines for showing films in the classroom.

The American Constitution: The Road from Runnymede Narrated by Christopher Reeve, this film traces U.S. history from the sealing of the Magna Carta in 1215 to the Constitutional Convention in 1787. The film focuses on the English roots of American democracy, particularly the effects of political events in the 17th century.

Liberty! The American Revolution This six-part PBS documentary follows the story of American independence from 1763 to 1788. Use these two episodes with this chapter:

- Episode 2, "Blows Must Decide, 1774–1776," highlights the story of the colonies' dramatic move to declare independence from Great Britain in 1776.
- Episode 6, "Are We to Be a Nation? 1783–1788," features the struggles of the newly independent colonies as they try to form a new nation.

Following are possible responses for each section of the Reading Notes.

Section 3.2

Religious and Classical Roots

- Ancient Judaism stressed that people should seek to create a just society based on respect for the law. Colonial thinkers based their notion of justice on this idea.

- Christians believed in natural law, the idea that a universal set of moral principles existed. Many colonists believed that a human law that violated natural law was unjust and should be changed.

- Ancient Greeks introduced the idea of direct democracy, or decision making by all citizens. Direct democracy took root in New England's town meetings, where citizens gathered to solve local problems.

- From ancient Romans came the idea of representative government, or decision making by elected officials. This idea would be the basis of U.S. government.

English Roots

- The Magna Carta defined the rights and duties of English nobles, set limits on the monarch's power, and established the principle of the rule of law. The colonists had great respect for the traditions of English government.

- The Petition of Right demonstrated the idea of limited government by affirming that the king's power was not absolute. The idea of limited government was one of the principles that colonists admired in English government.

- The English Bill of Rights reaffirmed the principle of individual rights established by earlier documents. One reason the colonists rebelled was to secure their individual rights, which they believed had been denied to them.

English Enlightenment

- Thomas Hobbes first introduced the idea that government was the result of a social contract between people and their rulers. His social-contract theory laid the groundwork for the idea that government was formed by the consent of the people.

- John Locke wrote about the idea that all people were equal and enjoyed certain natural rights, such as the right to life, liberty, and property. This idea exerted a powerful influence on colonial thinkers and would be used to justify the revolution.

French Enlightenment

- Montesquieu introduced the idea of separation of powers, in which governments are organized to prevent any one person or group from dominating others. Americans applied this idea to their colonial governments.

- Jean-Jacques Rousseau believed in the idea that a government formed by a social contract was legitimate if it was based on popular sovereignty. Some colonial leaders, including Thomas Paine, agreed with this idea that the government should be based on the will of the people.

Section 3.3

1619, Virginia House of Burgesses: This was the legislative branch of the colony where elected officials made decisions. The House of Burgesses was the first elected assembly in the colonies; other elected assemblies would follow.

1620, Mayflower Compact: Before settlers from the *Mayflower* landed, they drew up this compact for governing their new colony. They agreed to live in a civil body politic and obey just and equal laws enacted by representatives. This was the first written framework for self-government in the colonies.

1763, French and Indian War: After the war, Britain reversed its policy of "benign neglect" by imposing new taxes and restrictions on the colonies. Before this time, colonies had been accustomed to managing their own affairs, with Britain rarely interfering in the day-to-day business of government.

1765, Stamp Act: The British government required Americans to buy stamps to place on various documents. Colonists felt that, as British citizens, only their elected representatives could tax them; with no colonial representation in Parliament, the taxes were illegal.

1775, Battles at Lexington and Concord: Massachusetts militia troops clashed with British soldiers, marking the beginning of the American Revolution. This event revealed that tensions between the colonies and the British government were so high that armed conflict was inevitable.

1776, Declaration of Independence: This document called for a final break between the colonies and Britain. It set forth a vision for a new kind of nation in which the government is formed to protect people's unalienable rights and gets its powers from the consent of the governed.

Section 3.4

1. State constitutions showed that lawmakers were committed to constitutionalism—the idea that government should be based on an established set of principles. These principles included popular sovereignty, limited government, the rule of law, and majority rule. State constitutions also created a government with three branches to separate powers, and most began with a statement of individual rights.

2. The main weaknesses of the Articles of Confederation were, first, that Congress could not levy taxes to raise money to support an army or repay debts. Congress could not control trade among the states; instead, states set up trade barriers and quarreled among themselves. Also, there was no executive to enforce laws and no court system to settle legal disputes. States could and did ignore laws passed by Congress. These weaknesses meant that the national government did not have enough power to accomplish what it needed to do.

3. Possible answer: One challenge faced by the delegates was how to determine representation in the new government. Some delegates favored a unicameral legislature in which all states had equal representation. Others favored a bicameral legislature with representation based on population. The resolution was to have a bicameral legislature. In one house, representation was based on population. The other house had equal state representation. Another challenge was over slavery. The resolution was to count slaves as three-fifths of a free person for determining taxation and representation. A third challenge was over how to choose the president. Some delegates thought Congress should do it, while others favored popular elections. The resolution was to set up the Electoral College.

Sections 3.5 to 3.6

Federalists	Anti-Federalists
• Favored the creation of a strong federal government that shared power with the states. • Believed that because the national government represented so many people, it would be less likely to fall under the sway of factions. • Believed that separation of powers in the Constitution kept the national government from becoming too powerful.	• Preferred the loose association of states established under the Articles of Confederation. • Feared that a strong national government would lead to tyranny. • Believed that states are better able to represent people's rights and preserve democracy. • Were concerned that the Constitution did not contain a bill of rights.

The debate over the ratification of the Constitution was resolved by an agreement that a bill of rights would be added to the document. In 1789, James Madison introduced a series of proposed constitutional amendments in Congress. These amendments were a list of rights, including those discussed at state ratifying conventions and found in various documents. Congress eventually approved 12 amendments, 10 of which were ratified at that time.

The United States Constitution

How and why did the framers distribute power in the Constitution?

Overview

Students examine the Constitution to understand its guiding principles and the basic structure of the government it created.

Preview Students examine an outline of the Constitution and draw inferences about the intentions of the framers in creating our government.

Activity In a Social Studies Skill Builder, students delve into the Constitution during three engaging challenges that require them to examine specific provisions of the document as well as its overarching principles.

Processing Students propose amendments to the Constitution and describe why they believe these changes are needed.

Objectives

In the course of reading this chapter and participating in the classroom activity, students will

- examine the fundamental governing principles on which the Constitution is based and how those principles are embodied in the document.

- analyze how the Constitution establishes a limited government in which powers are distributed among different levels and branches.

- summarize how the various elements of the Constitution exemplify efforts by the framers to divide power.

- propose and defend amendments to the Constitution.

Materials

Government Alive!
Power, Politics, and You

Transparencies 4A–4C

CD Tracks 1–6

Lesson Masters

- Notebook Guide 4
  (1 per student)

- Notebook Handout 4
  (1 per student)

- Student Handouts 4A
  and 4C (3 copies of
  each, cut apart)

- Student Handouts 4B,
  4D, and 4E (1 of each
  per pair)

- Information Masters
  4A–4D (1 transparency
  of each)

Preview

Suggested time: 15 minutes

1   **Introduce the activity.** Explain that, throughout this chapter, students will take on the role of law students progressing through three years of law school. To be accepted into law school, they must first pass the Law School Admissions Test. Part of the LSAT requires them to demonstrate logical and analytical reasoning. This first task will test whether they can logically piece together an incomplete outline of the Constitution in a timed exam. (**Note:** If possible, seat students individually in rows, as if they were taking a high-stakes exam.)

2   **Have students complete *Notebook Handout 4: Outline of the U.S. Constitution.*** Distribute Notebook Handout 4, and give students a few minutes to complete the outline (in pencil, so they can correct mistakes later) using the Word Bank on the page and without using the Constitution as a reference. Then project *Information Master 4A: Outline of the U.S. Constitution*, and have students check and correct their work. Have them put the handout into their notebooks.

3   **Have students complete Preview 4.** Distribute *Notebook Guide 4*, and have students answer the Preview questions in their notebooks. Then discuss the questions and their answers.

4   **Explain the connection between the Preview and Chapter 4.** Explain that students will now learn how the Constitution, despite being over two centuries old, still guides our government and courts in day-to-day decision making. They will examine the document in depth to learn how the framers distributed power in order to protect us from abuses of power as well as how they assigned power to different branches of government and to the states.

Notebook Handout 4

Information Master 4A

Reading

Speaking of Politics Encourage students to use the following terms as they complete their Reading Notes for the chapter: *due process, republican government, checks and balances, federalism, independent judiciary, strict construction, loose construction,* and *judicial review.*

1   **Introduce the Essential Question and have students read Section 4.1.** Then ask students to consider possible answers to the Essential Question: *How and why did the framers distribute power in the Constitution?*

2   **Introduce a form of questioning commonly used in law school.** Assume the role of a law professor and explain that for the duration of students' time in law school, classes will be conducted using the following method. You will call on individuals at random to answer each question, addressing them by last name, such as "Miss Brown." If a student is unable to answer a question, he or she may reply, "May I have cocounsel?" and then call on another student for assistance. Use this method to ask students these questions about Section 4.1:

- Why did Dwight Lopez file a lawsuit against his school district?

- Is the issue Lopez presented a constitutional issue? In other words, is it

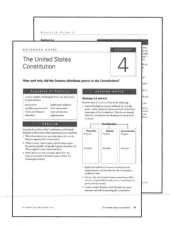

Notebook Guide 4

a case in which the Constitution will be consulted in order to make a decision?

- If you were the lawyer assigned to represent Lopez in this case, on what grounds might you argue that his constitutional rights were violated?

3 **Students will read Sections 4.2 to 4.6 and complete the Reading Notes during the classroom activity, as indicated in the procedures that follow.**

Social Studies Skill Builder

Challenge 1

Suggested time: 50–75 minutes

1 **Introduce the activity.** Congratulate students on being accepted into law school. To survive the next three years, they will need extensive knowledge of the Constitution and its principles. Each part of this activity will further familiarize them with the provisions of the Constitution, as well as how it embodies some basic governing principles and acts as the foundation for our government. Have students, in unison, repeat the following oath:

I do hereby promise to abide by the code set forth by this law school. I will not lie, cheat, or steal, as it is my aspiration to enter the honored profession of law practice. Toward this end, I will uphold the principles of the Constitution in each and all of my actions.

2 **Have students read Sections 4.2 and 4.3 and complete the corresponding Reading Notes.**

3 **Introduce Challenge 1: Constitutional Law 1.** Remind students that as 1L (first-year law) students, it is vital that they thoroughly understand the contents of the Constitution. To this end, Challenge 1 will acquaint them with the rules and operations of the U.S. government as enumerated in the Constitution.

4 **Put students into pairs, and have them complete Challenge 1.** Give each pair two or three cards cut from *Student Handout 4A: Constitutional Law 1 Cards* and a copy of *Student Handout 4B: Constitutional Law 1 Matrix*. Tell students that they will find the answer to each question directly in the Constitution (which is reprinted in the Resources section of the Student Edition) and can use their outlines from the Preview to guide them to the right article and section. As pairs record answers on the matrix, have them exchange cards with another pair or retrieve new cards from a "card bank" of remaining cards placed in an accessible location. Continue until most pairs have completed all 20 cards. (**Note:** Consider completing one card as a class before beginning the activity.)

5 **Debrief Challenge 1.** Project *Information Master 4B: Completed Constitutional Law 1 Matrix* and review it with students. Then ask,

- What do you notice about how the Constitution deals with power?
- Based on your examination of the Constitution so far, what are some ways that the framers distributed power in the Constitution?
- Why do you think they distributed power as they did?

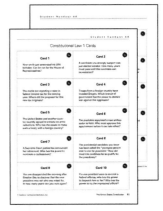

Student Handout 4A

Student Handout 4B

Information Master 4B

The United States Constitution **39**

Challenge 2

Suggested time: 50–75 minutes

1 **Teach students about the six governing principles of the Constitution.**
Project *Information Master 4C: Guiding Principles of the Constitution.* Have
students complete Question 1 of the Reading Notes for Section 4.4 as you discuss the six principles. (**Note:** Students will read the section after completing
the challenge.)

2 **Introduce Challenge 2: Constitutional Law 2.** Congratulate students on successfully completing 1L. Explain that as 2L students, they will now be expected
to understand the larger principles embodied by the Constitution. For this
next challenge, they will be asked to look up certain provisions and decide
which of the six guiding principles is being exemplified.

3 **Put students into pairs, and have them complete Challenge 2.** Give each pair
one or two cards cut from *Student Handout 4C: Constitutional Law 2 Cards*
and a copy of *Student Handout 4D: Constitutional Law 2 Matrix.* Explain that
they must find the article, section, and clause listed on the card and read that
provision of the Constitution. On Student Handout 4D, they will record as
many principles as they believe are exemplified within that provision and a
short explanation of why those principles apply. As pairs record their answers,
have them exchange cards with another pair or retrieve new cards from the
card bank. Continue until most pairs have completed all 10 cards. (**Note:**
Consider completing one card as a class before beginning the activity.)

4 **Have students read and complete the Reading Notes for Section 4.4.** As they
read, have them check their answers on Student Handout 4D, verifying which
principles they correctly identified. Then have them complete Question 2 of
the Reading Notes for Section 4.4.

5 **Project *Information Master 4D: Completed Constitutional Law 2 Matrix***
and debrief Challenge 2. Ask students to identify any principles they listed
that are not on the matrix and give justification for them. Then ask, *How do
these principles embody the concerns that the framers had about a government
with too much power?*

Information Master 4C

Student Handout 4C

Student Handout 4D

Information Master 4D

Challenge 3

Suggested time: 50–75 minutes

1 **Have students read Section 4.5 and complete the corresponding Reading Notes.**

2 **Introduce Challenge 3: Understanding Constitutional Law in Preparation for the Bar Exam.** Congratulate students on successfully completing their year as 2L students and explain that at the completion of their year as 3L students, they must pass a final exam before they can practice law. To prepare for this exam, they will undergo one final challenge. The challenge will focus on constitutional law and will require them to synthesize all they have learned about the Constitution by analyzing three Supreme Court cases that involve interpretations of the document.

3 **Put students into pairs, and have them analyze the first constitutional case study for Challenge 3.** Give each pair a copy of *Student Handout 4E: Background on Three Constitutional Cases*. Project *Transparency 4A: Constitutional Case 1* and play CD Track 1, "Constitutional Case 1," which, in addition to the handout, gives background on this first case study. Have students complete the tasks on Transparency 4A. When they have finished, ask them to share what sections of the Constitution might provide an answer to the question posed on the transparency, their predictions of what the Supreme Court will decide, and what in the Constitution led them to those predictions.

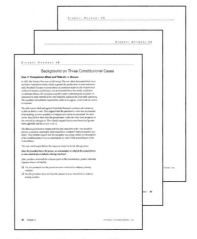

Student Handout 4E

4 **Reveal the outcome of the first case.** Play CD Track 2, "Outcome of Case 1," which gives an overview of what happened in the case and how the Constitution was used to decide the case. Discuss students' reaction to the decision and whether they agree with it.

5 **Repeat Steps 3 and 4 for the second and third cases.** Use *Transparency 4B: Constitutional Case 2* and CD Tracks 3 and 4 for the second case. Use *Transparency 4C: Constitutional Case 3* and CD Tracks 5 and 6 for the third case.

6 **Debrief the activity.** Ask,

- How and why did the framers distribute power in the Constitution?

- How do modern circumstances present challenges to carrying out the original intentions of the Constitution?

- Do you think the Constitution still works today? Why or why not?

Transparencies 4A–4C

Power, Politics, and You

Have students read the "Power, Politics, and You" section of the chapter, and facilitate a class discussion by asking the questions below. Consider having students discuss the questions in pairs or small groups first.

- What are the benefits and detriments of zero-tolerance policies in schools?
- Do you believe that the student in this article was denied due process, or was she simply breaking a known rule and therefore subject to punishment?
- Are zero-tolerance policies constitutional?

Processing

Suggested time: 15 minutes

1 **Have students complete the Processing activity on Notebook Guide 4.** Students will propose amendments to the Constitution and discuss why they believe these changes are needed.

2 **Have the class vote on the proposed amendments.** Ask volunteers to read their proposals aloud. Remind students that for a proposal to pass through Congress and move to state legislatures, their amendment must receive two-thirds of their classmates' votes in its favor. Have students vote on a few proposed amendments to see whether the class supports them.

Quicker Coverage

Streamline the Activity Have pairs complete only one or two of the challenges, or have students examine only one or two of the case studies in Challenge 3.

Simplify the Processing Hold a class discussion instead of having students complete the Processing assignment individually.

Deeper Coverage

Analyze Other Constitutional Court Cases Have students visit the National Constitution Center connections at www.teachtci.com to locate recent news stories in which questions of constitutionality have arisen. Use the NCC's Constitution Newswire page to find current cases and stories in which the courts were asked to decide on constitutional issues. Consider assigning groups of four students the task of summarizing each issue and presenting a question, using the format on Student Handout 4E as a model. Have groups present their case studies to the class, and ask the class to use their knowledge of the Constitution to decide what is constitutionally acceptable. Students might also visit the Oyez Project, U.S. Supreme Court Media, Web site at www.oyez.org.

Assessment

Masters for the chapter assessment appear in the *Lesson Masters*.

Mastering the Content

| 1. A | 2. B | 3. C | 4. B | 5. B |
| 6. C | 7. A | 8. A | 9. D | 10. A |

Exploring the Essential Question

1. Possible answers: limited government, separation of powers, checks and balances

2. Madison argued that because people are imperfect (not angels), the government must be constructed to keep those who govern from abusing their power. The Constitution does this by limiting the power of any one branch and allowing each branch to check the power of the other two.

3. Accept any specific example of checks and balances as correct answers.

English Language Learners

Make the Constitution More Concrete When introducing the Preview, consider briefly comparing the Constitution to a rulebook for a game that students often play—in other words, the Constitution is the rulebook for how our country is run. Then allow students to consult the Constitution during the Preview.

Support Developing Language Skills Provide support during the challenges. For example:

- For Challenge 1, rewrite the questions on Student Handout 4A in simpler language. Card 3 might read, *Who has the power to propose an increase in federal income tax rates?*

- For Challenge 2, give students Information Master 4D with a multiple-choice selection of three principles in the third column. Omit the answers in the "Explanation" column for students to complete during the challenge.

- In Challenge 3, provide a template for students to complete while listening to the audio tracks. The template should highlight the important information students will need to discuss the case. For example:

  Who are the two parties involved in this case?

  What is the issue to be decided by the Supreme Court?

  One party, the _____, argues that _____.

  The other party, _____, argues that _____.

Learners Reading and Writing Below Grade Level

Simplify the Processing Consider an alternative Processing assignment. For example, require students to write about one specific power each branch has and draw a simple illustration to represent that power.

Learners with Special Education Needs

Offer a Resource During the Preview, allow students to refer to the Constitution.

Make Class Discussions Easier During the law school questioning of the Reading Notes, allow students to raise their hands, or preselect the questions students will be expected to answer.

Offer Guidance with the Challenges Consider these suggestions:

- After working with each card, have students check their answers with you.

- Reduce the number of cards students must complete. Choose cards that provide the key information. Provide a copy of the completed notes to students who are unable to complete all the cards.

- On the matrix for Challenge 1 (Student Handout 4B), fill in the article numbers and some section numbers to offer some information about where in the Constitution the answers can be found.

- In Challenge 3, provide a cloze activity (the passages from Student Handout 4E with some words omitted) to help students focus on the important facts and better understand the case.

Advanced Learners

Create an Amendment Timeline As an alternative to the Processing assignment, have students examine how difficult it actually is to amend the Constitution. Have them create a simple timeline showing the flag-protection amendments that have been proposed since the 1989 decision in *Texas v. Johnson*. (The First Amendment Center, at www.firstamendmentcenter.org, has a timeline students can use.) Underneath their timelines, have them list two or three conclusions that can be drawn from the information on the timeline.

Research a Recently Proposed Amendment As an alternative to the Processing assignment, have students research a recently proposed amendment to the Constitution. Have them describe the proposed amendment and then argue in a paragraph whether or not they would vote for it if they were members of Congress.

U.S. Supreme Court Cases: You Make the Call

Have students read the summary of Case 1, *New London v. Kelo,* which relates to the primciple of eminent domain, in the "U.S. Supreme Court Cases: You Make the Call" section of the Student Edition. Have volunteers share key facts from the case and the question before the Court. Then facilitate a Response Group–type discussion asking students to "make the call" on how the Court should decide the case and why. Finally, have students read the actual Supreme Court decision.

National Constitution Center

Have students visit the National Constitution Center connections at www.teachtci.com and search by court case to find other relevant cases, such as those in Challenge 3, in which the Supreme Court decided questions of power within the government.

Internet Connections

For related research materials on the Constitution, refer students to Online Resources at www.teachtci.com.

Multimedia

Please follow school and district guidelines for showing films in the classroom.

Seizing Power: The Steel Seizure Case Revisited This one-hour film explores the 1952 decision by President Harry S. Truman to seize the nation's steel mills to maintain steel production in support of the war effort in Korea. Steel industry leaders sued the president to get their property back. The arguments made before the Supreme Court about presidential power in times of war and national crisis remain compelling today.

Following are possible answers for each section of the Reading Notes.

Sections 4.2 and 4.3

1. Possible answer:

Preamble

Purpose: To define the broad purposes of the republican government created by the document and to set out specific goals for the nation

Example: The words "to form a more perfect Union" establish a goal of cooperation among the states and between the states and the national government.

Articles

Purpose: To establish and define the powers of the three main branches of government as well as to establish relations among the states, the supremacy of national law, and the amendment process

Example: Article 1 establishes the legislative branch and lays out the powers of Congress, including the power to make laws.

Amendments

Purpose: To list formal changes to the Constitution and to ensure the protection of individual civil liberties

Example: The First Amendment protects the freedoms of religion, speech, press, assembly, and petition.

2. Enumerated powers are those specifically listed in the Constitution. Congress is given the power to collect taxes, for example. Implied powers are those that stem from Clause 18 of Section 8 in Article 1, which allows Congress to make all laws necessary for carrying out its duties.

3. The three branches of government divide power and responsibility in such a way that no single branch can become too powerful. The legislative branch, for example, can make laws and approve treaties. The executive branch enforces the laws and negotiates treaties. The judicial branch interprets the law and judges whether laws and executive actions are constitutional.

4.

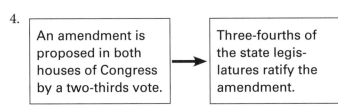

| An amendment is proposed in both houses of Congress by a two-thirds vote. | → | Three-fourths of the state legislatures ratify the amendment. |

Section 4.4

1, 2. Possible answers (symbols will vary):

Popular sovereignty

Explanation: Power resides with the people, and people elect their leaders.

Example: Article I, Section 2, Clause 1: Members of the House of Representatives are chosen by the people.

Rule of law

Explanation: Government is guided by laws, rather than by an individual or group.

Example: Article VI, Section 2: The Constitution is the supreme law of the land.

Separation of powers and checks and balances

Explanation: Power is divided among three government branches, and a system of checks and balances limits the power of any one branch.

Example: Article I, Section 7, Clause 2: Congress must present every proposed law to the president for approval before it becomes a law.

Federalism

Explanation: Power is divided between the central government and the individual, state, and local governments.

Example: Article V: Congress can propose amendments to the Constitution, which the states must ratify.

Independent judiciary

Explanation: The judicial branch is separate to prevent abuses of power and influences by the other two branches.

Example: Article III, Section 1: Judges hold office for a life term, and their pay cannot be lowered while they are in office.

Individual rights

Explanation: Civil liberties and basic rights are guaranteed.

Example: First Amendment: This amendment establishes that the government cannot take away freedoms of religion, speech, press, assembly, or petition.

Section 4.5

1. Strict construction is a literal reading of the Constitution by examining the original language of the document and the intent of the framers. Loose construction is a belief in a flexible reading of the Constitution, taking into account modern values and realities.

2. Possible answer:

Marbury v. Madison, 1803

Facts: William Marbury, appointed to a federal judgeship by outgoing President Adams, was denied his commission by incoming President Jefferson. Marbury argued that the Supreme Court could force Secretary of State Madison to perform his official duty and deliver Marbury his commission.

Summary: The Court struck down as unconstitutional the law on which Marbury had based his case.

Significance: Established the principle of judicial review

McCulloch v. Maryland, 1819

Facts: After Congress created a Second Bank of the United States, several states, including Maryland (which opposed the creation of a national bank), charged a tax on the bank's branches. James McCulloch, cashier of the Maryland branch, refused to pay the tax.

Summary: The Court held that the power to create a national bank was supported by the Elastic Clause, but that states did not have the power to tax a national bank as that would put state law above federal law.

Significance: Asserted a broad expansion of the powers of Congress and that federal law trumps state law

United States v. Nixon, 1974

Facts: Senate discovers that President Nixon secretly recorded conversations in the Oval Office. President Nixon claimed executive privilege after the Senate asked him to hand over the recordings.

Summary: The Court decided against Nixon, saying that executive privilege must be considered in light of the circumstances.

Significance: Reinforced the principle of rule of law—that even presidents are subject to the law

The Bill of Rights and Civil Liberties

How are your rights defined and protected under the Constitution?

Overview

Students study the Bill of Rights, with a particular focus on debates over the protection of civil liberties contained in the First Amendment.

Preview Students examine a school-based situation involving a conflict of rights and then explain what they think is fair.

Activity In a Problem Solving Groupwork activity, students simulate a Supreme Court hearing on a First Amendment case that focuses on a conflict of rights.

Processing Students examine a current event involving a conflict of rights and argue what they believe is constitutional and fair.

Objectives

In the course of reading this chapter and participating in the classroom activity, students will

- examine the Bill of Rights and Supreme Court decisions and explain the evolution of the first 10 amendments.
- discuss the meaning and significance of each right secured by the Bill of Rights.
- debate landmark Supreme Court cases to explore what happens when rights conflict.
- evaluate a current situation involving a conflict of rights to determine what they believe is constitutional and fair.

Materials

Government Alive!
Power, Politics, and You

Transparency 5

CD Track 7

Lesson Masters

- Notebook Guide 5 (1 per student)
- Notebook Handout 5 (1 per student)
- Student Handouts 5A–5D (20 copies of each)
- Student Handout 5E (1 per group, plus 1 transparency)
- Information Masters 5A–5C (1 transparency of each)

9 graduation gowns (optional)

Preview

Suggested time: 10 minutes

1 **Have students complete Preview 5.** Distribute *Notebook Guide 5.* Students will examine a school-based situation in which a conflict of rights is at issue and explain what they think is fair.

2 **Have students share their responses in pairs or with the class.**

3 **Explain the connection between the Preview and Chapter 5.** Tell students that they will now learn how the Bill of Rights protects individual civil rights and civil liberties. They will also examine many cases throughout history that involve a conflict of rights between two individuals or between an individual's rights and the government's need to protect society.

Notebook Guide 5

Reading

Speaking of Politics Encourage students to use the following terms as they complete their Reading Notes for the chapter: *civil liberties, civil rights, incorporation, libel, slander, prior restraint, self-incrimination,* and *double jeopardy.*

1 **Introduce the Essential Question and have students read Section 5.1.** Then ask,

- What rights did Charles Schenk feel he had?

- What rights did the government feel it had?

- In this conflict between Schenk's right to protest the draft and the government's right to arrest someone they believed was compromising public safety, who did the Supreme Court side with? On what grounds?

2 **Before conducting the activity, have students read and complete the Reading Notes for Sections 5.2 and 5.3.** Distribute *Notebook Handout 5: The Bill of Rights,* and have students follow the directions on Notebook Guide 5 to fill in the first row of the table.

3 **After the activity, have students read and complete the Reading Notes for Sections 5.4 to 5.7.** In the process, they will complete the table on Notebook Handout 5. Also consider the alternative reading and note-taking strategy in the first option under "Quicker Coverage."

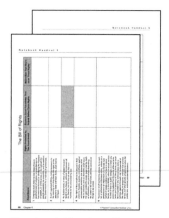

Notebook Handout 5

Problem Solving Groupwork

In Phase 1 of the activity, students prepare arguments for a mock Supreme Court hearing. In Phase 2, they conduct the hearing. Prepare materials for both phases of the activity in advance.

Phase 1

Suggested time: 100 minutes

1 **Divide the class into four equal-size groups.** Each group will prepare arguments for one of the four Supreme Court cases.

2 **Introduce the activity.** Explain that students will now become members of a legal team in order to simulate the proceedings of four actual Supreme Court cases, each dealing with a conflict of rights.

3 **Assign each group a Supreme Court case by distributing the appropriate copy of *Student Handouts 5A to 5D: Case Briefs.*** The cases to be argued are the following:

- *Hazelwood v. Kuhlmeier* (1988)
- *Wallace v. Jaffree* (1985)
- *Bethel School District No. 403 v. Fraser* (1986)
- *Board of Education of Westside Community Schools v. Mergens* (1990)

4 **Divide each group into two legal teams: one to play the part of the Petitioners and the other to play the part of the Respondents.** Approximately four students will then argue each side of each case. Explain that the Petitioner in each case is the party who is initiating the lawsuit, or bringing an action before the Court. The Petitioner is listed first in each court case. The Respondent is the party against which an action is brought; they are listed second.

5 **Review the procedures for the hearings.** Project *Information Master 5A: Supreme Court Hearing Procedures* and review the arrangement of the room and the steps for conducting the hearing.

6 **Review the steps for preparing a legal argument.** Distribute *Student Handout 5E: Preparing Your Case* to each group. Project a transparency of the handout as you review the directions. Ask that each legal team assign team members to roles based on each person's strengths and interests. Explain that, regardless of the role, everyone will have the opportunity to take part in the Supreme Court presentation.

7 **Monitor teams as they prepare their legal arguments.** Encourage students to do additional research on the precedent cases described on their handouts. Consider providing graduation gowns or similar robes for students to wear as Supreme Court Justices.

8 **Assign nine students to act as Justices for each of the four cases.** Assign the students from each case (Petitioners and Respondents) to act as Justices for one of the other cases. Give each group of nine students the appropriate copy of Student Handouts 5A to 5D, and explain that they will be presiding as Supreme Court Justices for that case. Instruct them to prepare for the hearings as follows:

- Read the background and appropriate precedents for the case.
- Note the important facts in the case.
- Prepare one thoughtful question for the Petitioners and one for the Respondents.

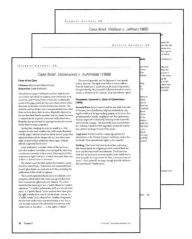

Student Handouts 5A–5D

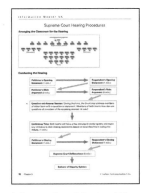

Information Master 5A

Student Handout 5E

Phase 2

Suggested time: 100 minutes

1 **Project Information Master 5A.** Review the procedure for the presentation of the oral arguments. Have students arrange the classroom according to the diagram. Explain that anyone who is not part of a legal team or the Supreme Court for a particular case will represent the Media.

2 **Prepare for the first set of legal arguments and debates.**

   - Have the Petitioners and Respondents for the first case get into position.

   - Have the Supreme Court Justices assigned to this case review the notes and questions they prepared. However, don't seat them yet.

   - Tell the Supreme Court Justices and the members of the Media that they will be required to keep track of the case's main facts by drawing a T-chart in their notebooks labeled "Petitioners" and "Respondents." As they listen to the case being argued, they should note key facts and strong arguments that they hear. This will help them form an opinion about the case at its conclusion. Alert the Media that they will be asked to discuss and offer opinions about the case at the conclusion of the hearing.

   - Project the appropriate "Case Summary" and "Question for the Court" on *Information Master 5B: Case Summaries and Outcomes.* Review the facts of the case for the Justices and the Media.

Information Master 5B

3 **Open this session of the Supreme Court.** Consider doing the following:

   - After the Respondents, Petitioners, and Media have been seated, appoint a Chief Justice. Then ask the Justices for this case to leave the room for a moment.

   - Project *Transparency 5: The Supreme Court* behind where the Justices will be seated.

   - Play CD Track 7, "Opening a Session of the Supreme Court," and ask all students to stand as the Justices enter the room.

   - Before the Justices are seated, have them perform the "conference hand-shake." They shake hands with one another as a reminder that their differences of opinion will not prevent them from trying to achieve justice.

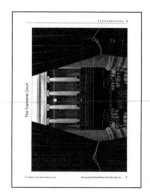

Transparency 5

4 **Hold the first Supreme Court hearing.** Follow the steps on Information Master 5A to conduct the hearing.

5 **Discuss the case.** After both sides have presented their closing statements, have the Supreme Court Justices leave the room to deliberate. During this time, facilitate a discussion with the Media about the key arguments for both sides. Poll the Media to see which party they believe will win the case.

6 **Reveal the Supreme Court holding.** Once the Justices return, have the Chief Justice read the majority opinion to the class and announce the number of Justices who voted for this opinion. For example, the Chief Justice might say, *In a 5-4 decision, the Supreme Court holds in favor of the respondent and concludes that the statute in question does indeed violate the First Amendment.*

Ask Justices in the majority to explain the reasoning behind their holding. Then allow Justices in the minority to do the same. Finally, reveal the actual decision made by the Court by projecting the appropriate "Case Outcome" from Information Master 5B.

7 **Repeat Steps 3 to 6 for the remaining Supreme Court cases.** Rotate a new group into the roles of Petitioners, Respondents, Media, and Supreme Court Justices for each case.

8 **Debrief the activity.** Ask,

- Based on what you have learned in this chapter, how are rights defined and protected under the Constitution?

- How does the Supreme Court determine whose rights prevail in certain situations?

- To what degree do you believe the Constitution is still an adequate reference for resolving these conflicts?

Power, Politics, and You

1 **Have students read the "Power, Politics, and You" section of the chapter and take the survey.**

2 **Discuss the survey.** Consider tallying students' responses for each question and analyzing the overall trends in the responses. Then ask,

- In general, what are the views of this class on the rights guaranteed by the First Amendment?

- When an individual's speech is offensive to others, what does this class generally believe takes precedence: the individual's rights to free speech or the good of society as a whole?

- When freedom of the press conflicts with government's attempts to keep our society safe, what does this class believe takes precedence?

3 **Discuss the national results.** Have students examine the results from the "State of the First Amendment" survey, or project *Information Master 5C: "State of the First Amendment" Survey Results, 2006,* which displays the information in graph form. Ask,

- Do the results of any of these questions surprise you? Which ones?

- How do our class results compare with the national results?

- What does this survey tell us about the concerns of the American people in general?

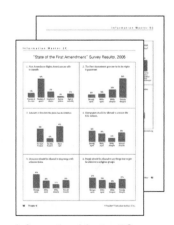

Information Master 5C

Processing

Suggested time: 20 minutes

1 **Have students complete the Processing assignment.** Students will examine a current event involving a conflict of rights and argue what they believe is constitutional and fair. For some examples of current news stories that relate to constitutional issues, visit the National Constitution Center connections at www.teachtci.com.

2 **Discuss the examples.** Call on a few volunteers to share the conflicts they chose, describe the two sides of the conflict, and explain what they believe is constitutional and fair.

Quicker Coverage

Break Up the Reading Divide students into expert groups of four. Assign each group to read and to complete the corresponding Reading Notes for one of Sections 5.4 to 5.7. You may have to assign two groups to the same section. Allow students to meet in their groups for a few minutes to discuss the answers and to clarify any information they may have found confusing. Then ask students to number off within their expert groups. Form new jigsaw groups by having all number 1s, number 2s, and so on, meet. In each jigsaw group, have students share the information from their Reading Notes with the rest of the group.

Streamline the Activity Instead of having groups argue these cases as a Problem Solving Groupwork activity, consider making transparencies of one or two cases from Student Handouts 5A to 5D and conducting this activity as a Response Group activity. Divide students into groups of three. After reading through the "Facts of the Case," have the Response Groups imagine they are Supreme Court Justices who must debate whether they should decide in favor of the Petitioner or the Respondent. Have each group select a Chief Justice to reveal the group's decision and participate in some class debate. Finally, project the appropriate "Case Outcome" from Information Master 5B to reveal the actual decision.

Deeper Coverage

Survey Others About the First Amendment Expand on the "Power, Politics, and You" feature by having students ask an adult, such as a parent or grandparent, to complete the "State of the First Amendment" survey. Have students bring the results to class and compare the findings across generations.

Research Current Supreme Court Cases Instead of using the cases provided for the Problem Solving Groupwork activity, have groups research and argue cases that are on the current Supreme Court docket. See the Findlaw Web site at supreme.lp.findlaw.com/supreme_court/docket/index.html for a list of current cases. Have students research the case's background and possible precedents. If possible, review the outcomes of the cases with the class once the cases are decided by the Court.

Assessment

Masters for the chapter assessment appear in the *Lesson Masters*.

Mastering the Content

1. C	2. D	3. D	4. C	5. A
6. C	7. A	8. D	9. B	10. B

Exploring the Essential Question

1. The first question the Supreme Court considered was whether the Fourth Amendment applies to public school officials. It held that it did.

2. The Court sought in its decision to balance the privacy rights of students with the needs of school administrators to maintain an orderly learning environment.

3. A student search is constitutional if it is based on a reasonable suspicion that it will show that the student has violated the law or school rules.

4. Possible answers:

   - No. Random locker checks are unconstitutional because they are not based on a reasonable suspicion that an individual student has violated the law or school rules.

   - Yes. Random locker checks are constitutional if there is a reasonable suspicion that some students are breaking the law or school rules by keeping drugs or guns in their lockers.

English Language Learners

Support the Reading To assist students with the Reading Notes for Sections 5.3 to 5.6, provide an underlined and annotated copy of the Bill of Rights as they write their summaries. Also, pair students with more fluent readers to discuss cases that set precedents in these areas.

Offer a Sample Argument Provide support during the Supreme Court activity by drafting an argument for one of the cases before having students frame their own arguments.

Modify the Processing Provide several news articles with clear examples of conflicting rights for students to choose from.

Learners Reading and Writing Below Grade Level

Simplify the Reading Notes To help students complete the Reading Notes for Sections 5.3 to 5.6, provide a cloze passage for the amendment summary, with words or phrases omitted, for students to complete. In the column for the precedents, identify the cases but let students explain them.

Create a Table During the Supreme Court presentations, provide a table that students can fill out when they are acting as Justices or the Media.

Important Court Case Facts	Respondent Viewpoint	Petitioner Viewpoint	Actual Court Decision

Simplify the Processing Provide a template like the one below for students to complete. Do an example as a class before having students work independently.

- The conflict of rights in this situation is between these two parties: . . .
- These two parties are in conflict because . . .
- The rights held by the first party are . . .
- The rights held by the other party are . . .
- The party who should win this conflict is . . .
- I think this because . . .

Learners with Special Education Needs

Support the Activity During the Supreme Court activity, do one or all of the following:

- Create an additional role within each group, such as a paralegal who types the completed brief or a document clerk who makes sure all the completed work is in order.

- Require students to have their work checked off at each stage when they are developing their arguments. Use Student Handout 5E as a guide for checking student work.

- Provide a one-page overview of each case, with the main points bulleted, followed by a two- or three-sentence summary of the precedents.

- Allow the use of note cards for presenting the student's portion of the argument.

Advanced Learners

Draw on Personal Experience During Phase 2 of the activity, have students play the role of current Supreme Court justices by examining and deciding the case from what they know of the viewpoints held by those justices. Have them research their particular justice's biography and examine his or her opinions in recent cases. Or have students voice their own opinions while acting on the Supreme Court, and then assign them a particular justice after the class court has decided the case. They can then analyze whether their assigned justice would have agreed with the class decision.

U.S. Supreme Court Cases: You Make the Call

Have students read the summaries of Cases 2 and 3, *United States v. O'Brien* and *United States v. Miller,* which relate to individual rights under the First and Second amendments, in the "U.S. Supreme Court Cases: You Make the Call" section of the Student Edition. Have volunteers share key facts from the case and the question before the Court. Then facilitate a Response Group–type discussion asking students to "make the call" on how the Court should decide the case and why. Finally, have students read the actual Supreme Court decision.

NATIONAL CONSTITUTION CENTER

National Constitution Center

For the Processing assignment, have students locate current news stories that relate to constitutional issues by visiting the National Constitution Center connections at www.teachtci.com.

Internet Connections

For related research materials on the First Amendment and the Bill of Rights, refer students to Online Resources at www.teachtci.com.

Multimedia

Please follow school and district guidelines for showing films in the classroom.

The Constitution: That Delicate Balance This 13-part Emmy award–winning series (Columbia University, 1984) on constitutional issues has two one-hour episodes that pertain to the first 10 amendments. Part 8, "National Security and Freedom of the Press," asks students to consider how much information the public has the right to know about national security issues. Part 9, "School Prayer, Gun Control, and the Right to Assemble," focuses on a small town and a number of First and Second amendment controversies.

Future Fright: Losing the Bill of Rights This 24-minute video (AIMS Multimedia, 1998) poses the question, *What would happen if our government eliminated the Bill of Rights?* After living in a remote jungle without media access, the Gordon family returns to the United States to realize that the Bill of Rights is no longer in effect. Viewers are left to contemplate what choices they would make if faced with a world in which basic rights are not guaranteed.

Following are possible answers for each section of the Reading Notes.

Section 5.2

1. Civil liberties are freedoms that are an individual's birthright, such as the freedoms of speech, religion, and assembly. They are not something the government can legitimately take away. Civil rights are rights of citizenship that come with being a member of society, such as the right to a trial by jury and the right to legal counsel.

2. The Fourteenth Amendment denies the states the ability to infringe on civil liberties and rights. Though narrowly interpreted at first, the amendment eventually prevented states from abridging the rights of U.S. citizens. In *Gitlow v. New York,* the Court reversed the previous limitations it had set on the Fourteenth Amendment and held that the Due Process Clause extended the reach of the Bill of Rights to the states.

3. The Supreme Court reviews the decisions made by lower courts. It does not retry cases. If the Court reverses a decision made by a lower court, the case usually returns to a lower appeals court to allow for a decision that fits with the current Supreme Court opinion.

Sections 5.3 to 5.6

Illustrations will vary.

First Amendment

Rights protected: The First Amendment guarantees the separation of church and state, establishes that people are free to follow the religious practices of their choice, allows citizens to express ideas freely, protects the media from censorship, and allows people to assemble and to petition the government about grievances.

Precedents: In *Engel v. Vitale,* the Court struck down state-sponsored prayer in schools. In *Lemon v. Kurtzman,* the Court established the "Lemon test" to determine whether the Establishment Clause has been violated. In *West Virginia Board of Education v. Barnette,* the Court held that the government must show a compelling interest in forcing people to obey a law that violates their religious convictions. In *Brandenburg v. Ohio,* the Court created a two-part test to determine whether speech creates a "clear and present danger." In *Texas v. Johnson,* the Court held

that flag burning is protected symbolic speech. In *Near v. Minnesota,* the Court declared that government attempts at prior restraint are unconstitutional, except under special circumstances.

Second Amendment

Rights protected: This amendment guarantees citizens the right to own firearms.

Precedent: In *United States v. Miller,* the Court supported the conviction of two men who had not registered a sawed-off shotgun on the grounds that because militias would not use these guns, the government has a right to regulate them.

Third Amendment

Rights protected: This amendment prohibits citizens from being forced to house soldiers.

Fourth Amendment

Rights protected: This amendment protects people's privacy by prohibiting unreasonable searches and seizures without a warrant and ensuring that a warrant is issued only if there is probable cause and if police are specific about what they are looking for.

Precedents: In *Katz v. United States,* the Court established the notion of a "reasonable expectation of privacy" when deciding whether a warrant is needed. In *Terry v. Ohio,* the Court expanded the rights of police to search individuals if they have a reasonable justification for doing so.

Fifth Amendment

Rights protected: This amendment protects suspects from self-incrimination. It also protects them against double jeopardy and says that the government cannot take property for public use without paying a fair price for it.

Precedent: In *Miranda v. Arizona,* the Court set forth a procedure for ensuring that suspects know their rights, now called Miranda rights.

Sixth Amendment

Rights protected: This amendment explains how trials are to be carried out to protect the rights of the accused: quickly, publicly, and in front of a jury, with all evidence presented to the defendant, who has the right to legal counsel.

Precedents: In *Gideon v. Wainwright,* the Court determined that the guarantee of a lawyer should not depend on a defendant's ability to pay. In *Sheppard v. Maxwell,* the Court determined that press coverage should not interfere with a defendant's right to due process.

Seventh Amendment

Rights protected: This amendment guarantees trial by jury in most civil lawsuits.

Eighth Amendment

Rights protected: This amendment protects suspects from excessive bail, fines, or cruel and unusual punishment.

Precedents: In *In re Kemmler,* the Court held that any method of execution is acceptable, as long as it does not involve "torture or lingering death." In *Furman v. Georgia,* the Court held that capital punishment is "cruel and unusual" when inconsistently applied, causing states to rewrite their laws to apply capital punishment more consistently. In *Gregg v. Georgia,* the Court held that the death penalty is constitutional.

Ninth Amendment

Rights protected: This amendment acknowledges that rights other than those specified in these amendments may exist and offers protection of these unenumerated rights.

Precedent: In *Griswold v. Connecticut,* the Court declared that the Ninth Amendment includes the right to privacy.

Tenth Amendment

Rights protected: This amendment limits the powers of the federal government to those specifically granted by the Constitution and reserves other powers to the states and the people.

Precedent: In *United States v. Morrison,* the Court held that violent crime between individuals is an issue for the states.

Federalism: National, State, and Local Powers

How does power flow through our federal system of government?

Overview

Students analyze the purpose and function of the U.S. federal system of government, identifying the roles and responsibilities of national, state, and local governments.

Preview Students examine the advantages and disadvantages of sharing decision making with their parents.

Activity In a Response Group activity, students discuss three case studies illustrating the challenges of defining state and national powers in the federal system.

Processing Students create a public service flyer to help young people understand how to use the federal system to create change in issues of importance to them.

Objectives

In the course of reading this chapter and participating in the classroom activity, students will

- identify the benefits and drawbacks of the federal system.
- analyze historical and current challenges to defining national and state powers.
- summarize the roles and responsibilities of national, state, and local governments.
- demonstrate how to use the federal system to create change in a public issue.

Materials

Government Alive! Power, Politics, and You

Transparencies 6A–6D

Lesson Masters

- Notebook Guide 6 (1 per student)
- Student Handouts 6A–6C (1 each per student)

Preview

Suggested time: 15 minutes

1 **Have students complete Preview 6.** Distribute *Notebook Guide 6*. Students will examine the advantages and disadvantages of sharing decision making with their parents.

2 **Have students share their responses in pairs or with the class.**

3 **Explain the connection between the Preview and Chapter 6.** Point out that just as students share decisions with their parents, there is a system of shared powers between the national and state governments. This system is called federalism. As in a family, this system has many benefits, but there are also drawbacks that can cause tension and conflict. In this chapter, students will learn about the roles and responsibilities of the different levels of government, as well as analyze the purpose and function of the U.S. federal system.

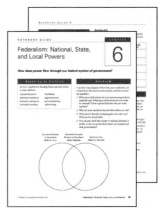

Notebook Guide 6

Reading

Speaking of Politics Encourage students to use the following terms as they complete their Reading Notes for the chapter: *expressed powers, interstate commerce, intrastate commerce, unfunded mandate, devolution, apportionment, gerrymandering,* and *redistricting.*

1 **Introduce the Essential Question and have students read Section 6.1.** Then ask,

- Why did the gray wolf population become a government issue?
- What were the national government's arguments?
- What were the state governments' arguments?
- How do you think power might flow through our federal system of government?

2 **Have students read and complete the Reading Notes for Section 6.2 *before* the Response Group activity and for Sections 6.3 to 6.5 *after* the activity.** Consider the alternative reading and note-taking strategy in the first option under "Quicker Coverage."

Response Group

Suggested time: 60 minutes

1 **Place students in groups of three and introduce the activity.** Explain that groups will look at specific issues that challenge the definitions of national and state powers in the U.S. federal system. Each issue is illustrated by a case study in which either the national government or a state government faced conflict in exercising its powers. After examining the facts and arguments, groups will determine whether, according to the U.S. federal system, a legitimate use of power exists.

2 **Have students hypothesize the main issue of the first case study.** Project the photograph at the top of *Transparency 6A: United States v. Lopez* (covering the text at the bottom). Ask,

- What interesting details do you see?

- What federalism issue do you think this photograph represents?

- Do you think the national government or the state governments should have the power to control guns near schools?

3 **Have groups read the first case study.** Distribute and have students read *Student Handout 6A: Federalism and Gun Control Laws.*

4 **Have groups discuss the case study.** Project *Transparency 6D: The Federal System,* and have groups discuss the questions on Student Handout 6A. (**Note:** The federal system diagram also appears in Section 6.2 of the Student Edition.) Each group will need to come to an agreement on Question 3 and be ready to share their response with the class. (**Note:** Consider having groups use excerpts from the Constitution to support their responses. To help students identify excerpts that relate to federalism, have them visit the National Constitution Center connections at www.teachtci.com.)

5 **Facilitate a student-centered discussion of the case study.**

- Have each group appoint a Presenter.

- Select one Presenter to stand and share his or her group's response to Question 3.

- Ask all other Presenters to raise their hands, and have the first Presenter call on one of the others by name. Encourage lively debate by having students call on Presenters whose answers differ from theirs.

- Have the new Presenter, and subsequent Presenters, begin his or her response as follows: *[Name of previous speaker], our group agrees/disagrees with your group because . . .*

You might provide additional support by distributing the "Engaging in Civil Dialogue" handouts from the *Doing Democracy* toolkit and briefly reviewing with students how to use them.

6 **Reveal the outcome.** Tell students that this issue was ultimately resolved in the Supreme Court. Project Transparency 6A, and review the outcome of the case.

7 **Repeat the procedure for the remaining case studies.** Appoint a new Presenter for each case study.

- For the second case study, use *Transparency 6B: Lorillard Tobacco Company v. Reilly* and *Student Handout 6B: Federalism and Tobacco Advertising Laws.* In Step 2 above, replace the third question with, *Do you think the national government or the state governments should have the power to regulate cigarette advertising?*

- For the third case study, use *Transparency 6C: Alaska v. EPA* and *Student Handout 6C: Federalism and Air Pollution Laws.* In Step 2 above, replace the third question with, *Do you think the national government or the state governments should have the power to limit air pollution?*

Transparencies 6A–6C

Transparency 6D

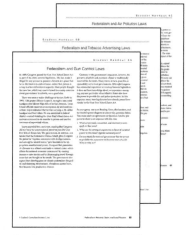

Student Handouts 6A–6C

8 **Debrief the activity with the class.** Ask the questions below. Consider having students discuss the questions in their groups first.

- What challenges did you have in determining who had the power in each case study?

- What do these case studies reveal about our federal system of government?

- How does power flow through our federal system of government?

Power, Politics, and You

Suggested time: 20 minutes

1 **Conduct a short activity to introduce students to the magnitude of the health insurance crisis.**

- Have all students stand and count off by 7s. Ask all but the 1s to sit down. Explain that the students standing represent the 15.3% of Americans who did not have health insurance in 2005.

- Have students stand again and count off by 13s. Ask all but the 1s to sit down. The students standing represent the uninsured living in the state with the fewest number of uninsured people in 2005—Minnesota, with 7.9%.

- Have students stand and count off by 4s. Ask all but the 1s to sit down. The students standing represent the uninsured living in the state with the most uninsured people in 2005—Texas, with 23.6%.

- Have students stand and count off by 9s. Ask all but the 1s to sit down. The students standing represent the 10.9% of Americans under 18 that did not have health insurance in 2005.

- Have students stand and count off by 3s. Ask just the 1s to remain standing. The students standing represent the 30% of Americans aged 19 to 29 that did not have health insurance in 2005.

2 **Discuss the exercise.** Ask,

- What did you find interesting about this exercise?

- Why do you think health insurance coverage differs from state to state?

- Why should the health insurance crisis be of concern to you?

3 **Have students read the "Power, Politics, and You" section of the chapter, and then facilitate a class discussion by asking the questions below.** Consider having students discuss the questions in pairs or small groups first.

- Why are the uninsured a growing concern for national and state governments?

- How have some states proposed to address the health insurance crisis?

- Should providing health insurance to all be a government responsibility? If so, should it be a responsibility of the states? Or should the national government make health care a universal right, no matter where you live?

Processing

Suggested time: 30 minutes

1   **Introduce the topic of the Processing activity.** Tell students that a 2006 study conducted by the Center for Information and Research on Civic Learning and Engagement found that only 10 percent of young people age 15 to 25 felt they could personally make a *great* difference in solving community problems. Another 45 percent felt they could make *some* difference. The study cited a number of reasons for this lack of confidence, including a distrust of government, misinformation, and low interest. Explain that students will now create a public service flyer to help young people understand how to use the federal system to effect change in issues of importance to them.

2   **Have students complete the Processing activity.** Consider having students share their finished flyers in pairs or having volunteers share theirs with the class. You may also want to have the class select one or two flyers to publish and distribute throughout the school or community.

Quicker Coverage

Break Up the Reading Place students in groups of three to read and complete the Reading Notes for Sections 6.3 to 6.5, dividing the reading so that each student is responsible for one section. Then have students take turns sharing the information from their assigned section with the group.

Shorten the Activity Have students analyze and discuss a single case study rather than all three. The case presented on *Student Handout 6C: Federalism and Air Pollution Laws* is recommended, as it demonstrates a struggle of both the national and state governments to define their powers in the federal system.

Deeper Coverage

Expand the Activity Have groups examine one or more additional case studies that explore the challenges to define national and state powers in the federal system. Consider these case studies and the corresponding Supreme Court decisions:

- Federalism and auto emissions laws: *Massachusetts v. Environmental Protection Agency* (2007)

- Federalism and assisted suicide laws: *Gonzales v. Oregon* (2006)

- Federalism and disability laws: *Tennessee v. Lane* (2004)

Information on these cases, including transcripts of oral arguments, can be found at the Oyez Project, a multimedia archive on the Supreme Court, at www.oyez.org.

Research State or Local Government Have students find out more information about the organization and function of their state or local government. They might work in pairs to prepare for and conduct an in-person, phone, or online interview of a public official. Or they might attend a public meeting to learn about a specific function of their state or local government. Provide additional support by distributing the "Attending a Public Meeting" and "Contacting and

Interviewing Experts" handouts from the *Doing Democracy* toolkit and briefly reviewing with students how to use them.

Assessment

Masters for the chapter assessment appear in the *Lesson Masters*.

Mastering the Content

1. B	2. D	3. C	4. C	5. D
6. B	7. D	8. C	9. C	10. A

Exploring the Essential Question

1. This is a concurrent power. The national and state governments share the power to make energy policy.

2. Possible answer: Efforts to promote solar energy in California make sense given that state's sunny climate. It is in the economic interest of Midwestern states to promote the production of biofuels because it creates a market for crops grown by farmers in that largely agricultural region. It makes sense for New York City to promote the use of gas-saving taxis to reduce fuel use and environmental concerns about air pollution in that densely populated urban area.

3. Possible answers:

   - Yes. States seem to be adopting a variety of approaches to energy policy based on their resources, economies, and interests. Those that work best are likely to be adopted by other states and the national government.

   - No. While states are adopting varied approaches to energy policy, these approaches are not often very innovative or experimental. Because they mainly serve local economic interests, they are not likely to be adopted by other states and the national government.

English Language Learners

Provide a Template For the Response Group activity, provide groups with a matrix like the one below for recording responses to the questions on Student Handouts 6A to 6C. Then encourage Presenters to consult the matrix for talking points in the class discussion.

	Gun Control Laws	Tobacco Advertising Laws	Air Pollution Laws
Expressed, Concurrent, and Reserved Powers			
Strongest Argument for National Power			
Strongest Argument for State Power			
Your Group's Opinion			
Supreme Court Decision			

Guide the Processing Activity Show an example of a public service flyer. Help students locate contact information for their own flyers by providing an online or print directory of government agencies. Also consider having students choose a topic relevant to their individual experience, such as immigration policy.

Learners Reading and Writing Below Grade Level

Color Code the Case Studies In the Response Group activity, have groups use three colors to highlight the key points of the case studies on Student Handouts 6A to 6C: one color for the powers, one for the national government's arguments, and one for the state governments' arguments. Review the highlighted information as a class before groups discuss the questions on the handouts.

Graphically Support the Reading Notes For the Section 6.4 Reading Notes, provide a graphic organizer of a tree with three branches. Label each branch so students can record notes about state legislatures, state governors, and state courts systems. Instruct students to briefly describe and identify two or more roles for each branch.

Learners with Special Education Needs

Supply Venn Diagrams Give students two blank Venn diagrams, one for the Preview assignment and one for the Section 6.2 Reading Notes.

Outline the Case Studies Provide a bulleted set of notes outlining the narrative of each case study on Student Handouts 6A to 6C. Include information relevant to each of these questions: *What is the conflict? What are the national government's strongest arguments? What are the state governments' strongest arguments?*

Create a Class Public Service Flyer For the Processing activity, work as a class to create a single public service flyer about an issue of concern to students. Have the class choose an issue and then work in groups to research information for the class flyer.

Advanced Learners

Enhance the Public Service Flyers Have students provide additional information for their public service flyers. Ask them to suggest ideas for what people can do to get involved in this issue, such as organizing a letter-writing campaign or proposing a law. Provide additional support by distributing the "Organizing a Letter-Writing Campaign," "Lobbying on an Issue," or other appropriate handouts from the *Doing Democracy* toolkit and briefly reviewing with students how to use them.

 **National Constitution Center**

For the Response Group activity, have groups quote the Constitution as support for their responses. Help students identify appropriate excerpts from the document by visiting the National Constitution Center connections at www.teachtci.com.

Internet Connections

For related research materials on federalism, refer students to Online Resources at www.teachtci.com.

Multimedia

Please follow school and district guidelines about showing films in the classroom.

The Constitution: That Delicate Balance This 13-part Emmy Award–winning series (Columbia University, 1984) brings to life key constitutional issues by featuring live debates on controversial topics. In Part 13, "Federalism," Senators Orrin Hatch and Daniel Moynihan debate the topic of federalism. This series can be viewed online at no cost at Annenberg Media, www.learner.org.

Democracy in America This 15-part series (Educational Film Center, 2003) explores important topics in American democracy, such as citizenship and civil rights. In Part 3, "Federalism: U.S. v. the States," viewers follow modern conflicts between the national and state governments over the distribution of powers in the federal system, including the story of the gray wolf in Yellowstone National Park. This series can be viewed online at no cost at Annenberg Media, www.learner.org.

The Supreme Court This 2007 PBS series examines the history of the Supreme Court, from its creation to its years under Chief Justice William Rehnquist. Of interest to the topic of federalism is Episode 1, "One Nation Under Law," which discusses early cases that establish federal authority under the Marshall Court. Modern cases supporting devolution, such as *United States v. Lopez*, are explored in Episode 4, "The Rehnquist Revolution." Clips can be viewed online at www.pbs.org.

Following are possible answers to each section of the Reading Notes.

Section 6.2

Expressed powers: Powers specifically granted to the national government, such as coining money and making treaties with other countries.

Concurrent powers: Powers shared by the national and state governments, such as levying taxes and establishing courts.

Reserved powers: Powers reserved for the states, such as overseeing public schools and regulating businesses.

The benefits of a federal system include protecting individuals against the tyranny of the majority, promoting unity without imposing uniformity, allowing states to act as testing grounds for innovative solutions to common problems, and encouraging political participation. The drawbacks include inconsistent laws and policies from state to state and the tension they sometime create between state and federal officials.

Section 6.3

Dual federalism (1790–1933): The national and state governments maintained a fairly strict division of powers. The two levels of government were part of a whole, but each had its own clearly delineated area.

Cooperative federalism (1933–1960): The national and state governments shared more powers and worked together. One difference from dual federalism was that the national government provided grants-in-aid to state and local governments for specific programs.

Regulated federalism (1960s): The national and state governments continued to share powers. The national government continued to provide funds to state governments but outlined strict regulations for how the money could be spent. These regulations were sometimes unfunded mandates, meaning they came without adequate funding.

New federalism (1970s–1990s): The national and state governments shared fewer powers as devolution returned power to the states. The national government provided funds to state governments but encouraged them to find their own solutions to problems.

Section 6.4

1. State constitutions show that both the national and the state governments have power to govern in our federal system. The national government has limited power and reserves a good amount of power for the states. The U.S. Constitution requires every state constitution to support "a republican form of government," but each state is left to organize its government as its citizens choose. Nebraska, for example, has a unicameral legislature. Alabama is unique in allowing local amendments to its constitution.

2. Illustrations will vary. Possible answer:

   Role of state legislatures: Responsible for enacting laws, levying taxes, and creating budgets. Responsible for apportionment of seats in the U.S. House of Representatives and state legislatures.

   Role of state governors: Responsible for managing the executive branch of the state government. Have various powers, such as preparing the state budget, commanding the state National Guard, and issuing executive orders. May serve as ambassadors for the state and play a major role in promoting its economic development.

   Role of state courts system: Trial courts handle most cases that affect citizens' daily lives. Lower-level trial courts include municipal courts and small claims courts. Higher-level trial courts deal with major criminal cases and lawsuits. Appeals courts handle cases that are appealed from trial courts.

Section 6.5

Counties, parishes, and boroughs

Organization: Traditionally headquartered in the county seat, which is often the most centrally located town in the county. Headed by an elected board of commissioners or board of supervisors.

Purpose: Original purpose was to provide government services to rural residents. Duties might include law enforcement, court operations, road construction, and public assistance.

Mayor-council system

Organization: Voters elect a mayor and a city council. The mayor is the chief executive, and the council is the city's lawmaking body.

Purpose: Purpose is to govern a city. The mayor's duties and powers vary from city to city.

Commission system

Organization: Voters elect commissioners. Commissioners enact ordinances.

Purpose: Purpose is to govern a city. Commissioners also serve as department heads to carry out duties.

Council-manager system

Organization: Voters elect a city council. City manager is hired to fulfill day-to-day operations.

Purpose: Purpose is to govern a city. Combines the democratic rule of a city council with the professional management expertise.

Special-purpose districts

Organization: Specialized, separate units of governments. May overlap geographic boundaries of cities and countries. Have their own elected leaders and taxing authority.

Purpose: Usually carry out one specialized function, such as providing fire protection or running a hospital.

UNIT 3

Political Participation and Behavior

7 Citizen Participation in a Democracy 75

How can you make a difference in a democracy?

Visual Discovery

8 Parties, Interest Groups, and Public Policy 85

Political parties and interest groups: How do they influence our political decisions?

Experiential Exercise

9 Public Opinion and the Media 97

To what extent do the media influence your political views?

Experiential Exercise

10 Political Campaigns and Elections 107

Elections and voting: Why should they matter to you?

Experiential Exercise

Citizen Participation in a Democracy

How can you make a difference in a democracy?

Overview

Students learn about the rights and responsibilities of U.S. citizenship and how citizens can influence all levels of government.

Preview Students analyze a photograph of a lunch counter sit-in and predict the problem being addressed and the tactics people in the picture are using to try to effect change.

Activity In a Visual Discovery activity, students identify forms of civic participation that individuals or groups have used to effect change on the local, national, and international levels.

Processing Students identify and develop plans of action to address particular issues.

Objectives

In the course of reading this chapter and participating in the classroom activity, students will

- examine paths to U.S. citizenship and the rights and responsibilities of U.S. citizens.

- analyze methods of bringing about political change or maintaining the status quo.

- identify forms of civic participation.

- develop a plan to address a local, national, or international problem.

Materials

*Government Alive!
Power, Politics, and You*

Transparencies 7A–7D

CD Tracks 8–10

Lesson Masters

- Notebook Guide 7
  (1 per student)

- Student Handouts 7A
  and 7B (1 of each per
  pair)

- Information Master 7
  (1 transparency)

Preview

Suggested time: 10–15 minutes

1 **Have students complete the Preview.** Distribute *Notebook Guide 7*. Project *Transparency 7A: Lunch Counter Sit-In*, or direct students' attention to the photograph on Notebook Guide 7. Then ask,

- What interesting details do you see?
- What actions do these people appear to be taking?
- What problem or problems do you think these people are trying to address?
- What do you think the results of their actions were?

As the class discusses possible answers to each question, have students record answers in their notebooks. (**Note:** See the "Multimedia" section for suggestions of video clips on lunch counter sit-ins.)

Notebook Guide 7

2 **Give students background information on the image.** Explain that, in the 1960s, many major retailers in the South had segregated lunch counters. In protest, people organized sit-ins to force the companies to change their segregation policies. In this photograph, college students hold a sit-in at a Walgreens lunch counter. Sometimes protesters were taunted and even attacked by onlookers. Walgreens, and other retailers, chose to close their lunch counters rather than to serve the students.

John R. Salter (also known as Hunter Bear), a prominent civil rights activist and a university professor in Mississippi, described a Woolworths lunch counter sit-in he participated in in Jackson, Mississippi, as "the most violently attacked sit-in during the 1960s . . . A huge mob gathered, with open police support while the three of us sat there for three hours. I was attacked with fists, brass knuckles and the broken portions of glass sugar containers, and was burned with cigarettes." As a result of the sit-ins, cafes and lunch counters eventually ended their segregation policies.

Transparency 7A

Now ask students, *Do you think you could carry out actions like these for a cause you believe in? Why or why not?*

3 **Explain the connection between the Preview and Chapter 7.** Tell students that they have just seen one example of a form of civic participation that helped draw attention to a societal problem in the 1960s: the lack of civil rights for African American citizens. In this chapter, they will learn more about the process of becoming a U.S. citizen and closely examine the rights and responsibilities of citizenship. They will look at how some Americans have effectively used civic participation to address problems facing their communities, their country, and the world. Throughout the chapter, they will examine such important questions as, *What does it take to become a U.S. citizen? What does it mean to be a citizen? How can ordinary people make a difference in a democratic society like the United States?*

Reading

Speaking of Politics Encourage students to use the following terms as they complete their Reading Notes for the chapter: *citizenship, lawful permanent resident, undocumented immigrant, naturalization, ideology, liberalism, conservatism,* and *civil society.*

1 **Introduce the Essential Question and have students read Section 7.1.** Then ask,

- What does Robert D. Putnam say about how the participation of Americans in civic, social, and religious groups has changed over the past century and a half?

- Do you think this change in behavior is cause for concern? Why or why not?

2 **Have students read Sections 7.2 to 7.5 and complete the Reading Notes** *before* **the Visual Discovery activity.** Consider the alternative reading and note-taking strategy in the first option under "Quicker Coverage."

Visual Discovery

Suggested time: 75–90 minutes

1 **Introduce the activity.** Explain that students will now analyze photographs to predict what actions the subjects of the images are taking to help address a societal problem. They will then examine corresponding case studies to learn about the problems and to identify the forms of civic participation that individuals or groups engaged in to address those problems.

2 **Have pairs examine the forms of civic participation.** Place students in pairs. Give each pair a copy of *Student Handout 7A: Forms of Civic Participation* to review. Ask students to circle the words or phrases that best describe each form of civic participation.

3 **Introduce the first case study.** Project *Transparency 7B: A School for Iqbal* and have students analyze the photograph. Ask, *What do you see here?* Tell students that this is a Pakistani boy named Iqbal Masih. Iqbal worked for six years in bonded labor for a carpet manufacturer. After he escaped, he spoke out against bonded labor and argued that children should be sent to school rather than to work. Then ask, *What actions might Iqbal and others have taken to address the problem of bonded labor? What might the results of their actions have been?*

4 **Have students analyze the first case study.** Distribute *Student Handout 7B: Civic Participation Case Studies* to each pair. Ask pairs to read along with the first case study as you play CD Track 8, "A School for Iqbal." Have them underline any forms of civic participation from Student Handout 7A that they see being used in this case study. (**Note:** The following forms of civic participation are used in this case study: fundraising, creating a Web site, organizing a letter-writing campaign, communicating with a public official, testifying before a public body, giving a speech, and joining a campaign or an interest group.)

Student Handouts 7A and 7B

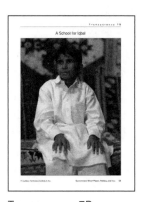

Transparency 7B

5 Review the forms of civic participation that were used in the case study.
Ask volunteers to share the forms of civic participation they identified.
Then ask,

- Did the actions these people took make a difference? If so, for whom?
  (You may need to encourage students to look beyond the obvious and
  immediate beneficiaries of these actions to help them see the full impact.)

- Do you think you could carry out actions like these for a cause you believe
  in? Why or why not?

6 Repeat Steps 3 to 5 for the second case study.

- Use *Transparency 7C: The Ryan White CARE Act* to introduce the case
  study. Ask, *What do you see here?* Tell students that this is Ryan White and
  his mother. Ryan was a teenager from Indiana who developed AIDS from
  a blood transfusion he had received as a child. At the time, Ryan faced a lot
  of discrimination because little was known about AIDS. Then ask, *What
  actions might Ryan and others have taken to address the problem of the lack
  of AIDS education? What might the results of their actions have been?*

- Use CD Track 9, "The Ryan White CARE Act" and have students analyze
  the case study. (**Note:** The following forms of civic participation are used
  in this case study: giving an interview or a speech, testifying before a public
  body, and starting an interest group.)

Transparency 7C

7 Repeat Steps 3 to 5 for the third case study.

- Use *Transparency 7D: Mothers Against Drunk Driving* to introduce the
  case study. Ask, *What do you see here?* Tell students that this is a display at
  a candlelight memorial service for victims of drunk driving, sponsored by
  the group Mothers Against Drunk Driving. Then ask, *What actions might
  people have taken to address the problem of drunk driving? What might the
  results of their actions have been?*

- Use CD Track 10, "Mothers Against Drunk Driving" and have students
  analyze the case study. (**Note:** The following forms of civic participation are
  used in this case study: starting an interest group, organizing a fundraiser,
  giving an interview or a speech, testifying before a public body, communicating with a public official, organizing a protest, and writing a press release.)

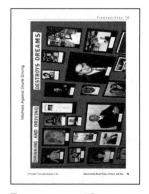

Transparency 7D

8 Debrief the activity by having students apply what they have learned. Project *Information Master 7: Applying Forms of Civic Participation* and conduct
the exercise as follows:

- Draw a spectrum across the board with ends labeled "Not Likely to Be
  Effective" and "Likely to Be Effective."

- Assign each pair to one of the forms of civic participation listed on Student
  Handout 7A and have them write that form in large letters on a sheet of
  paper. In order to represent all 15 forms of civic participation, you may
  need to assign some pairs to more than one form of civic participation or
  combine some pairs into groups of four.

Information Master 7

- Reveal the situations on Information Master 7 one at a time, and have students follow the instructions to arrange themselves along the spectrum.

- Once students have arranged themselves along the spectrum, hold a brief discussion in which students debate whether the forms of civic participation are placed appropriately. Do this for each situation before revealing the next situation.

Power, Politics, and You

1 **Introduce students to the "Power, Politics, and You" section of the chapter.** First, in their pairs from the activity, have students read the introductory information about the U.S. naturalization test.

2 **Have students take the citizenship test.** Explain that one student in each pair will act as the official administering the naturalization test and the other will act as the immigrant seeking to become a U.S. citizen. Each "official" should choose 10 questions from the test—at least one question from each section—to ask the "immigrant" orally. Officials must check the immigrants' answers and reveal whether the answers were correct or not. Then have partners switch roles and repeat the exercise with 10 new questions.

3 **Debrief the activity.** Remind students that they have been taught this content in social studies and history classes since grade school. Then ask the questions below. Consider having students discuss the questions with their partners first.

- If you were trying to become a U.S. citizen right now, would you have passed this test?

- How well does this test prepare naturalized citizens to make a difference in a democracy?

- Should all citizens have to pass a test like this every five years in order to maintain their citizenship?

Processing

Suggested time: 20–30 minutes

Have students complete the Processing activity in their notebooks. In the activity, students identify a problem and then develop a plan for engaging in forms of civic participation to address the problem. Provide additional support by distributing the appropriate handouts, depending on which actions students choose, from the *Doing Democracy* toolkit and briefly reviewing with students how to use them.

Quicker Coverage

Break Up the Reading Divide students into four groups, and assign each group one of Sections 7.2 to 7.5. Have groups read their section and complete the corresponding Reading Notes. Then have them lay their notebooks open on their desks. Have groups rotate to review the versions of the Reading Notes for another section, complete their own notes for that section, and move to a new section.

Complete Only the Debriefing Instead of having students complete the entire Visual Discovery activity, use only the last step in which they apply the forms of civic participation to representative situations. This will be most effective if used immediately after students complete the Reading Notes for Section 7.5.

Shorten the Activity Use only one or two of the case studies in the Visual Discovery activity, or reduce the number of situations discussed in the debriefing.

Deeper Coverage

Complete Civic Action Projects Expand on the Processing assignment by guiding students in completing civic action projects. The *Doing Democracy* toolkit has step-by-step directions and support for such projects, such as how-to guides for a variety of civic actions, including how to write a press release, run a fundraiser, conduct an effective meeting, and speak before a public body.

Assessment

Masters for the chapter assessment appear in the *Lesson Masters*.

Mastering the Content

1. A   2. D   3. B   4. D   5. B
6. D   7. C   8. A   9. A   10. C

Exploring the Essential Question

1. all except vote

2. Possible answers: Yes; political activity involves working with politicians and government officials, while community service is focused on helping people or the community. No; community service may involve working with public officials on projects. It may also lead to political activity as volunteers see the need for public action or policy changes.

3. Possible answer: Participation in a social or recreational club might make people more aware of issues in the community. It might also help people gain the skills they need to participate with others in political and community activities.

4. Accept statements either in support of or in opposition to a curfew law as long as the student explains his or her position. Possible actions include attending and speaking out at a city council meeting, circulating a petition, contacting public officials, and organizing a demonstration.

English Language Learners

Review Various Ideologies For the Reading Notes for Section 7.4, before students rate their connections with each ideology, briefly review the section to make sure students clearly understand the different ideologies.

Provide Historical Context While projecting Transparency 7A during the Preview, provide a short written or verbal description of lunch counter sit-ins in case students are unfamiliar with the historical background. This will help them understand the context clues and answer the spiral questions.

Learners Reading and Writing Below Grade Level

Build Vocabulary Give students a list of key vocabulary along with the case studies. Consider these terms:

A School for Iqbal: bonded labor, Scholastic Web site, Punjab province, Amnesty International, congressional hearing, Operation Day's Work

The Ryan White CARE Act: hepatitis, AIDS, transmitted, presidential commission, foundation

Mothers Against Drunk Driving: task force, Capitol Hill, presidential commission, fatalities, blood alcohol concentration level

Learners with Special Education Needs

Simplify the Debriefing To foster better comprehension, decrease the number of forms of civic participation used in the exercise by choosing just 7 to 10 of them, rather than using all 15.

Provide a Template Offer students a template for the Processing assignment outlining the specific requirements for their plans of action.

Problem:

Why it is a problem:

Fact 1:

Fact 2:

My plan to address that problem (use at least two forms of civic participation):

Modify the Reading Notes Adapt the Reading Notes to simplify their completion.

- For Section 7.3, provide a template for the flier students are to create.
- For Section 7.4, provide definitions of the ideologies so that students only have to create simple illustrations for and rate the ideologies.

Advanced Learners

Draw on Current Events Have students read newspapers or online news sources and identify three forms of civic participation mentioned in them. Require them to turn in copies of the articles, along with a short written explanation of each describing the situation and analyzing how effective that method of civic participation was in that situation.

U.S. Supreme Court Cases: You Make the Call

Have students read the summary of Case 4, *United States v. Virginia,* which relates to the Fourteenth Amendment's Equal Protection Clause, in the "U.S. Supreme Court Cases: You Make the Call" section of the Student Edition. Have volunteers share key facts from the case and the question before the Court. Then facilitate a Response Group–type discussion asking students to "make the call" on how the Court should decide the case and why. Finally, have students read the actual Supreme Court decision.

National Constitution Center

Consider using parts or all of the National Constitution Center's service-learning curriculum: "America Volunteers," "Being American," or "Just Vote!" For more information, visit the National Constitution Center connections at www.teachtci.com.

Internet Connections

For related research materials on citizenship and civic participation, refer students to Online Resources at www.teachtci.com.

Multimedia

Please follow school and district guidelines about showing films in the classroom.

A Time for Justice This 38-minute Academy Award–winning documentary (Guggenheim Productions, 1994) is about the men and women who served as foot soldiers in the civil rights movement of the 1950s and 1960s. It includes archival footage and interviews from participants in civil rights marches, sit-ins, freedom rides, and the like.

Eyes on the Prize The PBS Web site for this series maintains a "Video and More" section that includes two hours of video from the original 14-hour series. Consider having students watch Parts 1 and 2 of "Non-Violent Protests, 1960," which contain archival footage of the growing movement, including lunch counter sit-ins, marches, and interviews with leaders, participants, and onlookers.

Following are possible answers for each section of the Reading Notes.

Section 7.2

Civic rights: U.S. citizens can vote; can hold public office; can claim certain social and economic benefits.

Civic responsibilities: U.S. citizens must obey laws; must pay taxes; must cooperate with public officials; must register for military service if they are 18-year-old males; are expected to be informed about and participate in public affairs.

Section 7.3

Fliers should include the required information—requirements for becoming a citizen, application for naturalization, interview with an immigration official, citizenship ceremony, and rights that new citizens gain—and be organized in an appropriate how-to format. Illustrations will vary.

Section 7.4

1. Answers should include an explanation of the importance of at least one shared American value: liberty, equality, democracy, individualism, free enterprise, justice and the rule of law, patriotism, optimism, and civic duty.

2. Symbols and ratings will vary. Possible explanations:

   liberalism: favors an active role for government in solving society's problems

   conservativism: favors a limited role for government in economic affairs

   socialism: wants to limit economic inequality by ensuring a fair distribution of wealth

   libertarianism: believes in personal freedom and minimal government intervention

   environmentalism: is deeply concerned about conservation and protection of the environment

   centrism: holds a mix of liberal, conservative, and perhaps environmental views; crosses party lines based on issues and candidates

Section 7.5

1. Answers should include an explanation of social capital and an evaluation of its importance.

2. Answers will vary.

Parties, Interest Groups, and Public Policy

Political parties and interest groups: How do they influence our political decisions?

Overview

Students learn about the influential role of political parties and interest groups in government and public policy.

Preview Students analyze their political beliefs and reflect on their preconceived notions about, and affiliations with, political parties.

Activity In an Experiential Exercise, students work in groups to create informational Web sites about simulated presidential candidates and interest groups, before participating in a meet-and-greet to learn about the relationship between politicians and interest groups.

Processing Students register to vote and then answer questions about their party choice and the role of parties in government and society.

(**Note:** Chapter 8 is the first of a three-part Experiential Exercise. See the second option under "Deeper Coverage" for tips on how to connect this activity to the activities students will participate in for Chapters 9 and 10.)

Objectives

In the course of reading this chapter and participating in the classroom activity, students will

- analyze the roots of political parties and the role parties play in the political process and public policy development.
- identify the organization of political parties, including third parties, and evaluate how participation in parties affects the government.
- analyze the platforms of political candidates and parties.
- evaluate the significance of interest groups in terms of their goals, methods, and influence on government and public policy.

Materials

Government Alive! Power, Politics, and You

Lesson Masters

- Notebook Guide 8 (1 per student)
- Student Handouts 8A and 8E (1 of each per student)
- Student Handout 8B (6 copies)
- Student Handout 8C (1 copy)
- Student Handout 8D (1 copy, cut into cards)
- Student Handout 8F (3 copies, cut apart)
- Information Masters 8A and 8B (1 transparency of each)

envelopes (optional)

poster paper and markers

voter registration or preregistration forms (optional)

Preview

Suggested time: 15 minutes

1 **Have students complete the Preview.** Distribute *Notebook Guide 8*. Students will analyze their political beliefs and reflect on their preconceptions about, and affiliations with, political parties.

2 **Have students share their responses.** Designate each corner of the room to represent one of the following: Democrat, Republican, independent, or third party. Tell students to go to the corner that best describes their self-selected political affiliation. Have students in each group quickly discuss the reasons they chose that affiliation. Then call on one member of each group to quickly share a couple of the group's reasons. (**Note:** If students are uncomfortable revealing their political affiliations, hold a class discussion instead about the factors that influence a person's choice of political party.)

3 **Have students assess their views on political issues.** Distribute *Student Handout 8A: Political Issues Survey*. Have students complete the survey and tally their scores to see where they fall along a political spectrum.

4 **Debrief the Preview.** Ask,

- Were the results of the survey consistent with your party choice in the Preview?

- In this survey, all issues were weighted equally. In reality, what specific issues might have more or less weight in a person's decision to become affiliated with one party over another?

- Why do you think people join political parties? What might be some of the advantages and disadvantages of joining one?

5 **Explain the connection between the Preview and Chapter 8.** In the Preview, students began to analyze their own political leanings, the issues that define political parties, and the reasons people join political parties. In the chapter, they will learn more about two organizations that influence and shape public policy in the United States: political parties and interest groups. This chapter and activity are designed to better educate students about political parties in preparation for their registering to vote in the Processing assignment.

Notebook Guide 8

Student Handout 8A

Reading

Speaking of Politics Encourage students to use the following terms as they complete their Reading Notes for the chapter: *political party, interest group, platform, two-party system, pluralism, political action committee (PAC), lobbying,* and *public policy.*

1 **Introduce the Essential Question and have students read Section 8.1.** Then ask,

- Who sponsored the two 2004 ads discussed in this section?

- What were the sponsors of these ads hoping to accomplish?

- How are interest groups and political parties similar?

Then ask students to consider possible answers to the Essential Question: *Political parties and interest groups: How do they influence our political decisions?*

2 **Assign the Reading Notes.** Have students read and complete the Reading Notes for Sections 8.2 and 8.3 *before* conducting the Experiential Exercise. Have them read and complete the notes for Section 8.4 *during* the exercise as indicated in Phase 2 of the Experiential Exercise that follows.

Experiential Exercise

To introduce the activity, explain that students will be working either as an interest group representative or in a group representing a candidate from one of the two major political parties. Candidate groups will meet with interest group representatives to form alliances that will help their candidates get elected and help the interest groups call attention to their issues.

Phase 1

Suggested time: 90–120 minutes

1 **Prepare materials.** Make copies of Student Handouts 8B, 8C, and 8D and Information Master 8A as noted in the materials list.

2 **Introduce this phase of the activity.** Tell students that they will be assigned to learn about and represent a simulated presidential candidate or interest group. So that others can learn about their candidates or interest groups, they will be creating poster versions of informational Web sites with position statements or talking points covering the major issues in a fictitious presidential campaign.

3 **Create candidate groups and interest groups.** Divide students as follows:

- Create six groups of three students each. Each group will represent one of the six candidates.

- Create two groups of six students each. One group will represent the liberal interest groups. The other will represent the conservative interest groups.

If you have a small class, consider eliminating a liberal and a conservative candidate or eliminating one of the types of interest groups (such as the environmental interest groups) from both the liberal and conservative profiles.

4 **Have students learn about their candidates or interest groups.**

- Assign candidate groups to candidates by distributing *Student Handout 8B: Campaign Team Roles* and one version of *Student Handout 8C: Candidate Profiles* to each candidate group. Have groups use Student Handout 8B to assign roles and then review Student Handout 8C to learn about their candidate. (**Note:** If there are fewer than three students in a group, eliminate the Research and Policy Director and have the Candidate and Campaign Manager share the responsibilities of the eliminated role. If there are more than three students in a group, assign two students to play the Research and Policy Director.)

Student Handouts 8B and 8C

- Distribute a liberal interest group profile card from *Student Handout 8D: Interest Group Profiles* to each student in the liberal group and a conservative interest group profile card to each student in the conservative group. Have students review the cards to learn about their interest groups.

5 **Project *Information Master 8A: Creating a Candidate or Interest Group Web Site* and review the directions.**

- After reviewing Step 1, point out the required features of the Web sites, such as the links and the list of issues. Consider asking groups to identify the required information in their candidate or interest group profiles.

- After reviewing Step 2, you might have groups write one position statement or talking point and check that they are on the right track.

- Have groups use poster paper and markers to create large Web sites that will be easy to read.

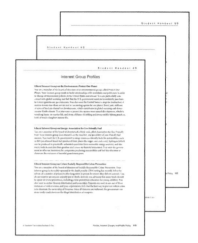

Student Handout 8D

6 **Have groups post their Web sites and learn about the other candidates and interest groups.** Explain that during a campaign, political candidates regularly meet with representatives from interest groups. Students will now have a chance to learn about the candidates and interest groups in preparation for the meet-and-greet to follow. Tell candidate groups to identify and record in their notebooks interest groups whose positions or goals align with their own and with whom they would like to meet. Interest group representatives should do the same for the candidates. Also consider these tips:

- Set a time limit (approximately 15 minutes) for groups to circulate and learn about the other candidates and the interest groups.

- For classroom-management purposes, you might have groups rotate in set two- or three-minute intervals.

Information Master 8A

Phase 2

Suggested time: 60–75 minutes

1 **Prepare materials.** Make copies of Student Handouts 8E and 8F and Information Master 8B as noted in the materials list. Consider dividing the 90 Power Tokens cut from Student Handout 8F into envelopes labeled with each interest group's name and the number of tokens, following the guidelines in Step 3.

2 **Have students read and complete the Reading Notes for Section 8.4.** To save time, you might assign this for homework before Phase 2.

3 **Have students prepare for the meet-and-greet.** Explain that the meet-and-greet is intended to serve as a dialogue between the interest groups and candidates about which issues to focus on during the campaign. Project *Information Master 8B: Candidate and Interest Group Meet-and-Greet* and review the directions for Step 1. Then do the following:

- Have students create name tags that are large enough for students to easily identify each other. Members of candidate groups should include the candidate's name and campaign role. Members of interest groups should include the interest group name and the issue they represent.

Information Master 8B

- Distribute and review *Student Handout 8E: Recording Details About the Meet-and-Greet.*
- Distribute tokens from *Student Handout 8F: Power Tokens* to interest groups as follows: 10 tokens each to Good Cents for Earth and Association of Petroleum Distributors; 8 tokens each to Protect Our Planet, Citizens for One America, Association of American Health Care Providers, Association for Eco-Friendly Fuel, and Citizens United for Fair Immigration; and 6 tokens each to Socially Responsible Crime Prevention, Health Care for Everyone, Citizens United for Better Immigration, Safety on Our Streets, and Americans United for Responsible Choices.

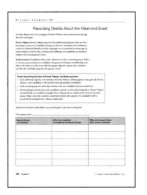

Student Handout 8E

4 Conduct the meet-and-greet. Remind students that the ideal outcome of the meet-and-greet is for candidates to secure endorsements and financial support (in the form of Power Tokens) from interest groups and for interest groups to find candidates who support their causes. Consider these tips:

- Encourage candidate groups to use the information they have gathered about their opponents to convince interest group representatives that theirs is the best candidate for that group to endorse. As there are more interest group representatives than candidates, you might also encourage candidate groups to split up and meet with as many interest groups as possible.

Student Handout 8F

- Remind interest groups that only one candidate will win the election. To have as much influence as possible, they might consider supporting multiple candidates with their Power Tokens.

- If candidates accept Power Tokens or an endorsement from an interest group whose cause they could not realistically support, penalize the candidates by confiscating some of their Power Tokens.

- Set a time limit (approximately 15 minutes) for the meet-and-greet.

5 Debrief the activity. Have each candidate group write its candidate's name in large letters on a sheet of paper. Below that, have the candidate groups write which interest groups endorsed their candidates and how many tokens they received. Ask one member from each candidate group to come to the front of the room with the group's sign. Have students quickly line up across the room from most successful to least successful based on how many endorsements and Power Tokens each candidate received. Then ask,

- Which candidates did the best? Why do you think interest groups were more likely to support these candidates?

- What is the relationship between candidates and interest groups?

- How might this relationship be beneficial for democracy? How might it be harmful?

You might also have students research their real-life elected officials and the PACs that have donated to them. To find this information, visit the National Constitution Center connections at www.teachtci.com.

Power, Politics, and You

1 **Help students understand the problem inherent with the "red state" and "blue state" classification.**

   - Draw a spectrum along the board, labeled "Democrats (Blue)" on the left and "Republicans (Red)" on the right.

   - Tell students that for the purpose of this exercise, they need to choose to be a Democrat or a Republican; they cannot choose to be independent or a member of a third party. Assign Democrats to stand along the left wall of the classroom and Republicans to stand along the right wall.

   - Ask, *Are you content with only getting to be at the extreme ends of the spectrum? Why or why not? Would anyone like to move somewhere more toward the center of the spectrum?* Allow students who want to to move, and then ask them, *Why did you move toward the center?*

   Tell students that one potential problem with "red state" and "blue state" maps is that such maps show only the political affiliations of a majority of people in that state. They do not show that there may be many other people in that state (as many as 49.9%) who have a different political affiliation.

2 **Have students read the "Power, Politics, and You" section of the chapter.** Then ask,

   - According to Jonathan Rauch, why is it inaccurate to refer to a "red America" and a "blue America"?

   - What conclusions can you draw by comparing the two maps in this section?

Processing

Suggested time: 20 minutes

Have students complete the Processing activity on Notebook Guide 8. Suggest that they register to vote, selecting a party or an independent affiliation and then answering questions about the importance of political parties. (**Note:** Consider providing voter registration or preregistration forms for students, or have them register online. To complete online registration for all states that accept this method, visit the National Constitution Center connections at www.teachtci.com.) For students who are not eligible to vote, consider using the alternate Processing assignment in the third option under "English Language Learners."

Quicker Coverage

Substitute a Discussion for Phase 2 After Phase 1 of the Experiential Exercise, ask students the following questions instead of having them participate in Phase 2:

- Ask each candidate group, *Which interest groups would you be likely to seek endorsements from? Why?*

- Ask each interest group representative, *Which candidates would your group most likely support? Why?*

Follow up by asking the second and third debriefing questions from Phase 2.

Summarize Web Sites Rather than having students circulate to review the Web site posters, have each candidate group and interest group representative stand and take 30 to 60 seconds to explain the content of their site. Then move to Phase 2.

Deeper Coverage

Research Real Candidates or Interest Groups For the Experiential Exercise, have students research the biography, beliefs, and goals of candidates from a current or past election. Or create candidate biographies for students to use. You might also consider using real interest groups by choosing 12 groups whose beliefs align with the 12 fictitious groups in the activity.

Create a Three-Part Activity The activities for Chapters 8, 9, and 10 have been created so that a class can run a presidential election by doing all three activities back-to-back. If you plan to do all three activities, follow the "Deeper Coverage" options in Chapters 9 and 10 for linking these three activities together.

Create Actual Web Sites In Phase 1, consider having students create actual Web site home pages. Post each home page on a different computer in your classroom or a computer lab for students to view.

Assessment

Masters for the chapter assessment appear in the *Lesson Masters*.

Mastering the Content

1. B	2. C	3. D	4. C	5. B
6. A	7. C	8. A	9. B	10. D

Exploring the Essential Question

Possible answers:

1. The Business Roundtable most likely has the largest proportion of Republican members because the average Republican, like the typical corporate leader, is likely to be white, male, affluent, and opposed to excessive regulation of business.

2. The Business Roundtable might claim to serve the public and its members' interests by promoting economic growth, which helps businesses prosper and keeps Americans employed. United Farm Workers might claim to do so by ensuring that crops are grown in ways that are healthy for farmworkers and consumers. The Sierra Club might claim to do so by ensuring that wild places and ecosystems are protected for all Americans and future generations. The National Education Association might claim to do so by working to make public schools better places for teachers to work and for children to learn.

3. The National Education Association might use workshops and training to improve the skills of teachers, which would improve the effectiveness of public schools in teaching all students.

4. Examples might include recruiting new members, contributing money, supporting lobbying efforts, and participating in demonstrations.

English Language Learners

List Characteristics of Each Party Because some English language learners may not be familiar with the differences between Democrats and Republicans, have the class create a list of the characteristics of each party, including each party's stance on important issues. Students can consult the lists during the Preview.

Read the Survey Aloud During the Preview, read each survey statement on Student Handout 8A aloud and answer any questions students have.

Create a "Register to Vote" Brochure Modify the Processing assignment by having students create a brochure that encourages people to register to vote as a member of one of the major political parties, or of a third party, or as an independent. The brochure should

- explain the advantage of registering with that affiliation.

- include the party's stance on three or four major issues, or the student's stance on three or four issues if the student is encouraging people to register as independents.

- have creative touches, such as illustrations or a list of notable people affiliated with that party.

Learners Reading and Writing Below Grade Level

Highlight Key Facts Support students during the activity.

- Highlight key facts in the candidate and interest group profiles.

- Provide a talking-points summary of key facts for each candidate or interest group for use as a reference during the meet-and-greet.

Provide Summaries Help students understand the content of the chapter and handouts.

- Provide a bulleted summary of the main points from Sections 8.2 to 8.4 that students can consult when preparing for the activity.

- Modify the handouts for the candidates and interest groups by making them into bulleted summaries.

Learners with Special Education Needs

Model a Conversation Allow students to practice orally presenting information about their candidate or interest group prior to participating in the meet-and-greet.

Create Note-Taking Templates Provide additional support during the activity.

- Provide a template for interest group members to use when taking notes during the Web site review.

Candidate	Three Biographical Facts	Views on Two Issues	Does This Candidate Share Our Views?

- Provide a template for candidate group members to use when taking notes during the Web site review.

Interest Group	Views on Two Issues	Does This Interest Group Share Our Views?

Advanced Learners

Research PACs Have students research the amount of money that PACs have donated to their elected representatives. This information is easily available on the Open Secrets Web site, sponsored and maintained by the Center for Responsive Politics, or at the National Constitution Center connections at www.teachtci.com.

U.S. Supreme Court Cases: You Make the Call

Have students read the summary of Case 5, *Whitney v. California,* which relates to the activities of political parties, in the "U.S. Supreme Court Cases: You Make the Call" section of the Student Edition. Have volunteers share key facts from the case and the question before the Court. Then facilitate a Response Group–type discussion asking students to "make the call" on how the Court should decide the case and why. Finally, have students read the actual Supreme Court decision.

NATIONAL CONSTITUTION CENTER

National Constitution Center

Have students research their elected officials and the PACs that have donated to them. To find this information, visit the National Constitution Center connections at www.teachtci.com.

Internet Connections

For related research materials on influential role of political parties and interest groups, refer students to Online Resources at www.teachtci.com.

Following are possible answers for each section of the Reading Notes.

Section 8.2

1. Diagrams should include at least four of these functions: political parties get candidates elected, recruit candidates and support campaigns, help organize elections and inform voters, organize the government, develop platforms, or unite diverse interests and make collective action possible.

2. The first two political parties disagreed over how power should be distributed. Federalists wanted a strong national government. Democratic-Republicans wanted strong state governments and a weak national government.

3. Possible answers:

Democrats	Republicans
Support a strong federal government	Support limiting the size of the national government
Favor tax cuts for the poor and higher taxes for the affluent	Support giving more power to the states
Support government regulation of business	Favor lower taxes
Oppose prayer in schools	Oppose strong government regulation of business
Support abortion rights	Support prayer in schools
Support gun control laws	Oppose abortion
Support minimum wage laws	Oppose gun control laws
	Oppose minimum wage laws

4. In general, third parties are formed by people who are frustrated with the political system. Third parties allow people to express their opinions in constructive ways.

5. Descriptions should include such ideas as unaligned with a particular political party, tend to be centrist, and lean toward major parties at election time.

Section 8.3

Answers should include some of the following points on either side of the T-chart:

- Seek to achieve their goals at the expense of society as a whole
- Pose a threat to democratic government if their power goes unchecked
- Interest groups competing in a pluralistic society act as a check on tyranny and make government more representative
- Competition between interest groups prevents any one group from becoming too powerful
- Offer Americans a way to participate in the political process
- Speak out on issues of concern to their members and the public
- Present specialized information to government officials
- Monitor government actions to ensure members' rights and interests are protected
- Help keep people informed about their government
- Offer members benefits and a way to participate in a larger community of shared interests
- Contribute money to political parties and candidates
- PAC campaign contributions give interest groups too much influence over elected officials
- Influence the policy process by lobbying public officials on specific issues
- Carry out research and write policy proposals that support their goals
- Turn to litigation to influence policy
- Influence policy through grassroots mobilization

Section 8.4

Answers should include a mnemonic for the six steps of the policymaking process—issue identification, agenda setting, policy formulation, policy adoption, policy implementation, and policy evaluation—as well as an explanation of the steps the student feels are most important and least important.

Public Opinion and the Media

To what extent do the media influence your political views?

Overview

Students learn about the role that public opinion and the media play in American politics.

Preview Students analyze a political advertisement and identify the purpose of such media.

Activity In an Experiential Exercise, students work in groups to analyze persuasive techniques and then create and evaluate campaign commercials for presidential candidates.

Processing Students write position statements on the reliability and effectiveness of campaign commercials.

(**Note:** Chapter 9 is the second part of a three-part Experiential Exercise. See the second option in "Deeper Coverage" for tips on how to connect this activity to the activity students participated in for Chapter 8.)

Objectives

In the course of reading this chapter and participating in the classroom activity, students will

- analyze the role of the media in shaping public opinion.
- evaluate the extent to which the media act as a free press.
- analyze the influence of media coverage, political advertising, and public opinion polls on local, state, and national elections.
- identify persuasive techniques and their application in U.S. campaigns.
- write position statements about the influence of political advertising on voters.

Materials

Government Alive! Power, Politics, and You

Transparencies 9A–9D

Placards 9A–9H (2 sets)

Lesson Masters

- Notebook Guide 9 (1 per student)
- Information Master 9 (1 transparency)
- Student Handouts 9A and 9B (1 of each per group)

Preview

Suggested time: 15 minutes

1 **Have students complete Preview 9.** Distribute *Notebook Guide 9* and project *Transparency 9A: Adlai E. Stevenson Campaign Poster, 1952* or direct students to the image shown at the beginning of Chapter 9. Review the directions for the Preview with students. You may want to point out that Adlai Stevenson, who ran for president in 1952, belonged to the same political party as Franklin D. Roosevelt, who became president after Herbert Hoover during the Great Depression. Read each question aloud, and have students respond to them verbally and then record their responses in their notebooks.

2 **Have students share their responses in pairs or with the class.**

3 **Explain the connection between the Preview and Chapter 9.** Students have just considered how a campaign poster might have influenced voters in the 1952 presidential election and whether media messages are effective in shaping people's political views. They will now learn more about the various ways the media influence and are shaped by politics and public opinion.

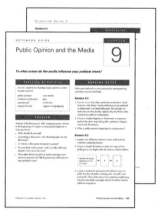

Notebook Guide 9

Reading

Speaking of Politics Encourage students to use the following terms as they complete their Reading Notes for the chapter: *public opinion, political socialization, opinion poll, margin of error, mass media, spin, media bias,* and *negative campaigning.*

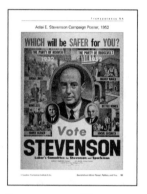

Transparency 9A

1 **Introduce the Essential Question and have students read Section 9.1.** Afterward, ask students to consider possible answers to the Essential Question: *To what extent do the media influence your political views?*

2 **Before conducting the activity, have students read Sections 9.2 to 9.5 and complete the Reading Notes.** Consider the alternative reading and note-taking strategy in the first option under "Quicker Coverage."

Experiential Exercise

Suggested time: 180 minutes

1 **Prepare the classroom.** Hang one set of *Placards 9A–9H: Campaign Posters* at three-foot intervals along one wall of the classroom. Hang the second set along another wall.

2 **Place students in groups of four and introduce the activity.** Explain that groups will first analyze campaign posters to identify the persuasive techniques used in them. Then they will use the techniques they learned about to write and produce 30-second campaign commercials for their assigned candidates.

Placards 9A–9H

3 **Have students review the persuasive advertising techniques presented in Section 9.5.** Then project Transparency 9A again and ask, *What persuasive techniques are used in this ad?* (name-calling, card-stacking, plain folks)

4 **Have students analyze Placards 9A to 9H.** Tell students they will visit the placards in pairs and quickly identify the persuasive advertising techniques used in each campaign poster, recording the placard letter and the techniques in their notebooks. Assign two students from each group to begin at each placard, and have pairs rotate until they have analyzed all the campaign posters.

5 **Review the advertising techniques used in the posters.** Project *Transparency 9B: Campaign Posters 9A–9D,* and have students quickly identify the techniques used in each poster. Then project *Transparency 9C: Campaign Posters 9E–9H* and repeat the process. Here are the techniques for your reference:

Placard 9A: name-calling

Placard 9B: card-stacking, plain folks, transfer

Placard 9C: transfer, glittering generalities, bandwagon

Placard 9D: testimonial

Placard 9E: bandwagon, transfer (**Note:** This poster also uses testimonial, as such celebrities as Clint Eastwood, Nelson Rockefeller, Wilt Chamberlain, and Barry Goldwater are pictured in the background. Though the technique was effective, it is unlikely students will identify these celebrities or this technique.)

Transparencies 9B–9D

Placard 9F: transfer

Placard 9G: transfer, glittering generalities

Placard 9H: card-stacking

Finally, ask, *Which advertising techniques do you think are the most effective, and why? The least effective, and why?*

6 **Have students analyze a sample campaign commercial.** Explain that a storyboard is a series of panels that shows the important visual and verbal components of a television show or commercial. Project *Transparency 9D: Storyboard for a Campaign Commercial,* and have students review the storyboard. Then ask,

- What is this commercial's message?
- What type of commercial—positive, negative, or issue based—is this?
- What persuasive technique or techniques are used?
- What do you think makes this commercial effective or ineffective?

7 **Review the requirements for creating campaign commercials.** Project *Information Master 9: Creating a Campaign Commercial* and review the steps with the class.

Information Master 9

8 Have groups prepare their campaign commercials.

- Give *Student Handout 9A: Candidate Profiles* and *Student Handout 9B: Storyboard for Campaign Commercial* to each group. Assign half the groups to represent candidate Cory Mathews and half to represent Taylor Andrews. Groups can refer to the opponent's profile, as well as their own, for preparing their commercials. (**Note:** The profiles are gender neutral, so male or female students can play the roles. Feel free to revise the names to reflect particular cultural backgrounds or genders.)

- Post or project Transparency 9D for students to review as they work on their storyboards.

- Circulate and provide guidance as students prepare and rehearse their commercials.

9 Have groups perform or "air" their campaign commercials. Have each group perform their commercial. Alternatively, have groups record their commercials ahead of time and then play the commercials in class. This will allow students to edit and add special features to their commercials using technology.

Student Handout 9A

10 Have students evaluate the commercials. As each commercial is presented, have students identify the type of ad and the persuasive techniques used, and record this information in their notebooks.

11 Debrief the activity. Ask,

- Which techniques do you feel were most effective? Least effective?

- Would any of these commercials make you more likely, or less likely, to vote for one of the candidates? Why?

- To what extent do you think political ads influence your political views? Can you think of any political ads that have greatly influenced viewers?

Student Handout 9B

Power, Politics, and You

Have students read the "Power, Politics, and You" section of the chapter, and facilitate a class discussion by asking the questions below. Consider having students discuss the questions in pairs or small groups first.

- Are voters protected from receiving false information from political candidates? Why or why not?

- Several states have sought to enact legislation to protect voters from receiving false information from political candidates. Why have those laws been so difficult to enforce?

- According to the principles of self-government, what is the responsibility of a voter during an election?

Processing

Suggested time: 20 minutes

1 **Have students complete the processing activity in their notebooks.** Students will write position statements on the reliability and effectiveness of campaign commercials.

2 **Debrief the Processing.** Ask, *What might be some of the advantages and disadvantages of campaign commercials?*

Quicker Coverage

Break Up the Reading Have students work in their groups to read and complete the Reading Notes for Section 9.5 in class before beginning the activity. Then assign students to read and complete the Reading Notes for Sections 9.2 to 9.4 as homework while they are working on the activity in class.

Use Fewer Placards During the activity, post only Placards 9A through 9D. Or, analyze the first four placards as a class by projecting Transparency 9B or using the Digital Teacher Resources to project the placards one at a time.

Eliminate the Performances Instead of having groups perform their commercials, post the storyboards around the room. Have groups circulate to quickly review them, identifying the type of ad and the techniques used in each.

Deeper Coverage

Analyze Political Commercials For the activity, consider setting up computer stations in a classroom, library, or technology lab where students can view television commercials from past political races. The American Museum of the Moving Image maintains the Living Room Candidate Web site, which makes available presidential race political commercials from 1952 to the present. To cover all of the techniques, consider using these commercials:

- 1952: Dwight D. Eisenhower, "The Man from Abilene" *(plain folks, card-stacking, transfer)*
- 1960: John F. Kennedy, "Jingle" *(glittering generalities, bandwagon)*
- 1984: Walter Mondale, "Rollercoaster" *(name-calling, transfer, card-stacking)*
- 1992: George H. W. Bush, "Arkansas 2" *(name-calling, card-stacking)*
- 1992: Bill Clinton, "We Can Do It" *(glittering generalities)*
- 2004: George W. Bush, "First Choice" *(testimonial, card-stacking)*

Continue from the Previous Activity Consider linking this activity to that in Chapter 8 as follows:

- Have students stay in their roles—candidate groups or interest group representatives—from Chapter 8, rather than using Student Handout 9A to assign roles.
- In this activity, have each candidate group create a commercial for their candidate or against one of their opponents.

- Put the 12 interest group representatives into two separate groups, one for the liberal interests and one for the conservative interests. Have each group create a commercial in favor of or opposed to one of the candidates or political parties, or have them choose a particular issue or set of issues around which they can endorse a candidate.

- You may want to post the candidate position statements from Chapter 8 for students to access while creating their commercials.

A "Deeper Coverage" option in Chapter 10 further extends this exercise, making it a three-part activity.

Analyze Real Candidates Consider creating and using your own profiles of current or past candidates from local, state, or national elections in place of the fictitious profiles on Student Handout 9A. You might use U.S. representatives, senators, or gubernatorial candidates during midterm elections and presidential candidates during the year prior to and the year of a presidential election. If it is an election year, you might direct students to the candidates' own Web sites to gather information.

Assessment

Masters for the chapter assessment appear in the *Lesson Masters*.

Mastering the Content

1. D	2. A	3. C	4. B	5. A
6. D	7. B	8. A	9. A	10. A

Exploring the Essential Question

1. about 63%

2. most trusting, Democrats; least trusting, Republicans

3. Republicans are most likely to see the media as biased. They are likely to think it is biased in favor of Democrats (or has a liberal bias).

4. Students should provide an explanation that supports their answer to the survey question.

English Language Learners

Activate Prior Knowledge To help students make concrete connections between the media and their own lives, consider drawing on their personal experience by asking how the media affects their lives (such as the clothing they wear or the music they listen to) prior to discussing the Essential Question in Reading Step 1.

Identify Key Candidate Information In the activity, consider having students underline key information about the candidate, and read and discuss the profiles with their group or the class, prior to preparing their commercials. This should help them identify appropriate political viewpoints to include in their commercials.

Learners Reading and Writing Below Grade Level

Streamline the Note-Taking Process Assign students to their groups of four for the activity prior to having them do the reading. Assign one or two groups to read each section, from Section 9.2 to Section 9.5, and to answer the Reading Notes questions for that section. Then have each group quickly create a poster or a transparency with the following information:

- section number and title
- key words (not whole sentences) that should be in the answer to each question for that section

Have each group quickly present their section by reviewing what content was covered and the answer for each question in the Reading Notes while the other students complete their Reading Notes for that section.

Learners with Special Education Needs

Support the Reading Notes Consider using one of these options:

- Provide a photocopy of the text with important passages underlined to help students find the answers to the questions.
- Reduce the number of questions for each section. The following questions focus on the main ideas of each section: Section 9.2, Question 2; Section 9.3, Questions 2 and 3; Section 9.4, Questions 1 and 4; Section 9.5, Question 1.

Support the Placard Analyses To help make determining the persuasive techniques used in the advertisements less abstract, offer students additional support. For example:

- Give a copy of the persuasive techniques from the text to each pair of students, and tell them to circle the word or phrase that best illustrates each technique. Have them use these pages as a resource as they visit the placards.
- Provide students with a multiple-choice checklist of two or three persuasive techniques for each placard, one of which is used in the advertisement, and have them choose which one of the techniques is used.
- Have groups check with you after analyzing each placard to make sure they correctly identified the persuasive techniques used before moving on to the next placard.

Advanced Learners

Evaluate Current Advertisements Have students research and evaluate the effectiveness of persuasive techniques used in current or recent local, state, or national elections. Consider having them find one example from each of three candidates and identify the following information for each:

- name of candidate and office sought
- persuasive techniques used in the advertisement
- brief description of the advertisement
- explanation of why the advertisement is or is not effective

Internet Connections

For related research materials on public opinion and the media, refer students to Online Resources at www.teachtci.com.

Multimedia

Please follow school and district guidelines for showing films in the classroom.

PBS Frontline: *News War* This four-part, four-hour series investigates current challenges and the future facing the news media, especially in regard to shaping the public agenda. The documentary is based on more than 80 interviews with key individuals from the print, broadcast, and electronic media, combined with behind-the-scenes access to several news organizations.

- Parts I and II, "Secrets, Sources, and Spin," examine the relationship between the president and the media, using anonymous sources and recent battles between the federal government and the press over First Amendment rights and the news media.

- Part III, "What's Happening to the News," examines the changing role of print and broadcast media and the rise of the new media.

- Part IV, "Stories from a Small Planet," examines media from around the world and reveals how journalism and politics in the United States are influenced by international forces.

West Wing, **Season 7, Episode 6, "The Al Smith Dinner"** In this episode, presidential hopefuls Matt Santos (D) and Arnold Vinick (R) face the first negative turn of their campaigns when a 527 pro-life organization airs a negative ad against Santos for his pro-choice stance. The episode centers on abortion politics but effectively highlights tough questions about the decision to "go negative" and examines the difficulty candidates face in getting their message out via the media. Consider forwarding through the scenes that take place in the West Wing, as they do not further the campaign storyline, and because students would need considerable background information to understand them.

Following are possible answers for each section of the Reading Notes.

Section 9.2

1. Answers should include a ranked list of six forms of political socialization—family, school, religion, peer groups, gender and ethnicity, and news media—and include an explanation for the top two ranked items.

2. Answers should include a simple illustration of each of the three ways public opinion is shaped: through the clash of special interest groups; by journalists, politicians, and other opinion makers; and by what politicians say it is.

3. Public opinion is important in a democracy because it guides leaders as they make public policy decisions, serves as a guard against hasty decisions, and serves as a kind of glue in a diverse society like America, where widespread agreement on basic political beliefs helps hold society together.

Section 9.3

1. A straw poll is an informal survey of opinion that can be highly inaccurate because it does not ensure that the population sampled is representative of the population as a whole. Scientific sampling involves selecting a small group of people who are representative of the whole population. The results of this type of survey are more likely to represent the views of the larger electorate.

2.

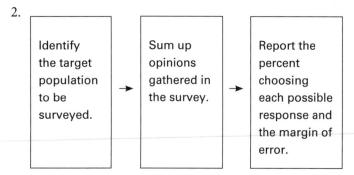

| Identify the target population to be surveyed. | → | Sum up opinions gathered in the survey. | → | Report the percent choosing each possible response and the margin of error. |

3. Answers should include a symbol and a brief explanation of whether each of the four types of polls should be used in political campaigns.

Section 9.4

1. Traditional media sources: newspapers, magazines, radio, or television. New media sources: talk radio, television talk shows, television news magazines, televised town hall meetings, cable comedy shows, blogs. Lists of pros and cons will vary.

2. In a democracy, a free press serves as a government watchdog, helps set the public agenda, and supports the free exchange of ideas, information, and opinions.

3. To attract and shape media coverage, public officials can stage events and invite the press. They can grant on- or off-the-record interviews with the press and can use these interviews to spin issues, float trial balloons, or leak information.

4. Though most Americans would say the media are biased, what is perceived as bias is more likely a reflection of how news organizations work. These organizations choose stories they know people will pay attention to. Also, people tend to pay attention to news that supports their views and tune out news that doesn't.

Section 9.5

Answers should include at least two of the following terms: *media consultant, issue ad, image ad, photo op, soap opera story, mudslinging.*

Political Campaigns and Elections

Elections and voting: Why should they matter to you?

Overview

Students study the U.S. electoral process.

Preview Students organize the steps in the electoral process for a presidential candidate and then determine how well this process helps the country to elect the best individual as president.

Activity In an Experiential Exercise, students participate in parts of the electoral process in a presidential race, from the primaries to the Electoral College.

Processing Students develop ideas for improving the U.S. electoral system.

(**Note:** Chapter 10 is the third part of a three-part Experiential Exercise. See the second option under "Deeper Coverage" for tips on how to connect this activity to the activities students participated in for Chapters 8 and 9.)

Objectives

In the course of reading this chapter and participating in the classroom activity, students will

- identify ways in which voting rights in the United States have expanded over time and identify the current qualifications for voting.
- analyze the process for nominating candidates at all levels of government.
- plan for and participate in a debate of current political issues.
- identify how elections are funded and how funding is regulated.
- analyze party identification and voter behavior in the United States.

Materials

Government Alive! Power, Politics, and You

Transparency 10

Lesson Masters

- Notebook Guide 10 (1 per student)
- Student Handout 10A (3 copies)
- Student Handout 10B (6 copies)
- Student Handout 10C (1 per student)
- Student Handout 10D (1 per audience member)
- Student Handout 10E (4 copies)
- Student Handout 10F (2 copies)
- Information Masters 10A–10C (1 transparency of each)

microphone

Preview

Suggested time: 15 minutes

1 **Have students complete Preview 10.** Distribute *Notebook Guide 10.* Have students complete the Preview, in which they will logically order the steps for running for president.

2 **Have students share their responses in pairs or with the class.** Focus the discussion on the complex nature of running for president.

3 **Explain the connection between the Preview and Chapter 10.** In the Preview, students organized the steps of the presidential election process. In the chapter, they will learn more about the electoral process at the local, state, and national levels, and evaluate whether that process is the most effective way to select the country's leaders.

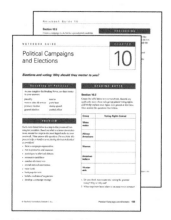

Notebook Guide 10

Reading

Speaking of Politics Encourage students to use the following terms as they complete their Reading Notes for the chapter: *plurality, winner-take-all system, primary election, general election, caucus, party base, stump speech,* and *coattail effect.*

1 **Introduce the Essential Question and have students read Section 10.1.**

2 **Have students complete the Reading Notes for Chapter 10.** Assign Sections 10.2 and 10.3 *before* conducting the Experiential Exercise. Then have students read Section 10.4 as indicated in the procedures that follow. *After* completing the Experiential Exercise, assign Sections 10.5 and 10.6.

Experiential Exercise

Explain that in this activity, students will take on the roles of presidential candidates and voters. The activity has three phases: a national town hall meeting and the state primaries, the national nominating conventions, and the popular and electoral votes. Students will have different responsibilities in each phase. (**Note:** If you have a limited amount of time to conduct this activity, see the options under "Quicker Coverage.")

Phase 1

Suggested time: 120 minutes

1 **Prepare materials.** Copy Student Handouts 10A to 10E and Information Master 10A as stated in the materials list. Cut apart the state primary ballots, keeping the Democrat and Republican ballots separate.

2 **Introduce the national town hall meeting.** Remind students that as part of their campaigning efforts, candidates regularly participate in nationally televised debates and town hall meetings to convey their ideas to voters. Students will simulate this campaign strategy by participating in a mock town hall meeting, a nationally televised event in which Democratic and Republican

candidates answer audience-prepared questions. (Remind students that in reality, only the nominee from each political party participates in this type of interparty debate.) Tell students that this meeting will be a focused debate in which the candidates debate four issues.

3 Assign groups for Phase 1.

- *Candidate groups:* Assign six students to play the six candidates, and have the candidates each select two students to serve as their campaign staff members. Each group of three students is a candidate group. To each candidate group, give the following: the appropriate version of *Student Handout 10A: Candidate Positions on Issues* (one per student); *Student Handout 10B: National Town Hall Meeting Prep for Candidates* (one per group); and *Student Handout 10C: Statistics on the Issues* (one per student).

- *Audience:* Group the remaining students into pairs. These students will play the role of audience members. Give *Student Handout 10C: Statistics on the Issues* and *Student Handout 10D: National Town Hall Meeting Prep for the Audience* to each audience member.

If you have a small class, eliminate two candidates or make the candidate groups smaller. This will ensure that you have enough audience members in this phase, as well as enough convention delegates and state representatives in Phases 2 and 3.

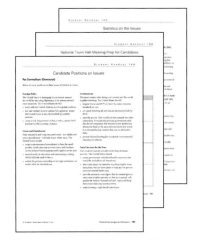

Student Handouts 10A–10D

4 Have students prepare for the national town hall meeting. Have candidate groups and audience members prepare for the national town hall meeting by completing Student Handout 10B or 10D. They should consult the statistics on the issues, from Student Handout 10C, to develop their questions and talking points. You might assign some or all of this preparation as homework.

5 Conduct the national town hall meeting and the state primaries. Project *Information Master 10A: The National Town Hall Meeting and State Primaries.* Have students set up the classroom and sit in the appropriate places. Review the directions for the debate, and then do the following:

- As the moderator, rotate through the audience at least twice, making sure each candidate is asked at least two questions.

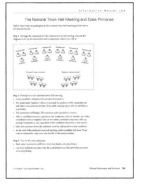

Information Master 10A

- After the meeting, tell students that after months of campaigning for the party's nomination, it is time for the primary elections. Remind them that primaries serve to select delegates to each party's national convention, who will then choose the party's nominee.

- Give members of the candidate groups the ballots cut from *Student Handout 10E: Ballots for the State Primaries* according to the political affiliations of their candidates. Also give half of the audience members Democratic ballots and the other half Republican ballots.

- Collect and tally the ballots. Record the name and the percentage of votes each Democratic candidate received in one column on the board, and those for each Republican candidate in a second column. Then circle the candidate from each party with the highest percentage of votes. Remind students that the parties' nominees are not officially selected until the conventions,

Student Handout 10E

but that these candidates will definitely have enough votes from delegates to secure the nominations of their respective parties.

6 **Debrief Phase 1.** Ask,

- *Audience:* Was this a good way to learn about the candidates? Why or why not?

- *Candidates:* How did it feel to be asked questions? What was exciting or challenging about the experience? What might you do differently if you had a chance to do this again?

- *Everyone:* Do you think this is the best forum for learning about the candidates and their positions? Do you think the primary process is an effective way to choose a party's nominee? How were the steps you took similar to or different from a real election?

Phase 2

Suggested time: 45–75 minutes

1 **Prepare materials.** Copy Student Handout 10F and Information Master 10B as indicated in the materials list.

2 **Explain the purpose of the national nominating conventions.** Remind students that in modern elections, the national convention is more of a formality with the goals of unifying the party and creating a party platform. It also gives the candidate a chance to address a national audience. In class, students will re-create portions of a convention for each political party.

3 **Have students prepare for the conventions.**

- Divide the class into two groups, Republicans and Democrats, based on students' political affiliations at the end of Phase 1.

- Distribute *Student Handout 10F: Preparing for the National Nominating Convention* to each party's nominee. Tell the two nominees that they are responsible for ensuring that the appropriate number of people take responsibility for and complete each job.

- Give the two groups time to prepare for the conventions.

- To save time, have the speakers prepare their own speeches and everyone else create signs at home the night before the conventions.

Student Handout 10F

4 **Conduct the conventions.** Project *Information Master 10B: The National Nominating Conventions* and follow these steps:

- Review the agenda for the conventions with the class.

- Give parties about five minutes to quickly and separately hold dress rehearsals. Consider giving a copy of Information Master 10B to each party's MC to help them facilitate the convention.

- Review the role of the press (played by all students who are not members of that party) with the class, emphasizing the importance of the members of the press reporting *independently* of their party affiliations in the activity.

Information Master 10B

- Allow the political party that does not currently hold the presidency (in real life) to hold its convention first. Project Information Master 10B to remind students of the order in which people will speak.

- After the first party holds its convention, consider having a few members of the press share answers to the two questions on Information Master 10B. Then switch groups and hold the second convention.

5 **Debrief Phase 2.** Ask,

- How would you describe the conventions?

- Do you think that national nominating conventions play an important and effective role in the electoral process?

- If the conventions have mostly become a formality, why do you think parties continue to hold them every four years?

- How were the steps you took similar to or different from a real election?

Phase 3

Suggested time: 50 minutes

1 **Prepare for the activity.**

- Make a transparency of *Information Master 10C: The Presidential Election.*

- Ask the presidential and vice presidential nominees from each party to select a third person to campaign with them. This might be a former candidate from their party who will try to get his or her former supporters to vote for the nominee, a well-known member of their party, or just someone who will be an effective campaigner.

- Assign each of the remaining students to a state by writing their names on the second page of Information Master 10C. Make sure both large and small states are represented. Because students will likely vote for the candidate from the party they belonged to in Phases 1 and 2, evenly divide the states with the most electoral votes between the two parties.

- Clear all desks and chairs from the center of the room, or find an auditorium or other large space to hold this part of the activity. Using masking tape, mark the corners of a large rectangle on the floor in front of the projection screen, and label the corners WA, ME, FL, and CA. The rectangle will represent the area of the United States; make sure it is large enough for all students to stand inside.

2 **Have students read and complete the Reading Notes for Section 10.4.**

3 **Have students participate in a round of campaigning.** Project Information Master 10C, and do the following:

- Project the second page of Information Master 10C so students can see their state assignments, and then project *Transparency 10: Map of Electoral Votes.* Have students representing Washington, California, Florida, and Maine stand near the taped corners on the floor. After students have assumed their positions, check their locations for accuracy.

Information Master 10C

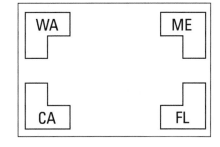

Transparency 10

- Remind students that during the campaigning session, the presidential and vice presidential nominees (and their campaigners) will crisscross the nation to meet voters. Emphasize that at this point the students representing states are no longer members of a particular party; instead, they represent the voters of a particular state. Thus they can choose a candidate from either party based on their own beliefs about the campaign issues and which candidates would be better for the offices of president and vice president.

4 **Conduct the popular vote.** End the campaigning, and remind students that they may vote for only one candidate team. Have students vote by a raise of hands or by writing on slips of paper the presidential and vice presidential candidates they would like to vote for. Then quickly calculate the *percentage* of the vote that each presidential/vice presidential team received, and reveal the outcome of the popular vote to the class.

5 **Conduct the electoral vote.** Tell students that the candidate they voted for in the popular vote happens to be the candidate who received the majority of votes in the state they represent. Therefore, that candidate will receive all the electoral votes from that state. Have students cast their electoral votes, then tally them and announce the winner (the candidate receiving the majority of electoral votes). (**Note:** Consider having students who represent states that divide their electoral votes based on the popular vote do so in this activity as well.)

6 **Debrief the activity.** Ask,

- *Candidates:* What pressures did you feel during the campaigning process?
- *States:* Which states received the most visits? Why was that so? Why were some states not visited?
- If the popular vote—instead of the Electoral College—elected the president, how might the campaign process be different?
- Do you think the Electoral College is the most effective way to elect the president?
- How were the steps you took similar to or different from a real election?
- What factors determined the outcome of the mock election? Does this reflect the selection of candidates and elected officials in real elections? Why?
- Are these factors the ones that should be determining elections?
- Does the best person for the job necessarily win? Why or why not?

Power, Politics, and You

Have students read the "Power, Politics, and You" section of the chapter, and then facilitate a class discussion by asking the questions below. Consider having students discuss the questions in pairs or small groups first.

- Which of the ideas offered do you think would be most useful in raising the percentage of people who vote in U.S. elections?
- Do you think that compulsory voting would be a good idea for America? Why or why not?

Processing

Suggested time: 15 minutes

Have students complete the Processing activity in their notebooks, in which they develop suggestions for improving the U.S. electoral system.

Quicker Coverage

Eliminate Phase 2 The national nominating conventions are an engaging classroom experience for students but are not pedagogically essential to the Experiential Exercise. To eliminate Phase 2, have each presidential nominee choose a vice presidential running mate after the popular vote in Phase 1, and then move on to Phase 3.

Conduct Only Phase 3 If you have very limited time, eliminate Phases 1 and 2 by making these adaptations to the activity:

* Divide the class into Democrats and Republicans. Give the Democrats the profile for Cory Mathews, and give the Republicans the profile for Taylor Andrews. Have each group learn about their candidate.

* Assign one student to represent the presidential nominee from each party. Have that student choose a vice presidential running mate.

Deeper Coverage

Sequence the Electoral Process During Step 2 of the Preview, put students into 10 groups. Give each group a sheet of paper with one of the 10 steps in the electoral process written on it. Draw a line across the board, labeled 1 on the left side and 10 on the right side. Have each group tape their step along the line where they think it belongs. Then have students discuss the placements and suggest any changes they feel are appropriate.

Link to Previous Activities Consider linking this activity to those in Chapters 8 and 9.

* Have students remain in their candidate groups from Chapters 8 and 9. Have students who represented interest groups in Chapters 8 and 9 become the Democratic or Republican supporters, depending on whether they represented liberal or conservative interest groups.

* Students will require less time in Phase 1 to prepare for the national town hall meeting, as they will already be familiar with all the candidates.

* Because students will be far more committed to particular candidates, emphasize the importance of voting for the *best* candidate in the primaries and the popular and electoral votes.

Debate Current Issues Add additional current domestic issues to the debate between the candidates.

* During Phase 1, give students background information—such as origins of the issue, current proposals for dealing with the issue, and the stance of major

parties on the issue. Require candidate groups to determine where their candidate, based on his or her other beliefs and the beliefs of the political party, would stand on the issue and to prepare to debate that issue along with the other issues.

- Require audience members to develop appropriate questions for candidates about the new issue as they complete Student Handout 10D.

Assessment

Masters for the chapter assessment appear in the *Lesson Masters*.

Mastering the Content

1. B	2. B	3. D	4. D	5. D
6. D	7. B	8. D	9. A	10. D

Exploring the Essential Question

1. Jerry Brown had the second largest number of votes at the Democratic National Convention. Patrick Buchanan had the second largest number of votes at the Republican National Convention.

2. Most Republicans supported the incumbent, George H. W. Bush, who was eligible for reelection. For the Democrats, there was no such single obvious presidential candidate as the primary season began.

3. Most states give all their electoral votes to the one candidate with the largest popular vote. As a result, candidates who win less than a plurality of popular votes receive no Electoral College votes.

4. If most of the people who voted for Ross Perot in 1992 had instead voted for George H. W. Bush, he might have defeated Bill Clinton. Perot may have drawn enough votes away from Bush to cause him to lose the election.

English Language Learners

Outline the Electoral Process Complete the Preview as a class by writing each step from the Preview, with a one-sentence description, on a separate sheet of paper. Have a class discussion about the sequence in which the events occur, and then tape the sheets to the wall in order. As events in the electoral process are simulated in class, point out what part of the process is occurring.

Support Student Participation During the Experiential Exercise, consider these ideas:

- In Phase 1, assign English language learners to the role of audience members.
- In Phase 1, help students better understand the four issues to be debated by first discussing them as a class.
- Prior to holding the national town hall meeting, model how to ask questions.
- Instead of holding the national nominating conventions, explain the process and then have students create campaign posters for the candidates for the upcoming election. Put these on display during the campaigning in Phase 3.

Offer Examples For the Processing activity, give students two or three news or op-ed articles that suggest changes to the electoral process. Allow students to choose one of the articles and write a paragraph explaining why they agree or disagree that the proposed change would be beneficial to the electoral system.

Learners Reading and Writing Below Grade Level

Create Mixed-Ability Groups Divide learners reading and writing below grade level among mixed-ability candidate groups. This will support them in completing Student Handout 10B.

Prepare Students to Participate Review the Reading Notes for Section 10.3 as a class before Phase 1 and those for Section 10.4 before Phase 3. This will ensure that students have the background information necessary for the upcoming activities.

Learners with Special Education Needs

Simplify the Sequencing To mirror what students experience in the activity, have them order just these five steps: *run in primaries and caucuses, participate in televised debates, electoral vote, attend national convention,* and *popular vote.*

Provide Templates Consider providing templates for the Reading Notes for Sections 10.2, 10.3, and 10.6.

Support the Experiential Exercise Consider these suggestions:

- Post the steps from the simplified Preview (given above) in the appropriate order, and point out the steps that are being simulated during each part of the activity.
- For the national town hall meeting, place learners with special education needs in the audience group.

- Assign students in the audience during the national town hall meeting to become familiar with just one of the four issues. Have them write a question for each candidate about that issue only.

- In Phase 2, assign students the role of making posters in preparation for the national nominating conventions.

- In Phase 3, provide students with their own copies of the map of electoral votes.

Advanced Learners

Use Current Data After students are assigned states in Phase 3, have them research how their state's electoral votes have been cast in the two previous presidential elections. They might also research the political parties of that state's current governor, U.S. representatives, and U.S. senators. On their nameplates, they should use red or blue to label their state as *Strong Republican, Weak Republican, Battleground, Weak Democrat,* or *Strong Democrat.* Candidates should use this information when deciding which states to visit, and students should vote according to their state's history and the strength of the candidates' campaigns.

Internet Connections

For related research materials on elections, refer students to Online Resources at www.teachtci.com.

Multimedia

Please follow school and district guidelines about showing films in the classroom.

The Candidate **(PG)** In this 1972 film by Michael Ritchie, Robert Redford stars as a prominent California lawyer who tries to unseat an incumbent senator who appears to be unbeatable. As his campaign gains attention and support, however, he begins to feel pressured to sell out on his original platform. *The Candidate* provides a raw look at the nature of U.S. political campaigns.

So Goes the Nation This 2006 documentary, directed by Adam Del Deo and James D. Stern, follows volunteer organizers for the John Kerry and George W. Bush campaigns in Ohio during the 2004 election. It focuses on the differing strategies used in the two campaigns in this crucial state. Be advised that despite the fact that this is a documentary, there is strong language used in several places in the film. You might want to select a few scenes to show students, highlighting each candidate's strategy.

Journeys with George In this 2002 documentary, Congresswoman Nancy Pelosi's daughter Alexandra, a network television producer for NBC, follows George W. Bush on the campaign trail during his 2000 presidential election campaign. Filmed entirely by Alexandra's handheld camcorder, the film gives a personal look at the presidential candidate.

The West Wing, **Season 7, Episode 7, "The Debate"** In this episode, presidential hopefuls Matt Santos (D) and Arnold Vinick (R) participate in a debate. Though they agree at the beginning to forgo standard debate rules, this still provides an interesting look at the differences between the Democratic and Republican candidates. It also offers one perspective on what a debate might look like were the candidates not beholden to sound-bite-length time limits for their responses.

The War Room This behind-the-scenes documentary of Bill Clinton's 1992 campaign, by directors D. A. Pennebaker and Chris Hegedus, includes extensive coverage of the major players in the campaign, including George Stephanopoulos and James Carville.

Following are possible answers for each section of the Reading Notes.

Section 10.2

White males

1789: only white property-owning males could vote

1820s: elimination of property requirement for white males

African Americans

1870: Fifteenth Amendment grants universal male suffrage

1920: Nineteenth Amendment grants women the right to vote

1964: Twenty-fourth Amendment bans poll taxes, which had kept many poor blacks from voting

1965: Voting Rights Act bans literacy tests and places voter registration in some parts of the South under federal authority; black suffrage increases dramatically in the South

Women

1920: Nineteenth Amendment grants women the right to vote

American Indians

1924: Indian Citizenship Act extends suffrage to American Indians

18-year-olds

1971: Twenty-sixth Amendment lowers voting age to 18

1. Answers will vary.

2. To encourage more people to vote, Congress passed the National Voter Registration Act, or Motor Voter Act, in 1993. The law requires that states allow residents to register to vote while applying for a driver's license and that states provide voter registration forms at social service offices and by mail.

Section 10.3

Form an exploratory committee: Gather a group of advisers to evaluate chances for election. Test the waters to determine the level of public support.

Join the race: Self-announce candidacy or wait to be drafted into the race by supporters.

Set up a campaign organization: Recruit volunteers and hire well-paid campaign professionals. Set up staff, consisting of a campaign manager, public opinion pollster, media consultant, fundraising specialist, accountants, lawyers, and press secretary. Set up offices in every state.

Raise funds: Dial for dollars and hold fundraisers. Set up direct mailings and Web site for fundraising.

Develop a campaign strategy: Develop a strategy for the primaries and caucuses that includes tone, theme, and targeting.

Campaign: Take part in parades, dinners, and other local events to meet voters. Appear as a leader who is in touch with ordinary people. Develop direct-mail campaigns to ask voters for support. Use the media, including the Internet, to reach out to millions of voters.

Run in primaries and caucuses: Run in primaries and caucuses in every state.

Attend the national convention: Choose vice presidential running mate. Work with party leaders to develop party platform. Attend convention and help unite party.

Section 10.4

presidential election: held every four years on even-numbered years; president, vice president, one-third of the Senate and all House members, and some state and local officials are elected

midterm election: held in even-numbered years between presidential elections; one-third of the Senate and all House members, most state governors, and some state and local officials are elected

off-year election: held in odd-numbered years, primarily for the election of local officials

term limit: a set time period for how long an official can serve; the president is limited to two terms, and the terms for state officeholders are set by the state constitutions

stump speech: a candidate's standard speech, variations of which are given throughout the campaign

polling place: location where votes are cast within a voting precinct

battleground states: states where a vote is likely to be close; candidates often concentrate their efforts here

electoral vote: votes cast by electors who have pledged to support the winner of the popular vote in their states

Section 10.5

Answers will vary.

Section 10.6

Sketches should include the following information:

age: The older people are, the more likely they are to vote.

education: Having a college degree dramatically increases the likelihood that a person will vote.

income: Middle-class and wealthy individuals are much more likely to vote than those living in poverty.

party affiliation: Party affiliation is the most critical factor influencing which candidate a voter will choose; voters tend to vote for candidates from their party.

issues: Voters, especially swing voters, tend to look for candidates whose views on issues are similar to their own.

candidate characteristics: Voters are sometimes drawn to candidates based on their characteristics, such as their image, personality, trustworthiness, or experience.

UNIT **4**

The Legislative Branch

11 Lawmakers and Legislatures   123

What makes an effective legislator?

Social Studies Skill Builder

12 Congressional Lawmaking   135

How do laws really *get made?*

Experiential Exercise

Lawmakers and Legislatures

What makes an effective legislator?

Overview

Students learn about the structure and important functions of the legislative branch of government.

Preview Students "meet" a newly elected member of Congress and identify information from the representative's background that may help him be an effective legislator.

Activity In a Social Studies Skill Builder, students become staff members for a newly elected member of Congress and participate in an orientation for new congressional staff to learn important aspects of being an effective legislator.

Processing Students research their own national or state legislators and evaluate their effectiveness.

Objectives

In the course of reading this chapter and participating in the classroom activity, students will

- analyze the formal and informal qualifications for members of Congress.

- identify the enumerated powers of the legislative branch and the checks provided by the Constitution to that branch on the other branches of government.

- compare the organization of the legislative branch at the national and state levels.

- analyze graphs, tables, diagrams, and political cartoons to understand the responsibilities and challenges of being a legislator.

Materials

Government Alive! Power, Politics, and You

Placards 11A–11H (2 sets)

Transparencies 11A and 11B

CD Track 11

Lesson Masters

- Notebook Guide 11 (1 per student)

- Student Handouts 11A–11H (2 sets)

- Student Handout 11I (1 per student)

- Information Masters 11A and 11B (1 transparency of each)

Preview

Suggested time: 15 minutes

1 **Have students complete the Preview.** Explain that students will now "meet" a newly elected member of Congress and identify information from the representative's background that may help him be an effective legislator. Distribute *Notebook Guide 11*, project *Transparency 11A: Congressman Joe Schwarz*, and have students complete the Preview.

2 **Have students share their responses in pairs or with the class.**

3 **Explain the connection between the Preview and Chapter 11.** In the Preview, students identified things that might make someone an effective legislator. In the chapter, they will learn more about the powers and functions of the legislative branch and what a legislator needs to do and know to be effective.

Notebook Guide 11

Reading

Speaking of Politics Encourage students to use the following terms as they complete their Reading Notes for the chapter: *constituent, pork, standing committee, joint committee, conference committee, appropriations, joint resolution,* and *casework.*

1 **Introduce the Essential Question and have students read Section 11.1.** Ask, *Which qualities described in the section do you think are most important for an effective legislator? Why?*

2 **Have students complete the Reading Notes for Chapter 11.** Consider breaking up the reading using the first option under "Quicker Coverage."

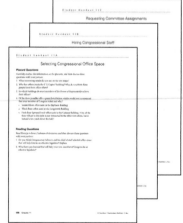

Transparency 11A

Social Studies Skill Builder

Suggested time: 90 minutes

1 **Prepare materials.** Make two copies of *Student Handouts 11A–11H: Orientation Materials.* Collate the handouts and *Placards 11A–11H: Orientation Materials* into two sets of eight folders (one set is shown below), for a total of 16 folders. Each folder will contain one two-page student handout and the corresponding placard or pair of placards.

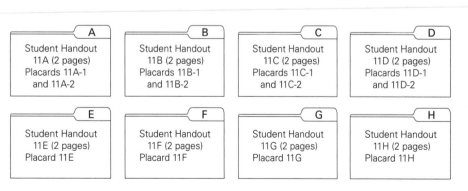

A	B	C	D
Student Handout 11A (2 pages) Placards 11A-1 and 11A-2	Student Handout 11B (2 pages) Placards 11B-1 and 11B-2	Student Handout 11C (2 pages) Placards 11C-1 and 11C-2	Student Handout 11D (2 pages) Placards 11D-1 and 11D-2

E	F	G	H
Student Handout 11E (2 pages) Placard 11E	Student Handout 11F (2 pages) Placard 11F	Student Handout 11G (2 pages) Placard 11G	Student Handout 11H (2 pages) Placard 11H

Student Handouts 11A–11H

2 **Place students in pairs and introduce the orientation for new congressional staff.** Explain that each pair will now take on the role of the staff members for a newly elected member of Congress. (**Note:** This new member is not Joe Schwarz. Students will learn about Congressman Schwarz later in the activity.) Students will participate in an orientation for new congressional staff that will prepare them to help their Congress member be an effective legislator. Play CD Track 11, "Congressional Staff Orientation Welcome," or read the script below.

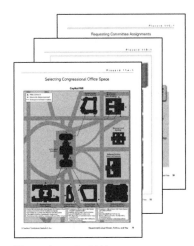

Placards 11A–11H

Hello, new congressional staff members, and welcome to Washington, D.C. My name is Katy, and I work for the Committee on House Administration. As you know, every two years a new group of representatives is elected to Congress. While many of these representatives are reelected, there are also some who are brand new, or what we call freshmen. Since you are the staff for these freshman members of Congress, it is vital that you learn about the inner workings of the legislative branch as quickly as possible.

To help you, the Committee on House Administration has developed a new congressional staff orientation. In this orientation, you will analyze various kinds of data and investigate the real-life case study of freshman congressman Joe Schwarz from Michigan. The goal of the orientation is to provide you with information that will help your member of Congress be an effective legislator. Good luck, and enjoy your next two years here on Capitol Hill.

3 **Distribute *Student Handout 11I: New Congressional Staff Orientation Notes.*** Have students tape the handout to a clean page in their notebooks.

4 **Conduct the activity.** Project *Information Master 11A: New Congressional Staff Orientation,* and have pairs follow the steps to complete their orientation notes. Begin the orientation by distributing one packet of orientation materials to each pair of students.

Student Handout 11I

5 **Debrief the activity.** For each of the eight topics, have students share what they learned that would help their new member of Congress to be an effective legislator.

6 **Wrap up the activity by creating a human spectrum.**

- On the board, draw a spectrum with ends labeled "Most Important" and "Least Important."

- Assign eight volunteers to Placards 11A to 11H. Ask them to come to the front of the room and, one at a time, hold up the placard and explain which topic it represents.

- Have pairs discuss which topic they think is the most important for being an effective legislator. Allow volunteers to go back to their partners to discuss the question, then return to the front of the room with their placards.

- Have someone begin the ordering by nominating which topic he or she thinks is most important and explaining the reasoning behind that choice. Encourage debate as students discuss each nominated topic and those holding the placards reposition themselves along the spectrum.

- For topics that are not considered very important, ask students to explain why they are *not* the most important.

Information Master 11A

7 Reveal what happened to Congressman Joe Schwarz in the 2006 election. Project *Transparency 11B: Republican Primary, Michigan Seventh District, 2006* and have students respond to the questions listed there. Then read or project a transparency of *Information Master 11B: Joe Schwarz and the 2006 Election*. Finally, ask,

- Overall, do you think Joe Schwarz was an effective legislator? Why or why not?

- Of all the topics you investigated, which contributed most to his being effective or ineffective?

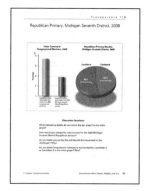

Transparency 11B

Power, Politics, and You

Have students read the "Power, Politics, and You" section of the chapter, and then facilitate a discussion by asking the questions below. Consider having students discuss the questions in pairs or small groups first.

- What reasons does Barack Obama give for why so many legislators are reelected?

- What are some of the challenges that Obama sees to being an effective legislator?

- Given these challenges, is being a legislator a job you might want? Why or why not?

Information Master 11B

Processing

Suggested time: 20 minutes

Have students complete the Processing activity in their notebooks. Students will use the Internet or other resources to create report cards evaluating the effectiveness of their own national or state legislator. Consider giving students the "Being a Public Watchdog" handout from the *Doing Democracy Toolkit* to help them with the assignment. Have students share their report cards in pairs or with the class.

Quicker Coverage

Divide and Conquer Have students work in groups of four, with each group dividing the reading so that each member is responsible for reading and completing the Reading Notes for one of Sections 11.2 to 11.5. Then have students take turns sharing the information from their assigned section and Reading Notes with their group.

Reduce the Workload Reduce the number of topics students investigate in the activity by creating packets for just Topics B, E, G, and H.

Deeper Coverage

Participate in a Fantasy Congress Have students closely follow the actions of key legislators and the progress of key legislation by participating in an online fantasy Congress league. Set up a league for your class at the Fantasy Congress Web site, www.fantasycongress.com, or have students join an existing league. As described on the site, Fantasy Congress "offers you the power to 'play politics.' As in other fantasy sports, you—the citizen—draft a team of real-life legislators from the U.S. Congress that will score points for your team based on their performance. Join and compete against a league of friends or form a league of your own! You earn points based on the productivity of your chosen members of Congress." There is no wagering involved and no cost to play.

Assessment

Masters for the chapter assessment appear in the *Lesson Masters*.

Mastering the Content

1. B	2. A	3. C	4. D	5. B
6. D	7. D	8. C	9. B	10. C

Exploring the Essential Question

1. Pork refers to publicly funded projects secured by legislators to benefit their home districts or states, such as federal projects and contracts.

2. Because of their work with constituents, incumbents have an advantage over challengers in elections. Service to constituents helps an incumbent build name recognition and attract grateful supporters and financial contributors. As a result, challengers most often lose against a well-liked incumbent.

3. Possible answer: My grandmother has applied for Social Security benefits but has not yet received any payments. A legislator might be more effective at solving that problem than I would be because he or she knows who to call and how to get action.

4. Possible answer:

   - well-organized: can set up a staff that handles issues efficiently and does not misplace information
   - persuasive speaker: is able to influence legislation that helps the district
   - empathic: understands constituent concerns and takes them seriously

English Language Learners

Model the Activity In the activity, work on the first four or five packets together as a class, as follows:

- Project a transparency of the placard.
- Have students discuss and share their answers to the questions from the corresponding student handout.
- Distribute the corresponding *Freshman Orientation* excerpt.
- Read the excerpt aloud or have students take turns reading paragraphs. Explain difficult words as they arise.
- Have students discuss and share their answers to the reading questions.
- Have pairs complete the corresponding section of the new congressional staff orientation notes. Ask volunteers to share their answers.

If appropriate, have pairs work independently on the last few packets. Depending on the class size, you may need to make more than two sets of the last few packets.

Learners Reading and Writing Below Grade Level

Focus Students' Reading Highlight key information on the *Freshman Orientation* excerpts.

Modify the Processing Have students create campaign posters for a real legislator who might run for reelection. Require that the posters reflect two ways in which the person has been an effective legislator.

Learners with Special Education Needs

Provide Context, Models, and Support Use any of these suggestions during the activity:

- Introduce Congressman Joe Schwarz, his district, and his state prior to the activity so that students have a clearer context for the information they will be reviewing.
- Lead students through the steps of analyzing information from one of the packets before assigning them to their pairs. If you do this with the whole class, project transparencies of the placards and student handouts and review them as a class.
- Have students complete Packets C, D, E, F, and G to get key information about the legislative role. As a class, review the information from the other packets.

Advanced Learners

Research and Read Have students read a biography of another member of Congress to find out what made or makes him or her an effective legislator and then write a review in which they identify three or more characteristics or qualities that made or makes that person an effective legislator. For each characteristic or quality, have students support their position with examples, excerpts, or quotations from the biography. Four appropriate biographies about former or current Congress members are listed below.

- Senator John McCain (R-AZ): Elizabeth Drew, *Citizen McCain*, New York: Simon and Schuster, 2002.

- Senator Barack Obama (D-IL): Barack Obama, *The Audacity of Hope: Thoughts on Reclaiming the American Dream*, New York: Crown, 2006.

- Representative Patricia Schroeder (D-CO): Pat Schroeder, *24 Years of House Work . . . and the Place Is Still a Mess: My Life in Politics*, Kansas City: Andrews McMeel, 1998.

- Representative Newt Gingrich (R-GA): Mel Steely, *The Gentleman from Georgia: The Biography of Newt Gingrich*, Macon, GA: Mercer University Press, 2000.

U.S. Supreme Court Cases: You Make the Call

Have students read the summary of Case 6, *City of Boerne v. Flores,* which relates to the powers of Congress, in the "U.S. Supreme Court Cases: You Make the Call" section of the Student Edition. Have volunteers share key facts from the case and the question before the Court. Then facilitate a Response Group–type discussion asking students to "make the call" on how the Court should decide the case and why. Finally, have students read the actual Supreme Court decision.

NATIONAL CONSTITUTION CENTER

National Constitution Center

For the Processing assignment, have students find out who their national and state legislators are and research information about them by visiting the National Constitution Center connections at www.teachtci.com.

Internet Connections

For related research materials on legislative power, refer students to Online Resources at www.teachtci.com.

Multimedia

Please follow school and district guidelines about showing films in the classroom.

Mr. Smith Goes to Washington In this 1939 Frank Capra movie, Jimmy Stewart plays the role of a freshman U.S. senator who learns the hard way what it takes to be an effective legislator.

The Power Game: How Washington Works In this PBS documentary, Emmy Award–winner Hedrick Smith of PBS's *Frontline* examines the Washington power structure to show the shadow government of staff, lobbyists, and the media, as well as of the elected government of Congress and the president.

Following are possible answers for the Reading Notes.

Section 11.2

1. *Formal qualifications:* resident of the state in which elected, U.S. citizen for at least 7 years (House) or 9 years (Senate), at least 25 (House) or 30 (Senate) years old

   Informal qualifications: college degree; background in business or law

2. Every 10 years, a national census is conducted, and results are used to calculate the distribution of House seats. States with a large increase in population may gain one or more seats; states whose population drops or stays the same may lose one or more seats. Each state is guaranteed at least one seat in the House.

3. Delegates seek to represent their districts by responding directly to the wishes and needs of their constituents. Trustees try to represent their districts by exercising their best judgment and assuming that their constituents trust them to do the right thing.

4. *Incumbents who have been reelected since 1945:* 90% in the House, 80% in the Senate

   Factors: Incumbents have higher name recognition. They have office resources—staff, mailing privileges, travel allowances—that help them keep in touch with voters. Incumbents generally receive more campaign contributions than do challengers. Incumbents can point to concrete achievements, such as federally funded projects, that they have won for their districts.

Section 11.3

1. Analogies will vary. Possible differences: The Senate allows for extended floor debate. The Senate has only 100 members. Senate terms are six years instead of two.

2. The House speaker has the most power in Congress. The speaker assigns bills to committees, appoints members to special committees and commissions, and decides what bills will be debated by the full House and when.

3. *Standing committees:* Permanent committees (such as the House Committee on Agriculture) that handle most legislative business and gather information from hearings and investigations.

   Subcommittees: Formed within standing communities, these do most of the work of reviewing proposed legislation.

   Select or special committees: Temporary committees formed to investigate a specific problem. They do not review legislation but may make recommendations to Congress.

   Joint committees: Permanent committees (such as the Joint Committee on the Library) made up of House and Senate members that are formed around issues of importance to both chambers.

   Conference committees: Temporary joint committees formed to iron out differences between two versions of a bill passed by the House and Senate.

4. Graphs will vary but should show an upward trend. Congressional staffers support Congress members, answer constituents' questions, write speeches, and draft bills.

5. Answers will vary.

Section 11.4

1. The enumerated powers of Congress are to levy and collect taxes, borrow money, regulate interstate and foreign commerce, coin money, and declare war. The Elastic Clause, which states that Congress can "make all Laws which shall be necessary and proper" for carrying out these powers, broadens Congress's power.

2. Diagrams should include these checks: oversight of executive agencies; Senate confirmation of key officials appointed by the president; impeachment and trial of federal officials, including the president; Senate ratification of treaties negotiated by the president; override of a president's veto of legislation; proposal of constitutional amendments.

3. Spoke diagrams should include these key powers:

   Enacting laws: New bills are first sent to a committee for review. If different versions of the same bill pass the House and Senate, a conference committee reconciles the differences. In 2005, only about 169 out of 7,000 bills actually became laws.

   Levying taxes: According to the Constitution, tax bills can originate only in the House. The federal government relies largely on income taxes for revenue.

   Power of the purse: Congress gets its power to spend from the Constitution. Congress must appropriate money for any federal project.

   Declaring war: Congress and the president share war-making powers, which sometimes causes tension between the two branches. U.S. soldiers have been sent into action abroad nearly 200 times, but Congress has declared war only five times. In 1973, Congress passed the War Powers Act, which requires Congress's approval for overseas troop deployments lasting longer than 90 days.

4. Cartoons will vary.

Section 11.5

1. *Similarities:* Both make laws. Both represent the voters in the state or district. Except for Nebraska, both are bicameral.

   Differences: State legislatures meet for less time each year than Congress does. In state legislatures, representatives average from one to nine staff members, as compared with 16 for members of the U.S. House and 40 for U.S. senators. Members of state legislatures are paid significantly less, averaging from $100 to $116,000 in 2007, depending on the state; members of Congress averaged $165,200 in 2007. In many states, legislators have term limits; there are no term limits for members of Congress.

2. Answers will vary.

Congressional Lawmaking

How do laws really get made?

Overview

Students learn about the process by which the legislative branch passes bills as well as about other factors that influence how laws really get made.

Preview Students propose bills that they would like to see passed into laws and create mental flowcharts of the steps they think are involved in making a law.

Activity In an Experiential Exercise, students create a mock House of Representatives to experience steps in the legislative process—including working in committee, party caucuses, and floor debates—as well as other factors that influence the lawmaking process.

Processing Students create mental flowcharts reflecting their increased understanding of the official process of how bills are passed through Congress as well as the other factors that influence that process.

Objectives

In the course of reading this chapter and participating in the classroom activity, students will

- explain the formal process of how a bill travels through Congress, including the role of committees.
- identify other factors that influence the lawmaking process.
- practice their persuasive speech and debate skills.

Materials

Government Alive! Power, Politics, and You

Lesson Masters

- Notebook Guide 12 (1 per student)
- Information Masters 12A–12C (1 transparency of each)
- Student Handouts 12A, 12B, and 12D (1 copy of each)
- Student Handout 12C (1 copy for every 3 students)
- Student Handout 12E (8 copies)

gavel (optional)

Preview

Suggested time: 15 minutes

1 **Have students complete the Preview.** Distribute *Notebook Guide 12.* Have students complete the Preview, in which they create mental flowcharts of the steps they think are involved in how a law gets made. Emphasize that in creating a mental flowchart, students should draw only from their own knowledge and not consult outside resources. Reinforce that there is no wrong answer; their mental flowcharts should simply reflect their current understanding of how a law is made.

2 **Have students share information from their mental flowcharts.** Ask, *How many of you have three or more steps in your flowcharts? Six or more? Nine or more? Anyone with 12 or more?* Have several volunteers share the step that they starred and why they think it is important. Ask the remaining students to raise their hands if they have the same step represented somewhere on their flowcharts, even if it is not starred.

3 **Explain the connection between the Preview and Chapter 12.** In this chapter, students will learn how laws are *really* made—not only the main steps in the legislative process of passing a bill, but also some of the unofficial and behind-the-scenes influences. By learning about all parts of the lawmaking process, students will better understand how laws are really made and will be better prepared to evaluate whether any changes or reforms are needed in the country's lawmaking process.

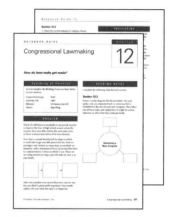

Notebook Guide 12

Reading

Speaking of Politics Encourage students to use the following terms as they complete their Reading Notes for the chapter: *congressional page, seniority rule, filibuster, cloture, hold, rider, Christmas tree bill,* and *logrolling.*

1 **Introduce the Essential Question and have students read Section 12.1.** Afterward, ask students to identify factors that could contribute to making the lawmaking process "complicated and untidy," as Representative Lee Hamilton put it.

2 **Have students complete the Reading Notes for Chapter 12.**

- Assign Section 12.2 *before* starting Phase 1 of the Experiential Exercise.
- Assign Section 12.3 *before* starting Phase 2 of the Experiential Exercise.
- Assign Section 12.4 *before* starting Phase 3 of the Experiential Exercise.
- *After* conducting the Experiential Exercise, assign Section 12.5.

Experiential Exercise

In this activity, students will create a mock House of Representatives to experience the steps of the legislative process. The activity has three phases: organizing the House, working in committee, and debating and voting.

Phase 1

Suggested time: 30 minutes

1   **Prepare materials.** Make a transparency of *Information Master 12A: Organizing the House* and a copy of *Student Handout 12A: House of Representative Role Cards* and *Student Handout 12B: Party Caucus Notes*. Cut out the role cards as follows:

- Prepare three or four more role cards for the political party with the majority in the *actual* U.S. House of Representatives than for the minority party. For example, for a class of 32 students, prepare 18 role cards for the majority party and 14 for the minority party. This will ensure that the majority party has at least one more member on each committee in Phase 2.

- If you do not need all 18 role cards for either party, eliminate the highest-numbered role cards for that party.

- If you have more than 33 students and need additional role cards, make more copies of Cards 16–18 for the Republican Party and of Cards 34–36 for the Democratic Party.

2   **Introduce Phase 1.** Explain that students will now take on the roles of newly elected or reelected members of the U.S. House of Representatives and will experience the process of trying to pass a series of bills. They will begin by learning their roles and helping to organize the new session of Congress.

3   **Distribute a role card to each student.**

- Explain that each student will play the role of the congressperson described on his or her role card, even if the party affiliation on the card does not reflect the student's own political beliefs.

- Students may be more engaged if they play roles that more closely mirror their own political orientation. Consider laying out the appropriate number of role cards per the instructions above and allowing students to select their own.

- Distribute Cards 1–3 for the Republicans and 19–21 for the Democrats to particularly motivated students, as these students will be the committee chairs.

- Ask students to create name tags by writing their name on their role cards.

- Have students carefully read the information on their cards.

4   **Project and have students follow the steps on Information Master 12A.** Here are some additional tips for conducting this phase of the activity:

- *Step 2:* Make sure each party selects strong students to act as party leaders. This will be important in Phase 3. Have party leaders add their titles to their name tags.

- *Step 3:* Distribute the party caucus notes to each party's leaders.

- *Step 4:* Provide a ceremonial gavel for the dean of the House, who will present it to the new speaker after he or she is sworn in.

- Collect the role cards at the end of each class period.

Information Master 12A

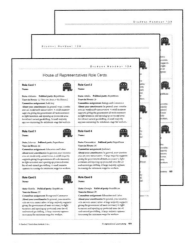

Student Handout 12A

Student Handout 12B

5 Debrief Phase 1. Ask,

- How did it feel to organize the House of Representatives?

- What role did party leaders play in this activity?

- In what ways was organizing the House similar to what really happens in Congress? In what ways was it different?

- What have you learned about how laws are really made?

Phase 2

Suggested time: 70 minutes

1 Prepare materials. Make a transparency of *Information Master 12B: Working in Committee*. Make enough copies for each committee member of the appropriate pages of *Student Handout 12C: H.R. Bills and Expert Testimony*. There is one bill and two pages of expert testimony for each committee. Consider having students review the bill and highlight key arguments in the corresponding expert testimony as homework. (**Note:** In place of the fictitious bills on Student Handout 12C, you may want to have students debate real bills that are currently under consideration in Congress or that were recently passed by the House or Senate. To find real bills, go to the National Constitution Center connections at www.teachtci.com. Be aware that using real bills negates the "About your constituents" section of the role cards. Review the bills with the class, and help students identify how conservative and liberal constituents would likely respond to each bill.)

Information Master 12B

2 Introduce Phase 2. Explain that students will now experience what it is like to work in committee.

3 Project and have students follow the steps on Information Master 12B. Here are some additional tips for conducting this phase of the activity:

- *Step 3:* Consider inviting parents, administrators, or students from other classes to read the expert testimony to each committee, as if they were witnesses.

- *Step 4:* Emphasize the importance of the committee chair's decision on the order of discussion of the amendments. There may not be time to debate every amendment.

- *Step 5:* Allow committees 10 to 15 minutes to discuss and vote on the amendments. Groups must then move to Step 6, even if they have not discussed all proposed amendments. Although this may cause frustration, it shows the power that the committee chair has in controlling debate.

Student Handout 12C

- *After Step 6:* If none of the bills makes it through committee, choose one or two to discuss on the House floor in Phase 3.

4 Debrief Phase 2. Ask,

- How did it feel to be a committee chair? What powers did you have to influence the work of your committee?

- How did it feel to be a member of the majority party? How were you able to influence or control the work in committee?

- How did it feel to be a member of the minority party? How were you able to influence the work in committee?

- What factors did you consider before making your final vote in committee? Which factor or factors influenced you the most and why?

- In what ways was working in committee similar to what really happens in Congress? In what ways was it different?

- What have you learned about how laws are really made?

Phase 3

Suggested time: 60–90 minutes

1 **Prepare materials.** Make a transparency of *Information Master 12C: Floor Debates and Final Voting.* Make enough copies of each of the bills and amendments that were approved by committee to pass out to House members. Have copies of expert testimony of each bill available for House members to review. Cut apart one copy of *Student Handout 12D: Floor Vote Strategy Notes* and 8 copies of *Student Handout 12E: Floor Vote Memos.*

2 **Introduce Phase 3.** Explain that students will now experience a full floor debate and vote.

3 **Project and have students follow the steps on Information Master 12C.** Here are some additional tips for conducting this phase of the activity:

- *Step 2:* Remind students that speaking during a floor debate is one of the best ways for members of Congress to impress voters back home. Encourage them to lobby hard with the committee chair or ranking minority member to get one of the limited speaking slots for the debate.

- *Step 4:* Distribute the strategy notes from Student Handout 12D to the appropriate House leaders. This will generate an atmosphere of intense, last-minute lobbying on the House floor.

  To increase the feeling of competing pressures placed on House members, distribute memos from Student Handout 12E to each House member. Give the "Memo from the President" to members of the current president's party. Randomly give two of the other two memos to each member of Congress.

- *Step 5:* If the voice vote appears close, prompt a student to raise his or her hand and request a standing vote.

4 **Debrief Phase 3.** Ask,

- How did it feel to participate in a floor debate and vote?

- What factors did you consider before making your final vote on the House floor? Which factors influenced you the most and why?

- In what ways was having a floor debate and vote similar to what really happens in Congress? In what ways was it different?

- What have you learned about how laws are really made?

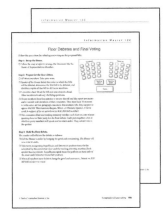

Information Master 12C

Student Handout 12D

Student Handout 12E

Power, Politics, and You

Have students read the "Power, Politics, and You" section of the chapter, and then facilitate a class discussion by asking the questions below. Consider having students discuss the questions in pairs or small groups first.

- What are some of the reasons Congressman DeLay offers for why partisanship should be praised?
- Why does Congressman Hamilton think compromise is key to the proper functioning of Congress?
- Reflect on what you have read in this chapter and what you experienced during the classroom activity. Which congressman's perspective do you think more accurately reflects how laws really get made? Why?
- Which congressman's perspective do you agree with and why?

Processing

Suggested time: 30 minutes

1 **Have students complete the Processing.** Students create new mental flow-charts demonstrating their increased understanding of the official process of how bills are passed through Congress, as well as the other factors that influence that process.

2 **Create several class flowcharts.** Have three or four students neatly copy their flowcharts onto the board. Allow others to come up in groups of three or four to add more details from their own flowcharts to one of those on the board. When all students have contributed to one of the class flowcharts, have students point out similarities and differences.

3 **Discuss the last Processing question.** Ask, *Do you think our system makes it too hard to get a bill passed into law? Why or why not?*

Quicker Coverage

Eliminate Working in Committee In Phase 1, assign the roles of speaker of the House, majority and minority leaders, and majority and minority whips to strong students. After the caucuses, skip directly to Phase 3 for the floor debate and vote.

Debate Just One Bill Complete Phases 1 and 2. In Phase 3, debate and vote on just one of the bills that passed out of committee.

Deeper Coverage

Simulate the Rules Committee An important step in the legislative process that is not simulated in the activity is the role of the House Rules Committee. Consider conducting the following steps between Phases 2 and 3 of the activity:

- The speaker selects five party members for the House Rules Committee, and the minority leader selects two members. The longest-serving member from the majority party serves as the committee chair.

- Majority party leaders meet with the Rules Committee members from their party; minority party leaders do the same with their members. Each group reviews the bills that were passed out of committee in Phase 2.

- Party leaders and committee members caucus for five minutes to determine whether their party supports or opposes each bill. If party leaders support a bill, they tell their committee members to vote to give the bill a closed rule, which allows for a floor debate and vote of the bill but does not allow amendments to be proposed. They also urge their members to vote to place that bill early in the order in which bills will be debated. If party leaders oppose a bill, they tell their committee members to vote to give the bill an open rule, which allows for a floor debate and vote and allows members to propose amendments to the bill. They also urge their members to vote to place the bill at the end of the order in which bills will be debated.

- After the party caucuses, have the Rules Committee chair reconvene the committee. The committee chair brings up the bills, one at a time. Each committee member has an opportunity to briefly explain why he or she thinks the bill should be given an open or closed rule. After each committee member has spoken, the committee votes on whether to give the bill an open or closed rule.

- The committee chair proposes whether the bill will be discussed first, second, or third. The committee votes on that proposal.

Use a Current Bill Have students research a current bill on a topic of interest to them. To search for current bills in Congress, have students do the following:

- Go to www.thomas.gov, and search bill text by keyword or phrase (for example, "stem cell").

- Click on a specific bill (such as H.R.3), and then click on "Bill Summary & Status."

- Click on "CRS Summary" to read a summary of the bill. Determine whether you support or oppose the bill and why.

- Return to the previous page and click on "Major Congressional Action" or "All Congressional Action" to determine where in the legislative process this bill currently is. If it has been assigned to a committee, find out which one.

- Have students draft and send a letter or e-mail to their representative or senator, urging him or her to support or oppose the bill they researched. The e-mail should include the bill number, a reference to where in the legislative process the bill currently is, a brief summary of the bill's main points, and one or more reasons why the bill should be supported or opposed.

Consider distributing the "Communicating with a Public Official" handout from the *Doing Democracy* toolkit and briefly reviewing with students how to use it to help structure their letters or e-mails. Students can write and send e-mails directly to their representatives or senators from the National Constitution Center Web site. Go to the National Constitution Center connections at www.teachtci.com.

Assessment

Masters for the chapter assessment appear in the *Lesson Masters*.

Mastering the Content

1. A	2. C	3. A	4. C	5. B
6. D	7. A	8. D	9. B	10. B

Exploring the Essential Question

1. The House Committee on Education and the Workforce held hearings on H.R.1.

2. It was conducted under a closed rule, allowing limited time for debate and limited amendments. This shows that the speaker wanted the bill to pass.

3. The history of H.R.1 supports the view that most of the work of Congress happens in committee. The bill spent far more time being studied, debated, marked up, and amended by the House Committee on Education and the Workforce, the House Rules Committee, and the conference committee than it did on the floor of the House or the Senate.

4. Possible answer: If my representative was on the House Committee on Education and the Workforce, I might have sent a letter expressing my views in March or April while it was studying the bill. Once the bill reached the House floor in early May, I might have contacted my representative. When the bill reached the Senate at the end of May, I might have communicated my concerns to my two senators.

English Language Learners

Annotate and Highlight Key Information Provide additional support during Phase 2 by providing annotations for key vocabulary in the H.R. bills and highlighting important facts and information in the expert testimony.

Encourage Peer Support Provide additional support during Phase 3 by allowing students to work in pairs or small groups as they review the proposed bills and expert testimony. Allow them to brainstorm possible reasons for supporting or opposing the bills before writing their one- or two-paragraph statements.

Learners Reading and Writing Below Grade Level

Consider having students read and complete the Reading Notes after each phase of the Experiential Exercise, rather than before. Their experiences in the classroom will help them to better understand the content in the reading.

Learners with Special Education Needs

Set Students Up for Success Provide additional support in Phase 1 by carefully choosing the role cards. Consider Republican Cards 16, 17, and 18 and Democratic Cards 34, 35, and 36. Speak to students individually to make sure they understand the perspective of the House member they are role-playing.

Meet in Small Groups Provide additional support in Phase 3 by doing the following:

- While the class prepares for the debate, meet in a small group with students to review the bill that will be debated. Have students read their role cards to determine whether their constituents would support or oppose the bill. Then review the expert testimony. Have students identify one or two arguments in the testimony either in support of the bill or in opposition. Finally, have them write a statement, using the appropriate arguments, to support or oppose the bill. Review their written statements to make sure the arguments support their position and are clearly stated. If appropriate, have each student practice reading his or her statement to the small group.

- While other students are doing last-minute lobbying before the floor vote, meet in a small group with these students and have them explain how they plan to vote on the bill and why. If appropriate, ask, *Would you change your vote if your party leader asked you to? If an individual or lobby group who had contributed several thousand dollars to your campaign asked you to? If a House member from the other party offered to support a bill that was important to you, if you changed your vote on this bill? If the president told you that it was important for the country for you to change your vote?*

Advanced Learners

Assign Subcommittee Work Once students have organized their committees in Phase 2, have them break into subcommittees of two or three students each. Have these smaller groups write a bill appropriate for their full committee to discuss and debate. Allow students to create these subcommittees. Explain that they can include members from both parties. Provide groups with copies of Student Hand-out 12C as examples of bills and expert testimony. This option will likely add two or three class periods to the activity. Student-generated bills should have a short title that clearly describes the purpose of the bill, be 150 words or fewer, be clearly written and easy to understand, and include the names of the main authors. Each subcommittee can also be required to research and write one or two pages of expert testimony, summarizing the main arguments, pro and con, on the proposed piece of legislation.

National Constitution Center

Instead of using the bills provided in this activity, have students debate real bills that are currently under consideration in Congress or that were recently passed by the House or Senate. To find real bills, visit the National Constitution Center connections at www.teachtci.com.

Internet Connections

For related research materials on making laws and public policy, refer students to Online Resources at www.teachtci.com.

Multimedia

Please follow school and district guidelines about showing films in the classroom.

West Wing, **Season 1, Episode 8, "Enemies"** A crucial banking bill is at risk when political rivals of environmentally sensitive President Jed Bartlet attach a land-use rider to it that would allow strip mining in some of the Montana wilderness.

West Wing, **Season 2, Episode 11, "The Leadership Breakfast"** As a bipartisan friendship breakfast with members of Congress nears, President Jed Bartlet's staff debate the merits of a patient's bill of rights and a minimum wage increase.

West Wing, **Season 6, Episode 17, "A Good Day"** Congressman Matthew Santos masterminds a plot to pass the president's stem cell bill while the Republicans are not looking.

Legally Blonde 2: Red, White, and Blonde **(PG-13)** This movie takes an issue and moves it through all the stages of policymaking. There are connections to agenda setting, committees, chairpersons, hearings, lobbying, building support for a bill, discharge petitions, and forming relationships with other Congress members and constituents.

Mr. Smith Goes to Washington Although this movie is from 1939, it includes excellent scenes explaining how a bill becomes a law and depicting a filibuster.

Following are possible answers to the Reading Notes.

Section 12.2

Three important tasks of party caucuses: to select party leaders, to form party committees, and to nominate party members to serve on standing committees. Possible explanation: Party leaders can use committee assignments to gain a member's loyalty. Members who receive prestigious or requested committee assignments understand that they "owe" the party leaders. In the future, on key votes, party leaders can use that debt to pressure a member to vote a particular way.

Section 12.3

1. If the current Congress is controlled by Democrats, Congressperson W would most likely be selected as chair. If it is controlled by Republicans, Congressperson X would most likely be selected. This is because committee chairs are always from the majority party, and the seniority rule usually gives the chair to the longest-serving member of the House (though the seniority rule is not as rigid as it once was).

2. Flowcharts could include the following steps:

   Hearings: Collect information from bill's sponsors, public officials, lobbyists, private citizens, and possibly celebrities. Subcommittee chairs control selection and scheduling of witnesses. Subcommittee chairs can move hearings along quickly or stretch them out, depending on whether they favor a bill.

   Markup: Members debate proposed amendments to bill and vote. Amendments must be passed by a majority of a quorum (one-third of the subcommittee). Members must sometimes choose between addressing the demands of their districts or states and gaining widespread support.

   Report: Subcommittee members vote on whether to report the bill to the full committee. The full committee can accept the bill, amend it further, or hold more hearings. The full committee votes on whether to report the bill to the House or Senate floor.

3. I would likely ask the committee to give this bill a closed rule. A closed rule allows for few or no amendments. Because I support the bill, I do not want to allow the opportunity for amendments to it.

Section 12.4

1. Similarities:

   - The majority party controls the agenda.
   - The speaker of the House and the Senate majority leader both have power of recognition during floor debate.
   - Both houses use voice votes, standing votes, and roll-call votes.

   Differences:

   - Debate in the House is restricted, often as little as one hour. Rules of the Senate include unlimited debate.
   - Passing a bill in the House requires a simple majority. Practically speaking, to do so in the Senate requires 60 votes, because a senator can filibuster a bill. It takes three-fifths of the Senate (60 votes) to end a filibuster.
   - House rules demand that amendments be related to the bill. In the Senate, riders that have nothing to do with the original bill can be attached to it.

2. Constituents, interest groups, party leaders, and colleagues; answers will vary.

Section 12.5

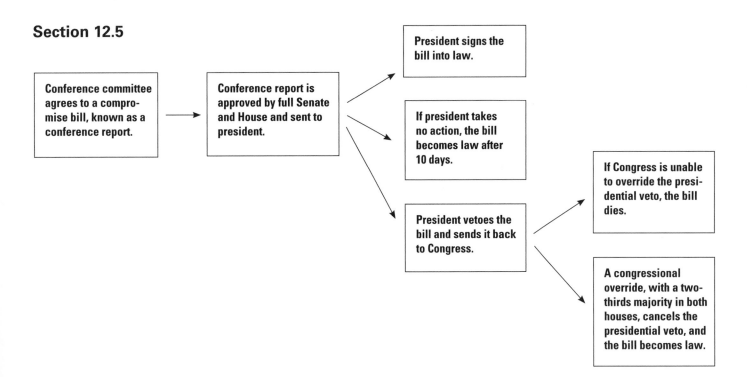

Conference committee agrees to a compromise bill, known as a conference report. → Conference report is approved by full Senate and House and sent to president.

President signs the bill into law.

If president takes no action, the bill becomes law after 10 days.

President vetoes the bill and sends it back to Congress.

If Congress is unable to override the presidential veto, the bill dies.

A congressional override, with a two-thirds majority in both houses, cancels the presidential veto, and the bill becomes law.

UNIT **5**

The Executive Branch

13 Chief Executives and Bureaucracies   151
*What qualities do modern presidents need
to fulfill their many roles?*

Problem Solving Groupwork

14 The Federal Budget   163
*Does the federal government budget and spend
your tax dollars wisely?*

Social Studies Skill Builder

Chief Executives and Bureaucracies

What qualities do modern presidents need to fulfill their many roles?

Overview

Students identify various roles that modern presidents fulfill and examine the structure and functions of the executive branch.

Preview Students examine a daily diary of a recent president to identify presidential roles and duties.

Activity In a Problem Solving Groupwork activity, students create interactive exhibits on a day in the life of a modern president for four presidential libraries and museums.

Processing Students write and conduct an opinion survey to evaluate the current president's job performance.

Objectives

In the course of reading this chapter and participating in the classroom activity, students will

- compare the formal and informal qualifications of national, state, and local chief executives.
- identify the responsibilities and roles of the modern president and the ways in which presidential power has increased over time.
- explain the organization and functions of the executive branch.
- describe the role and impact of government bureaucracies.
- evaluate the current president based on performance in various presidential roles.

Materials

*Government Alive!
Power, Politics, and You*

Placards 13A–13D (2 sets)

CD Tracks 12–16

Lesson Masters

- Notebook Guide 13 (1 per student)
- Information Master 13 (1 transparency)
- Student Handouts 13A–13D (2 copies of each)
- Student Handout 13E (8 copies)
- Student Handout 13F (1 per student)

8 large envelopes

Preview

Suggested time: 15 minutes

1 **Have students complete Preview 13.** Distribute *Notebook Guide 13* and project *Information Master 13: Appointments in a Modern President's Daily Diary.* Students will examine the daily diary to determine some of the roles and duties this president had to perform. Tell students that they are viewing just a small selection of appointments from this president on this day. The actual daily diary includes some 80 entries and runs six pages.

2 **Have students share their responses in pairs or with the class.** Then ask them to guess whose daily diary this is. Reveal that this is President Jimmy Carter's diary for April 24, 1980, the day he learned that an attempt to rescue American hostages held at the U.S. embassy in Iran had failed. (**Note:** You can obtain a full digital copy of this document from the Jimmy Carter Library and Museum Web site. Under the "Documents and Photographs" menu, select "President's Daily Diary, 1977–1981.")

3 **Explain the connection between the Preview and Chapter 13.** Tell students that a modern president has many roles and responsibilities, just as they saw in President Carter's daily diary. Two examples are his role as chief of state, which the president performed when accepting diplomatic credentials from various ambassadors, and as commander in chief, as when he met with the chairman of the Joint Chiefs of Staff. The president is also the chief executive—the head of the executive branch. In this chapter, students will learn more about these roles and responsibilities and about the organization and function of the executive branch.

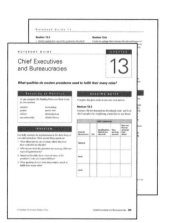

Notebook Guide 13

Information Master 13

Reading

Speaking of Politics Encourage students to use the following terms as they complete their Reading Notes for the chapter: *reprieve, pardon, cabinet, executive order, bureaucracy, pocket veto, administration,* and *whistle-blower.*

1 **Introduce the Essential Question and have students read Section 13.1.** Then ask,

 • What was typical about President Ford's day on April 28, 1975? What event occurred that was not typical?

 • What roles and responsibilities did the president perform on this day?

 • What qualities do you think modern presidents must have to fulfill their many roles?

2 **Have students complete the Reading Notes for Chapter 13.** Assign Sections 13.2 to 13.4 *before* conducting the Problem Solving Groupwork activity. *After* conducting the activity, assign Sections 13.5 and 13.6.

Problem Solving Groupwork

Suggested time: 90–120 minutes

1 **Prepare materials.** Create two sets of materials for each president. Place each set in a large envelope labeled with the president's name. Note that each handout is several pages long.

- Franklin Roosevelt: *Student Handout 13A* and *Placards 13A-1* and *13A-2*
- Lyndon Johnson: *Student Handout 13B* and *Placards 13B-1* and *13B-2*
- Richard Nixon: *Student Handout 13C* and *Placards 13C-1* and *13C-2*
- George H. W. Bush: *Student Handout 13D* and *Placards 13D-1* and *13D-2*

During the activity (see Step 7), groups will need to be able to play their audio clips at the same time. If available technology does not permit this, have groups use the written transcripts of the audio clips on the handouts instead.

Student Handouts 13A–13D

2 **Introduce the activity.** Tell students they will now work in groups to create an interactive exhibit on the day in the life of a modern president for a presidential library and museum. Each group will be assigned one president— Franklin Roosevelt, Lyndon Johnson, Richard Nixon, or George H. W. Bush— and will learn about a specific day when that president had to deal with an important crisis or event. They will design exhibits using artifacts—documents, audio clips, photographs, and objects—highlighting the various roles the president assumed on that day. Then they will serve as museum docents while visitors tour their exhibit to guess which roles the president performed on this day.

3 **Divide the class into eight groups and discuss the exhibits.** Assign two groups of students to each of the four presidents: Roosevelt, Johnson, Nixon, and Bush. Give each group a copy of *Student Handout 13E: Creating an Exhibit for a Presidential Library and Museum,* and review the directions for creating the interactive exhibits. Then give each group the appropriate envelope—containing a day-in-the-life overview, a daily diary, two documents, a transcript of an audio clip, and two photographs—and inventory the contents as a class.

Placards 13A-1 to 13D-2

4 **Monitor groups as they create their exhibits.** As groups complete Step 1 on Student Handout 13E, give each student a copy of *Student Handout 13F: Touring Exhibits in Presidential Libraries and Museums.* Allow groups adequate time—at least one full class period—to create their exhibits and rehearse their tours. If possible, provide access to CD Tracks 13–16 so groups can incorporate the audio clips into their exhibits.

5 **Arrange the room for the exhibit tours.** Clear the furniture to create four exhibit areas in the corners of the classroom. Assign a different presidential group to each corner, and give them a few minutes to set up their exhibits. The other four groups will play the role of visitors.

Student Handouts 13E and 13F

6 **Introduce the exhibit tours.** Play CD Track 12, "Hail to the Chief," as you welcome visitors to the opening of special interactive exhibits in four presidential libraries and museums. Explain that visitors will tour the exhibits to learn about the roles and responsibilities of the modern president by examining a day in the life of Presidents Franklin Roosevelt, Lyndon Johnson,

Richard Nixon, and George H. W. Bush. They will examine a variety of artifacts that are related to each president's day. They will connect these artifacts to specific times on the president's daily diary and then discuss how the artifacts illustrate one or more of the president's many roles.

7 **Conduct the exhibit tours.**

- Assign each group of visitors to one of the four exhibits.

- Allow several minutes for groups to tour the exhibits and interact with the museum docents and artifacts.

- Have groups rotate to the remaining three exhibits. Play CD Track 12 each time to cue groups to move to the next exhibit.

8 **Have docents and visitors switch roles and repeat Steps 5–7.**

9 **Debrief the activity by holding a class discussion.** Ask,

- What interesting things did you learn about the job of the modern president?

- In what ways did each president demonstrate his roles and responsibilities?

- What qualities do modern presidents need to fulfill their many roles? Give specific examples from the exhibits you have visited to support your answer.

Power, Politics, and You

1 **Poll the class.** As you ask these questions, record the results on the board:

- How many of you think you could be president?

- How many of you would want to be president?

- Of those who do not want to be president, what are your reasons?

2 **Have students read the "Power, Politics, and You" section of the chapter.**

3 **Facilitate a class discussion.** Ask the questions below. Consider having students discuss the questions in pairs or small groups first.

- How do the survey results compare to our classroom poll?

- Do you agree with the survey results? Why or why not?

- What kind of person do you think should be elected president?

Processing

Suggested time: 30 minutes

Have students complete the Processing activity, in which they create and conduct an opinion survey to evaluate the current president's job performance. Consider providing additional support by distributing the "Creating and Conducting an Opinion Survey" handout from the *Doing Democracy* toolkit and briefly reviewing with students how to use it. (**Note:** In an election year, you might have students instead create and conduct an opinion survey on the strength of the presidential candidates for each of the eight presidential roles or write and submit a letter to the editor supporting one or more candidates. Provide additional support by distributing the "Writing a Letter to the Editor" handout from the *Doing Democracy* toolkit.)

Quicker Coverage

Have Groups Visit Fewer Exhibits Pair groups assigned to different presidents, and have the two groups tour each other's exhibits.

Eliminate the Exhibits Instead of having groups create and tour exhibits, have students complete Student Handout 13F using the exhibit materials. Give each group the materials for one president. After students have completed their notes for that president, have groups exchange materials.

Deeper Coverage

Add Primary Sources to the Exhibits Have groups expand their exhibits with additional documents, photographs, audio recordings, and video clips. Text and visual resources can be accessed online at presidential library and museum sites. Audio and video resources can be downloaded from the American Presidency Project and the Presidential Timeline of the Twentieth Century sites.

Invite Guests to Tour the Exhibits Have all eight groups set up their museum exhibits in a large space such as a cafeteria, library, or hallway, and invite other classes, teachers, parents, or administrators to tour the exhibits. Ahead of time, have the class create a handout that briefly describes each of the eight presidential roles and post the handout next to the daily diary in each exhibit.

Assessment

Masters for the chapter assessment appear in the *Lesson Masters*.

Mastering the Content

1. D	2. D	3. A	4. A	5. B
6. D	7. C	8. A	9. B	10. A

Exploring the Essential Question

Possible answers:

1. commander in chief, get written opinions from department heads, grant reprieves and pardons, make treaties with advice and consent of Senate, appoint ambassadors and judges with advice and consent of Senate, recommend measures, call Congress into session, receive ambassadors, execute laws, commission officers

2. The Take Care Clause gives the president the power to enforce the laws and carry out acts of Congress. It is similar to the Necessary and Proper Clause in that it provides the president with the flexibility needed to deal with changing needs and circumstances.

3. The president has the power to command the armed forces, appoint and receive ambassadors, and negotiate treaties. Congress has the power to declare war. The Senate has the power to approve appointments of ambassadors and to ratify treaties. This division of powers gives the executive branch primary

responsibility for conducting foreign policy, but it must have the support, advice, and consent of Congress.

4. Being a good judge of character would help a president make wise appointments as well as grant reprieves and pardons wisely. The ability to see all sides of an issue would help a president negotiate treaties.

English Language Learners

Conduct an Alternative Preview Introduce the chapter by asking students to discuss the many roles they would have to play if they were the teacher for the day, such as rule enforcer and lesson planner. Then explain that the president also has multiple roles. Do the Preview assignment, but focus on the first two questions. As a class, connect student responses to the eight roles of the modern president. Give students a handout or post the roles around the classroom to serve as a resource.

Practice Exhibit Tours with Visitors Give students an opportunity to practice their exhibit tours by assigning the group with the same president to visit their exhibit first. Before groups move to the next exhibit, have the students discuss their tours and offer suggestions.

Learners Reading and Writing Below Grade Level

Annotate Student Handouts Review the primary source documents for each president (Student Handouts 13A–13D) ahead of time. Provide vocabulary support by writing synonyms for difficult words on the handouts.

Highlight Key Sections Reduce the amount of reading required for each primary source document by highlighting key phrases or sections on Student Handouts 13A–13D.

Learners with Special Education Needs

Simplify the Preview Use these prompts for the Preview assignment in place of those given:

1. Identify four activities the president participated in on this day.

2. Identify two people he met with during the day.

3. Name two qualities a president would need to do his job well.

Also consider highlighting key entries on the daily diary to reduce the amount of information students must examine.

Supply Templates for the Reading Notes Provide blank copies of the appropriate graphic organizers for the Reading Notes. Have students tape their completed notes into their notebooks.

Have Students Share a Role Create groups of five to allow two students to share a role. Alternatively, review the responsibilities of the roles with students ahead of time and have them select a role in which they feel most comfortable.

Use Prepared Questions Provide students with two or three questions for the Processing assignment as a model for creating their opinion polls.

Advanced Learners

Research the Federal Bureaucracy Have students work in pairs to learn about one office or agency in the executive office of the president, the cabinet, and the independent agencies. Have pairs describe the goals and responsibilities of each, name its head administrator, and list one specific action it has taken in the past year.

Evaluate the Importance of Presidential Roles Ask students to place the eight presidential roles on a spectrum from "Least Important Today" to "Most Important Today" and then write an essay explaining their evaluation, with specific examples.

Advise the President on Legislation Have students visit the Citizen Action Center at the National Constitution Center connections at www.teachtci.com to learn about a current piece of legislation and then write an e-mail or letter to the president with a recommendation to sign or veto the bill.

U.S. Supreme Court Cases: You Make the Call

Have students read the summary of Case 7, *Gonzales v. Oregon,* which relates to the powers of the executive branch, in the "U.S. Supreme Court Cases: You Make the Call" section of the Student Edition. For each case, have volunteers share key facts from the case and the question before the Court. Then facilitate a Response Group–type discussion asking students to "make the call" on how the Court should decide the case and why. Finally, have students read the actual Supreme Court decision.

National Constitution Center

To visit the Citizen Action Center to learn about current legislation, go to the National Constitution Center connections at www.teachtci.com.

Internet Connections

For related research materials on the executive branch and the modern presidency, refer students to Online Resources at www.teachtci.com.

Multimedia

Please follow school and district guidelines for showing films in the classroom.

The American President This 10-hour PBS series from 2000 examines the presidency from its earliest days under George Washington through the 20th century. The documentary profiles 41 of the nation's chief executives, ending with Bill Clinton. Each hour is organized thematically and features several presidents. For example, Episode 9, "Expanding Power," explores the presidencies of Andrew Jackson, Grover Cleveland, Theodore Roosevelt, and Richard Nixon.

The American President (PG-13) This 1995 romantic comedy, directed by Rob Reiner, follows the experiences of widowed president Andrew Shepherd with a government lobbyist. Viewers have ample opportunity to see Shepherd as he performs the roles of the modern president, such as acting as commander in chief and chief citizen after a bombing of U.S. military personnel overseas. The film also raises issues about what Americans want in their president, as the president faces a vocal campaign challenger.

Following are possible answers to each section of the Reading Notes.

Section 13.2

Chief Executives				
Level of Government	**Title**	**Qualifications (formal and informal)**	**How are they elected?**	**How can they be removed from office?**
National	President	• native-born citizen • at least 35 years old • have lived in U.S. for at least 14 years • cannot serve more than 2 terms • most are well-educated and have political experience • until 2007, have been white and male	Electoral College	A majority of the House votes to impeach, then two-thirds of the Senate must find the president guilty of wrongdoing.
State	Governor	• less stringent than for president • vary by state • some women and minorities have served as governors	a plurality or a majority of the vote; varies by state	Many states have recall procedures.
Local	Mayor	• less stringent than for president • vary by town or city • most towns or cities only require the mayor to be a legal adult • more women and minorities have been chief executives at local level than other levels	a plurality or a majority of the vote; varies by state	Many towns and cities have recall procedures.

Section 13.3

1. Descriptions will vary.

2. During the 1800s, most presidents acted mainly as "chief clerks." Other than carrying out the will of Congress, they assumed little authority beyond those powers granted them by the Constitution. When Franklin D. Roosevelt became president during the Great Depression, he transformed the role of president. He presented bills to Congress and got them passed and won passage of groundbreaking programs like Social Security and unemployment insurance. He continued to expand the presidential powers during World War II. The modern president is often viewed as the most powerful national leader in the world.

Section 13.4

1. Illustrations will vary.

   Chief executive: presides over federal bureaucracy; appoints some 2,000 federal officials; issues executive orders

   Chief of state: acts as ceremonial leader of government; represents United States at official functions at home and abroad; promotes national spirit

   Commander in chief: acts as head of armed forces; is responsible for operations of the U.S. military and security of the nation; can commit troops to action without a formal declaration of war

   Chief diplomat: oversees U.S. foreign policy; talks with foreign leaders; negotiates treaties

   Chief policymaker: sets policy agenda for Congress in the State of the Union address; proposes legislation; can call Congress into special session; can veto bills passed by Congress

   Chief manager of the economy: works with Congress to write the federal budget; works with Congress to set tax policy; appoints members of the Federal Reserve Board

   Chief of party: is the leader of his or her political party; works to ensure that the party does well in congressional elections; typically rewards loyal party members with political favors or appointments

   Chief citizen: embodies American ideals; serves the nation by acting in its best interests; informs, inspires, and comforts American people in times of crisis

2. The president can check the power of the legislative branch by approving or vetoing legislation passed by Congress or by invoking executive privilege. The president can check the power of the judicial branch by nominating judges to the Supreme Court and other federal courts.

Section 13.5

White House Staff: Presidents depend on the White House staff to provide them with guidance and advice. The chief of staff controls who gets to talk to the president. The president's personal lawyer, press secretary, and speechwriters are also part of the White House staff.

Executive Office of the President: The EOP provides support staff to the president. The agencies that make up the EOP perform a variety of specialized tasks for the president. The largest, the Office of Management and Budget, helps the president prepare an annual budget proposal to Congress. Other key agencies include the Council of Economic Advisers and the National Security Council. Presidents can add new agencies to the EOP to carry out their administration's goals.

Executive Departments: These carry out the work of the government in broad areas of public policy, such as agriculture, commerce, and labor. Today there are 15 executive departments, including the Justice Department, the Treasury Department, and the Department of Homeland Security. All 15 department heads are members of the president's cabinet.

Independent Agencies: These many agencies—such as NASA, the CIA, and the Federal Communications Commission—help implement federal policy. Though they still answer to the president, they are considered independent because they do not fall within executive departments.

Section 13.6

Analogies and drawings will vary.

The Federal Budget

Does the federal government budget and spend your tax dollars wisely?

Overview

Students examine the federal budget process and the roles and responsibilities of the president and federal bureaucracy in that process.

Preview Students analyze a set of typical monthly living expenses to understand the challenges of making budget decisions.

Activity In a Social Studies Skill Builder, students assume the role of budget experts in the Office of Management and Budget to recommend a spending plan for the president to submit to Congress.

Processing Students write a response evaluating how well the federal government budgets and spends their tax dollars.

Objectives

In the course of reading this chapter and participating in the classroom activity, students will

- examine the historical and modern roles of the president and the executive branch in the budget process.

- analyze the responsibilities and budgets of selected departments in the federal bureaucracy.

- compare the ways in which the national, state, and local governments raise revenue and make expenditures.

- defend a position on how well the federal government budgets and spends tax dollars.

Materials

Government Alive! Power, Politics, and You

Placards 14A–14F (2 sets)

Lesson Masters

- Notebook Guide 14 (1 per student)
- Station Materials 14A–14F (2 copies of each)
- Student Handout 14A (1 for every 2 students)
- Student Handout 14B (1 per student)

12 calculators

Preview

Suggested time: 15 minutes

1 **Have students complete Preview 14.** Distribute *Notebook Guide 14.* Students will analyze the typical monthly living expenses for a young adult to understand the challenges of making budget decisions.

2 **Have students share their responses in pairs or with the class.**

3 **Explain the connection between the Preview and Chapter 14.** Tell students that a personal budget has many similarities to a federal government budget. Just as they have necessary expenses, there are programs that the government is required by law to fund. If the government spends more money than it has, it faces options similar to those faced by students. All of these options come with consequences and difficult decisions. In this chapter, students will examine the federal budget process, including raising revenue and spending money, and the roles of the president and the executive branch in that process.

Notebook Guide 14

Reading

Speaking of Politics Encourage students to use the following terms as they complete their Reading Notes for the chapter: *balanced budget, budget surplus, federal deficit, national debt, progressive tax, regressive tax, entitlement,* and *earmarks.*

1 **Introduce the Essential Question and have students read Section 14.1.** Then ask,

• What were some of the proposals President Bush outlined in his 2007 State of the Union address?

• What was Bush's proposal for the federal budget?

• Why would the president be speaking about the federal budget?

2 **Have students complete the Reading Notes for Chapter 14.** Assign Sections 14.2 to 14.4 *before* conducting the Social Studies Skill Builder. *After* conducting the activity, assign Section 14.5.

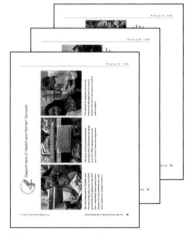

Placards 14A–14F

Social Studies Skill Builder

Suggested time: 60 minutes

1 **Arrange the classroom.** On one side of the room, create six stations to represent departments and agencies in the executive branch. Put two or three desks together to create each station. Place one of *Placards 14A–14F: Department and Agency Overviews,* a corresponding copy of *Station Materials 14A–14F: Department and Agency Budget Proposals* (each consists of two pages), and a calculator at every station. Set up six identical stations on the opposite side of the room.

2 **Place students in pairs and introduce the activity.** Explain that pairs will take on the role of budget experts in the Office of Management and Budget in the executive branch. Their job is to analyze budget proposals from six departments

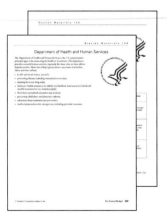

Station Materials 14A–14F

and agencies and create a spending plan for the president to submit to Congress. (**Note:** The proposed budgets in this activity are hypothetical but realistic.)

3 **Have pairs learn about the president's administrative priorities.** Distribute *Student Handout 14A: Executive Memorandum* to each pair. Tell students that this memo contains important information from the president about their job as budget experts. After pairs read the memo, ask,

- How many budgets did each department or agency propose? What are the differences between these three budgets?

- What are the president's administrative priorities? What role might these priorities play in creating your spending plan?

- What is the president's main concern for the spending plan to be submitted to Congress? (**Note:** Some students might find the following conversion helpful: $1,935,000 million = $1,935 billion = $1.935 trillion.)

Student Handout 14A

Tell pairs to use this memo as they develop their spending plans. Remind students that they will be asked to write a brief report to the president explaining how well their spending plan addresses the president's priorities and concerns.

4 **Review the steps for creating spending plans.** Distribute *Student Handout 14B: Proposed Spending Plan* to each student, and review the directions. Tell students they can visit the stations as many times as they would like, but they must visit each of the six stations at least once. Consider completing the notes for one station as a class.

5 **Have pairs create their spending plans.** Assign half of the pairs to the stations on one side of the room and the other half to the stations on the other side. Have students complete their spending plans in pencil in case they want to make changes. Remind students to compute their overall budgets after they have visited all six stations at least once. Allow enough time for students to revise their spending plans.

Student Handout 14B

6 **Have pairs write a report to the president.** Have pairs write a brief report explaining three reasons why their spending plan is the one to submit to Congress.

7 **Ask volunteers to share their spending plans and reports with the class.**

8 **Debrief the activity.** Ask,

- What challenges did you face in creating your spending plan?

- What are the benefits and consequences of cutting expenditures to balance the budget? What other options does the federal government have?

- In what ways is this similar to the actual budget process? In what ways is it different?

- Do you feel that the federal government budgets and spends your tax dollars wisely?

Power, Politics, and You

1 **Have students read the "Power, Politics, and You" section of the chapter.**

2 **Facilitate a class discussion.** Ask the questions below. Consider having students discuss the questions in pairs or small groups first.

   • Do you think there is a Social Security crisis? Why or why not?

   • Though the authors disagree about the future of Social Security, what do they both agree needs to be done?

   • What proposals have been offered to change Social Security? Which of these do you think provides the most promise?

   • What role should the federal government play in budgeting and spending tax dollars for *your* Social Security?

Processing

Suggested time: 20 minutes

Have students complete the Processing assignment, in which they evaluate how well the federal government budgets and spends their tax dollars. Have them share their responses in pairs or with the class.

Quicker Coverage

Break Up the Reading Divide students into groups of four, and assign each group one of Sections 14.2 to 14.4. Tell groups they will become experts on their assigned section and present the answers to those Reading Notes to the class. After students read and complete their Reading Notes, have each group transfer their answers onto a transparency. Tell groups to determine who will explain each component of the notes and to find interesting examples, facts, and statistics from the text to incorporate into their presentations.

Reduce the Number of Stations Limit the number of stations for the activity to four—Department of Health and Human Services, Department of State and Other International Programs, Department of the Treasury, and Social Security Administration—with a balanced budget figure of $1,887,000 million.

Deeper Coverage

Examine the Actual Federal Budget Have students examine the actual federal budget proposed by the president for the upcoming fiscal year at the Office of Management and Budget Web site. Have students read the president's message and view several of the budgets for individual departments and agencies. Then ask them to discuss these questions: *What are the president's priorities for this fiscal year's budget? In what ways do the budgets for individual departments and agencies reflect these priorities? Do you think the president's proposal budgets and spends your tax dollars wisely?*

Procedures

Learn About the Balanced Budget Amendment Have students research the proposals for a balanced budget amendment. Ask them to outline the arguments in favor of and against adding a balanced budget amendment to the Constitution and write an editorial supporting the side with which they most agree.

Assessment

Masters for the chapter assessment appear in the *Lesson Masters*.

Mastering the Content

1. C	2. A	3. D	4. B	5. A
6. D	7. B	8. B	9. B	10. D

Exploring the Essential Question

1. Mandatory spending is spending that is required by law and is not subject to the annual budget process. It consists mainly of spending on entitlements plus interest on the national debt.

2. Because annual spending exceeded revenue in 2006, the government had to borrow money to cover its expenses. Borrowing accounted for 9.3% of the revenue raised that year. The money borrowed was added to the national debt. Because loans to the government must be paid back with interest, borrowing has an effect on the federal budget. The spending graph shows that 8.3% of spending in fiscal year 2006 was used to pay interest on the national debt. This was money that otherwise could have been used to fund government services.

3. The budget could be balanced by raising more revenue, cutting discretionary spending, or doing some of each. Accept any answer that describes one or more of these options.

The Federal Budget   **167**

English Language Learners

Support the Activity Try these suggestions:

- Read Student Handout 14A as a class while students highlight or annotate the president's priorities. Then ask pairs to rewrite each priority in their own words.

- Review the placards ahead of time. Identify the main responsibility of each agency, and post these next to the placards at the stations.

- Give pairs an opportunity to practice presenting their spending plans to one another before they share them with the class.

Learners Reading and Writing Below Grade Level

Define Vocabulary for the Placards Identify any terms or phrases students may find challenging in the placards, and post their definitions next to the placards at each station.

Conduct a Prewriting Activity Before pairs write their memos to the president, conduct a prewriting activity. Have students work individually to list all the ways they think their spending plan has met the president's goals and then share those ideas with their partners.

Learners with Special Education Needs

Give Templates for the Reading Notes Provide copies of the appropriate graphic organizers for the Section 14.4 Reading Notes: a spoke diagram for Question 1 and a T-chart for Question 3. Have students tape their completed work into their notebooks.

Support the Spending Plans Consider these ideas:

- Total the mandatory expenditures and record the sum on Student Handout 14B.
- Color code each discretionary expenditure on the Station Materials. Highlight each expenditure in one color, and then highlight the corresponding box on Student Handout 14B in the same color.
- Ask a teacher's aide or parent to serve as an accountant. Instead of having pairs calculate their own totals, have them visit the accountant to receive their totals.

Advanced Learners

Offer Budget Options In addition to balancing the budget in the activity, offer pairs the choice of creating a budget with a modest deficit (by spending more than $1,945,000 million) or surplus (by spending less than $1,930,000 million). Have pairs determine which approach they will use before they start the activity, and allow them to revise their strategy as they complete their spending plans. When debriefing the activity, ask students to reflect on their choice of strategies, the challenges they faced with each, and what strategy they finally used.

U.S. Supreme Court Cases: You Make the Call

Have students read the summary of Case 8, *Clinton v. City of New York,* which relates to the president's budget-making powers, in the "U.S. Supreme Court Cases: You Make the Call" section of the Student Edition. For each case, have volunteers share key facts from the case and the question before the Court. Then facilitate a Response Group–type discussion asking students to "make the call" on how the Court should decide the case and why. Finally, have students read the actual Supreme Court decision.

Internet Connections

For related research materials on the federal budget, refer students to Online Resources at www.teachtci.com.

Multimedia

Please follow school and district guidelines for showing films in the classroom.

Dave (PG-13) This comedy from *Austin Powers* director Jay Roach relates the adventure of Dave Kovic, a small-town man who runs an employment agency and happens to look exactly like the president of the United States. In an unusual turn of events, Kovic is asked to fill in for the president. Consider showing students the scene in which Kovic meets with the cabinet to find funding for a project and asking them to reflect on whether the federal budget process is as easy as portrayed in the movie.

The West Wing, **Season 5, Episode 7, "Separation of Powers"** This episode follows the negotiations between the president's staff and congressional leaders about the upcoming fiscal year's federal budget. As each side tries to push its agenda, tensions grow to the point where the budget might not be approved in time.

The West Wing, **Season 5, Episode 8, "Shutdown"** This continues the story of the previous episode, in which the president and Congress cannot come to an agreement about the federal budget. To resolve the budget crisis, the president decides to shut down the government.

Following are possible answers to the Reading Notes.

Section 14.2

1. *1789–1921:* The legislative branch dominated the federal budget process. Proposals requesting the spending of federal funds originated in the House and were combined into a single spending bill. Once the House approved the bill, it went to the Senate. Usually, revenues and expenditures came out even, creating a balanced budget. The government typically raised taxes and borrowed money only in times of war.

   1921–1974: The executive branch gained more power to control the federal budget process. Faced with a huge war debt from World War I, Congress enacted the Budget and Accounting Act of 1921, which required the president to submit a proposed budget to Congress. This gave the executive branch more power to decide which agencies and programs received funding. Congress could override the president's recommendations, but it generally went along with the president's budget.

   1974–present: The legislative and executive branches have shared control of the federal budget process since 1974. In response to President Nixon's use of impoundment to object to congressional budget decisions, Congress enacted the Budget and Impoundment Control Act of 1974. The main change in the process was the creation of budget committees in the House and Senate to draft Congress's spending priorities.

2. When the Constitution was written, governments simply collected taxes and spent money as needed. When there was a shortfall, Congress raised taxes to bring in extra money. Passage of the Budget and Accounting Act of 1921 concentrated the budget-making process in the hands of the president. Over the years, many costly new programs led to deficit spending, because lawmakers did not want to raise taxes. This deficit spending led to a drastic increase in the national debt.

Section 14.3

Phase One: Budget requests are submitted to the Office of Management and Budget. The OMB reviews requests and prepares a budget proposal. President submits budget proposal to Congress.

Phase Two: House and Senate budget committees hold hearings and prepare budget resolutions. Budget resolutions from both houses go to conference committee to be reconciled. The full House and Senate approve the final version.

Phase Three: House and Senate Appropriations Committees work on appropriation bills. Congress works out differences between House and Senate appropriation bills. The 13 appropriations bills are sent to the president for approval.

Phase Four: The fiscal year usually begins in October. If the president and Congress cannot agree on appropriations bills, the president signs a continuing resolution to keep the government running. The president and Congress work out differences. If not, a budget crisis could result in a government shutdown.

Section 14.4

1. Diagrams should include the following information:

   Individual income tax: tax paid on an individual's or married couple's annual income

   Social insurance tax: tax deducted from a paycheck to fund Social Security and Medicare, among other programs

   Corporate income tax: tax paid by businesses on their profits

   Excise tax: tax paid on the sale of goods and services

2. A progressive tax is one in which the tax burden falls more heavily on the wealthy than on the poor, such as individual and corporate income taxes. A regressive tax is one in which the burden falls more heavily on poor than wealthy taxpayers, as a percentage of their income. Excise taxes are one example.

3. Diagrams should include the following information:

   Mandatory spending
   - Majority of federal spending.
   - Can be altered only by special legislation.
   - Includes interest on the national debt.
   - Includes entitlements, programs through which individuals receive benefits based on their age, income, or some other criteria; food stamps and Social Security pensions are two examples.

   Discretionary spending
   - Can be raised or lowered as Congress sees fit.
   - The largest chunk goes to defense.
   - The remaining money funds the many services provided by federal agencies.
   - There is frequent complaining about earmarks, or funds set aside for specific projects.

Section 14.5

State and local budgets
- Many state constitutions require a balanced budget.
- Some state constitutions restrict certain types of taxes.
- Citizens play a larger role in tax policy.
- Large share of budgets go to services for young people and their families.

Both
- Make budget decisions each year.
- Chief executive prepares budget, which is approved by legislature.
- Raise revenue through taxes.

Federal budget
- Face fewer limitations than do state and local governments.
- Can borrow money to fill gaps between spending and funding.
- Government makes tax policy.
- Bulk of spending goes to entitlements for the elderly and national defense.

UNIT **6**

Judicial Branch

15 Courts, Judges, and the Law 175
How is the U.S. judicial system organized to ensure justice?

Response Group

16 The Criminal Justice System 187
From doing the crime to doing time: How just is our criminal justice system?

Writing for Understanding

Courts, Judges, and the Law

How is the U.S. judicial system organized to ensure justice?

Overview

Students learn about the organization and function of the judicial system.

Preview Students analyze and discuss a montage of images that relate to the court system.

Activity In a Response Group activity, students analyze primary source documents, images, and a recording, as well as data and diagrams, to determine which type of court each set of information represents.

Processing Students write a comment for a blog in which they evaluate how effectively the U.S. judicial system ensures justice for all.

Objectives

In the course of reading this chapter and participating in the classroom activity, students will

- identify the organization and jurisdiction of federal, state, and local courts and the interrelationships among the various types of courts.

- determine the role that judges play in the court system and describe the ways they are appointed.

- explain the structure, function, and process of the Supreme Court.

- state and support an opinion on how effective the U.S. judicial system is in ensuring justice for all.

Materials

Government Alive! Power, Politics, and You

Transparency 15

CD Track 17

Lesson Masters

- Notebook Guide 15 (1 per student)
- Notebook Handout 15 (1 per student)
- Student Handout 15A (15 copies, cut into cards)
- Student Handouts 15B–15H (1 of each for every 3 students)
- Student Handouts 15C–15H (1 transparency of each)
- Information Master 15 (1 transparency)

Preview

Suggested time: 10 minutes

1　**Have students complete Preview 15.** Project *Transparency 15: Preview 15 Images* and distribute *Notebook Guide 15*. Students will analyze a montage of photographs that relate to the judicial system. Once they are finished, discuss their answers to the questions.

2　**Explain the connection between the Preview and Chapter 15.** Tell students that they will now learn how the judicial branch is structured and how it functions and become acquainted with the various courts that make up this system. After examining the judicial system closely, they will consider whether it is structured in a way that ensures justice or whether there are weaknesses in the system that might hinder the pursuit of justice.

Transparency 15

Reading

Speaking of Politics　Encourage students to use the following terms as they complete their Reading Notes for the chapter: *criminal law, civil law, burden of proof, defendant, prosecution, plaintiff, writ of certiorari,* and *legal brief.* (**Note:** Consider reviewing the term *jurisdiction,* which is defined in Chapter 4, because students will need to understand its meaning as they progress through the activity.)

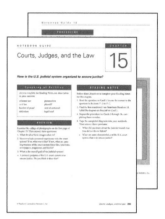

Notebook Guide 15

1　**Prepare materials.** Cut the cards from *Student Handout 15A: Judicial Branch Card Sort,* one set for every pair of students.

2　**Place students in pairs.**

3　**Introduce the Essential Question and have students read Sections 15.1 and 15.2.** Afterward, ask:

- What does the Constitution specifically say about the structure of the nation's judiciary?

- How did Congress decide to structure the rest of the nation's judicial system?

- What are the two kinds of legal conflicts, and how do they differ?

- How does the process by which jury members are selected help ensure justice in a courtroom?

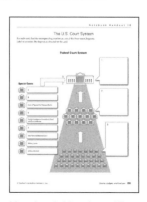

Student Handout 15A

4　**Have students read Sections 15.3 to 15.7 and complete the Reading Notes** *before* **conducting the Response Group activity.**

- Give each student a copy of *Notebook Handout 15: The U.S. Court System.*

- Distribute one set of cards from Student Handout 15A to each pair.

- Review the Reading Notes directions on Notebook Guide 15. Emphasize that students will use Notebook Handout 15 as a reference during the activity, so they should make their annotations clear and thorough.

- Model for students how to complete the Reading Notes by completing Card 1 as a class.

Note: The Reading Notes can be assigned for homework by giving each student his or her own uncut copy of Student Handout 15A to take home.

Notebook Handout 15

5 Debrief the reading. Ask,

- What did you learn about the judicial branch that you did not know before?

- What are some characteristics of the U.S. court system that help ensure justice? *(use of a jury to review and decide cases; a system of appeals that allows cases to be reviewed; courts with limited jurisdiction that specialize in certain cases; a dual court system)*

Response Group

Suggested time: 75 minutes

1 Place students in groups of three.

2 Introduce the activity. Explain that students will now use their knowledge of courts to further explore the judicial branch. They will work in their groups to examine sets of information relating to six types of courts and identify as many clues as possible in the information that will help them to decide which court each set of materials represents. They will then consult their Reading Notes and Chapter 15 to decide which court is represented and explain what the information reveals about the judicial branch as a whole.

3 Review the directions for the activity. Distribute *Student Handout 15B: Analyzing Court Materials* to each group and review the directions with the class. (**Note:** Consider projecting a transparency of the handout as you discuss how to complete this activity.)

4 Have students examine the information for the first court. Project *Student Handout 15C: Court 1* and distribute a copy to each group. Review the types of clues students should be looking for as they examine the information. Remind them that in trying to determine which court is represented, they should reference not only Notebook Handout 15 but also Chapter 15 in their books. Point out where they should write the name of the court and the evidence on their matrices. Then have groups complete the matrix for Court 1.

5 Debrief the information for the first court. Project *Information Master 15: Guide to the Courts* and reveal the information for Court 1.

- Call on a member of one group to reveal which type of court they identified and the evidence that led to that decision.

- Ask whether other groups found additional clues that this group failed to identify.

- Discuss what students wrote regarding what this court reveals about the judicial system as a whole.

- Have teams compute their score for this round by assigning 1 point to each piece of correct evidence they found that other groups also identified, 2 points for any correct evidence they found that no other groups identified, and 2 points for a correctly identified court.

Student Handout 15B

Student Handout 15C

Information Master 15

6 **Repeat Steps 4 and 5 for the remaining courts.** Have students analyze the information for each of Courts 2 through 6 by projecting and distributing *Student Handouts 15D–15H* as appropriate. When projecting Student Handout 15E and analyzing Court 3, play CD Track 17, "Guantánamo Bay Tribunal Proceedings."

7 **Debrief the activity.** Have teams compute their overall scores for the activity. Then ask,

- Why do different courts play different roles in the judicial branch?

- What safeguards are built into the organization of the U.S. court system to ensure justice?

- Are those safeguards working to ensure justice? How do you know?

- How effective do you think the U.S. court system is in ensuring justice?

Student Handouts 15D–15H

Power, Politics, and You

Have students read the "Power, Politics, and You" section, and facilitate a class discussion by having them respond to the questions below. Consider having students discuss the questions in pairs or small groups first.

- What problem is being discussed in this article? What are some efforts being made to address that problem?

- How could the high percentage of jury duty no-shows affect the judicial system's attempts to ensure justice?

- What do you think might be a solution to this problem?

Processing

Suggested time: 20 minutes

1 **Have students complete Processing 15.** Students write a Web log, or blog, in which they state and support an opinion on how effectively the U.S. judicial system ensures justice for all. You might provide additional support by distributing the "Posting Opinions on the Internet" handout from the *Doing Democracy* toolkit and briefly reviewing with students how to use it.

2 **Have students share their blogs.** Have each student pass the comment they added to the blog to at least one other student who then reads it and writes an additional comment. Once students receive their own blog comments back, ask volunteers to share what they wrote with the class.

Quicker Coverage

Shorten the Reading Notes Rather than having students complete the card sort in the Reading section, give each student a copy of Guide to Reading Notes 15 and simply discuss the diagrams and information as a class. Or send an uncut copy of Student Handout 15A home with students and have them complete the Reading Notes as homework.

Abbreviate the Activity Reduce the number of courts that students must examine from six to just three or four. Consider choosing courts that students may be more familiar with, such as Courts 1, 2, and 6.

Deeper Coverage

Suggest a Courtroom Visit After students have read Chapter 15 and completed the activity, assign them the task of visiting an actual courtroom to watch the proceedings. You might offer additional support by distributing copies of the "Attending a Public Meeting" handout from the *Doing Democracy* toolkit and briefly reviewing with students how to use it. When students observe the courtroom, have them note answers to the following questions to later report to the class:

- Who were the people involved in the case, and what were their roles?
- What was the topic of the case?
- Was the case decided? If so, what was the decision and how was it determined?
- What are your overall impressions of the courtroom and the judicial process?
- Did the trial process that you observed seem to achieve justice for all of the people involved?

Assessment

Masters for the chapter assessment appear in the *Lesson Masters*.

Mastering the Content

1. D	2. A	3. A	4. C	5. A
6. C	7. C	8. B	9. C	10. B

Exploring the Essential Question

1. Three levels. The Common Pleas Court of Cuyahoga County was the court of original jurisdiction.

2. Three levels. The Supreme Court was the court of last resort.

3. The Cuyahoga Country prosecutors had to prove their case beyond a reasonable doubt in both criminal trials of Sheppard. Sam Reese Sheppard had to prove his case by showing a preponderance of evidence at his civil trial.

4. Opinions will differ. Students may argue that the judicial system did not ensure justice because of the media circus surrounding Sheppard's first trial and the many appeals he had to make to get his conviction overturned. Or they may argue that the system did ensure justice by giving Sheppard a number of opportunities to argue his case before different levels of appellate courts and then, finally, a second trial.

English Language Learners

Use Video As an alternative Preview assignment, show students a short clip of a court proceeding and have them take notes on what they observe in the scene. Then discuss as a group the goal of the judicial system.

Support the Activity Consider these ideas:

- Model how to analyze Student Handout 15C so students will understand what is expected. Have volunteers point out various clues that might indicate which court is involved, such as that the case is heard by three judges, that the case is an appeal, and that one party in the case is the United States. Indicate where to write the information in the matrix.

- For each court students analyze, provide a list of three courts to narrow down the options.

- Once groups have analyzed each set of materials, complete the "What This Information Reveals About the Judicial System" column of the matrix as a class to ensure comprehension.

Learners Reading and Writing Below Grade Level

Support the Reading Notes Photocopy Section 15.2 to 15.7 and highlight key passages where students will look for information. Before conducting the Response Group activity, make sure students' Reading Notes contain correct and complete information.

Read the Blog Together During the Processing activity, read the blog postings as a class and have students highlight and discuss key points before formulating their responses.

Learners with Special Education Needs

Simplify the Preview Ask students to describe what they see in each image in the Preview. Then have them identify additional facts they know about the justice system.

Modify the Reading Notes Consider these suggestions:

- Require pairs to work on one question at a time and then check with the teacher for accuracy before proceeding to the next card.

- Provide a copy of Notebook Handout 15 with some of the items already completed and have students complete the remaining cards. Or provide Notebook Handout 15 with some of the longer answers as cloze passages and have students fill in the blanks.

- Provide page and section numbers on each card to help students locate the answers more easily.

Support the Activity For the Response Group activity, consider these suggestions:

- Provide a "cheat sheet" handout in table format that lists the six types of courts and the key identifiers of each court.
- Provide a copy of Student Handouts 15B–15G with the key clues that will help students determine the type of court circled or highlighted.
- At the end of each court analysis, project the answers to allow students to correct their information.

Add Structure to the Processing Have students address the following questions after reading the student blogs:

- What is courtwatcher's opinion of the U.S. justice system?
- Why does gavel_pounder disagree with that opinion?
- Do you think the U.S. justice system is structured in a way that ensures justice? Why or why not?

Advanced Learners

Examine Actual Court Cases Have students examine a specific case, such as the Terry Shiavo case, that has traveled through the justice system and made it to the Supreme Court and analyze whether the court system facilitated justice. Instruct students to create a timeline that details how the case moved through the system, including at least five dates related to the case with descriptions of what happened on each date and why it was significant. Then have them write a paragraph in response to this question: *To what extent does this case illustrate how the U.S. court system ensures justice?*

U.S. Supreme Court Cases: You Make the Call

Have students read the summary of Case 9, *Adarand Constructors v. Peña,* which relates to the issue of affirmative action, in the "U.S. Supreme Court Cases: You Make the Call" section of the Student Edition. Have volunteers share key facts from the case and the question before the Court. Then facilitate a Response Group–type discussion asking students to "make the call" on how the Court should decide the case and why. Finally, have students read the actual Supreme Court decision.

NATIONAL CONSTITUTION CENTER

National Constitution Center

For the Processing assignment, have students visit the National Constitution Center connections at www.teachtci.com to research current news stories that involve cases moving through the U.S. court system. Students should cite these cases in their blog comments as examples of justice being ensured or violated in the court system.

Internet Connections

For related research materials on the judicial branch, refer students to Online Resources at www.teachtci.com.

Multimedia

Please follow school and district guidelines for showing films in the classroom.

The Supreme Court This four-part PBS series from 2007 walks viewers through the history of the Supreme Court and shows how Court decisions have affected both society and history. The series highlights monumental cases—such as *Marbury v. Madison, Dred Scott v. Sandford,* and *Roe v. Wade*—and the issues that surround them.

The West Wing, **Season 1, Episode 9, "The Short List"** After a Supreme Court justice announces retirement, President Bartlet has the opportunity to affect the makeup of the Court by nominating a favorite judge. When he learns that the candidate's ideology conflicts with his own, he must decide whether to opt for another judge.

Following are possible answers to the Reading Notes.

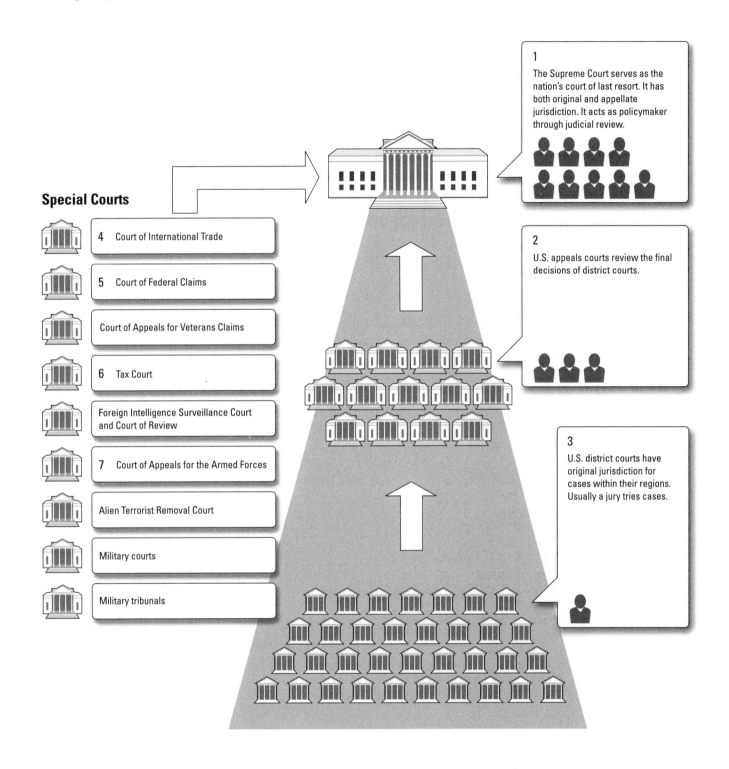

Special Courts

4   Court of International Trade

5   Court of Federal Claims

    Court of Appeals for Veterans Claims

6   Tax Court

    Foreign Intelligence Surveillance Court and Court of Review

7   Court of Appeals for the Armed Forces

    Alien Terrorist Removal Court

    Military courts

    Military tribunals

1
The Supreme Court serves as the nation's court of last resort. It has both original and appellate jurisdiction. It acts as policymaker through judicial review.

2
U.S. appeals courts review the final decisions of district courts.

3
U.S. district courts have original jurisdiction for cases within their regions. Usually a jury tries cases.

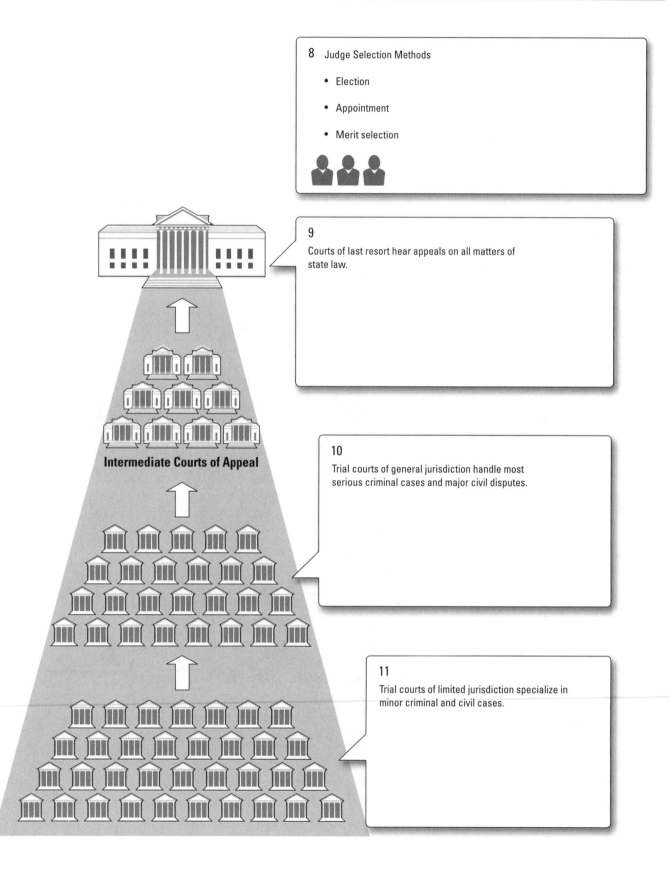

8 Judge Selection Methods

- Election

- Appointment

- Merit selection

9

Courts of last resort hear appeals on all matters of state law.

Intermediate Courts of Appeal

10

Trial courts of general jurisdiction handle most serious criminal cases and major civil disputes.

11

Trial courts of limited jurisdiction specialize in minor criminal and civil cases.

Federal Judge Selection Process

12

Senatorial courtesy allows senators to block nominations to federal courts in their home states.

13

Judges are nominated by <u>the president</u> and confirmed by <u>the Senate</u>.

Stages of a Supreme Court Case

14 A **writ of certiorari,** a document that the Supreme Court sends to a lower court ordering it to send up a complete record of a case, is granted.

Legal and amicus curiae briefs are filed.

Oral arguments are presented to the Court.

Justices meet in private conferences and decide to uphold or to overrule a previous decision.

15 Opinions are written.

- Majority opinions state the reasons for a Supreme Court decision.

- Dissenting opinions lay out the reasons for disagreeing with the majority.

- Concurring opinions lay out reasoning that differs from the majority opinion but reaches the same decision.

Schools of Thought About Judicial Review

16

Judicial activism asserts that the Court has both the right and the obligation to overturn bad precedents and promote socially desirable goals.

Judicial restraint holds that judicial review should be used sparingly by the Court and that elected officials should make policy decisions.

The Criminal Justice System

From doing the crime to doing time: How just is our criminal justice system?

Overview

Students examine the stages of the criminal justice system as well as the constitutional rights of those accused of a crime.

Preview Students reflect on a scenario in which class members are accused of a crime.

Activity In a Writing for Understanding activity, students review the criminal case of a death row inmate and write an amicus brief in support of or opposing his claim that his constitutional rights were denied.

Processing Students write a letter to the editor stating and defending a position on how just the U.S. criminal justice system is.

Objectives

In the course of reading this chapter and participating in the classroom activity, students will

- identify the constitutional rights of individuals in the criminal justice system.
- describe what happens during each stage of the criminal justice process.
- explain how an individual's due process rights uphold the principles of limited government and judicial review.
- analyze whether a defendant was afforded due process in the criminal justice system.

Materials

Government Alive! Power, Politics, and You

CD Tracks 18–21

Lesson Masters

- Notebook Guide 16 (1 per student)
- Student Handout 16 (1 copy per pair of students)
- Information Masters 16A and 16B (1 transparency of each)

Preview

Suggested time: 20 minutes

1 **Before class, prepare for the staged scenario.** Choose two students to assist you. Explain that you will accuse them of a fictitious crime and will ask them to leave the room. Tell them to look nervous as they walk out and to remain out of sight until you call on them to return.

2 **Conduct the staged scenario.** Assume a stern demeanor as students enter class. Dramatically tell the two students to gather their belongings and proceed directly to the principal's office. Then tell the remaining students that the principal has asked you to read the following statement aloud (replace *lockers* with *backpacks* or *cars* if more appropriate for your school):

In an effort to crack down on illegal activity, school officials conducted random searches this morning of student lockers. We were shocked and disappointed to find illegal substances in some of the lockers. All materials were confiscated and handed over to police officers. Any students involved will be taken into police custody. Please be reminded that possession of illegal substances on school property is considered a crime and will be prosecuted as such.

Pause for a few moments to allow students to react. Then ask whether students have any comments or questions about the announcement.

3 **Debrief the experience.** Explain that the scenario was staged and that school officials did not conduct locker searches. Invite the two students back into the classroom, and ask the class these questions:

- How did you feel when the students were sent out of the room and you heard the principal's statement?

- What rights, if any, should students have in such a scenario?

4 **Have students complete the Preview.** Distribute *Notebook Guide 16,* and have students list the rights that they believe a student accused of a crime should have. Ask volunteers to share their responses.

5 **Explain the connection between the Preview and Chapter 16.** Tell students that the Constitution guarantees certain rights to individuals accused of a crime. Explain that in this chapter they will examine the rights of the accused, as well as the stages of the criminal justice process, to evaluate how well the system promotes justice.

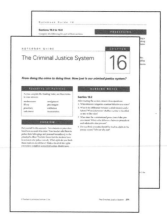

Notebook Guide 16

Reading

Speaking of Politics Encourage students to use the following terms as they complete their Reading Notes for the chapter: *misdemeanor, felony, grand jury, indictment, arraignment, plea bargain, restitution,* and *incarceration.*

1 **Introduce the Essential Question and have students read Section 16.1.**

2 **Have students complete the Reading Notes for Chapter 16.** Assign Section 16.2 *before* conducting the Writing for Understanding activity. Then have students read Sections 16.3 to 16.8 as indicated in the procedures that follow.

Writing for Understanding

Suggested time: 150 minutes

1 **Place students in pairs and introduce the activity.** Explain that pairs represent lawyer teams from the Criminal Bar Association, an organization that reviews criminal cases to ensure that the rights of the accused are upheld in the criminal justice system. Teams will examine three exhibits relating to the fictitious capital murder case of death row inmate Dwight Dexter and write a legal brief outlining whether they believe that Dexter was afforded his constitutional rights during the criminal justice process.

2 **Introduce the case.** Play CD Track 18, "The Murder of Floyd Babb." Then project and have students review *Information Master 16A: The Prosecution's Theory of Guilt*. Finally, ask, *What might implicate Dwight Dexter in the murder of Floyd Babb?*

3 **Have students read and complete the Reading Notes for Sections 16.3 and 16.4.**

4 **Have teams examine Exhibit A.** Play CD Track 19, "The Investigation into the Murder of Floyd Babb." Then distribute *Student Handout 16: Documents Relating to the Case of Dwight Dexter* and have teams examine the two documents in Exhibit A. As directed on Student Handout 16, have teams discuss the relevant questions related to the documents in Exhibit A and prepare a T-chart in their notebooks to begin collecting evidence about whether Dexter's rights were upheld in the criminal justice process.

5 **Lead a discussion about Exhibit A.** Ask the class, *Do you think the rights of Dwight Dexter were upheld in the criminal justice system? Why or why not?*

6 **Repeat the process for Exhibits B and C.**

- *Exhibit B:* Have students read and complete the Reading Notes for Sections 16.5 and 16.6. Then play CD Track 20, "The Trial of Dwight Dexter." Finally, have teams examine the two documents in Exhibit B, discuss the related questions, and add relevant information to their T-charts.

- *Exhibit C:* Have students read and complete the Reading Notes for Sections 16.7 and 16.8. Then play CD Track 21, "The Appeals Process of Dwight Dexter." Finally, have teams examine the two documents in Exhibit C, discuss the related questions, and add relevant information to their T-charts.

7 **Have students write amicus briefs.** Tell students that the Supreme Court has accepted the case and will consider whether Dwight Dexter's rights were upheld in the criminal justice system. Explain that teams will submit amicus briefs, documents that advise the Supreme Court on legal issues in a case. Project *Information Master 16B: Writing an Amicus Brief* and answer any questions. Then allow students adequate time to write their briefs.

8 **Reveal the Supreme Court decision and the current status of the case.** Explain to students that the case they have just examined was designed on the basis of an actual case decided by the U.S. Supreme Court. However, the names of the participants and their backgrounds have been changed, and

Information Master 16A

Student Handout 16

Information Master 16B

certain of the facts have been changed or embellished in order to highlight or introduce legal issues into the activity. Nothing in the hypothetical case presentation should be assumed to be an actual fact from the case, whose facts are fully set forth in the Supreme Court's opinon. Then read the following information aloud:

On February 24, 2004, the Supreme Court decided in favor of the petitioner, Delma Banks Jr. In a 7-2 decision, the Supreme Court overturned Banks' death sentence, concluding that he was denied due process. The Court remanded the case to the district court in Texas so that new evidence could be considered. At the time of publication of this book, Banks had not been afforded a retrial. He remained incarcerated at a federal prison in Livingston, Texas, where he was in solitary confinement 23 hours a day. He maintained his innocence.

9 **Debrief the activity.** Ask,

- Do you agree with the Supreme Court that Banks did not receive due process in the criminal justice system? Why or why not?

- Do you think that Banks deserves a retrial, even if he is guilty? Why or why not?

- Do you believe that justice was served in the Banks case? Why or why not?

- Based on this case and what you have learned in this chapter, how just do you think our criminal justice system is?

Power, Politics, and You

Have students read the "Power, Politics, and You" section of the chapter. Facilitate a class discussion by asking the questions below. Consider having students discuss the questions in small groups or pairs first.

- According to Howard Zehr, how does the view of crime and justice differ from the perspectives of retributive justice and restorative justice?

- How does restorative justice seek to empower victims? What are some examples?

- Do you think restorative justice promotes the notion of justice? Why or why not?

Processing

Suggested time: 20 minutes

Writing for Understanding activities generally fulfill the requirements of a Processing assignment. If you haven't conducted the classroom activity for this chapter, however, you may wish to assign this Processing activity, in which students write a letter to the editor reflecting on the Essential Question. Consider having students share their letters in pairs or with the class. You might provide additional support by distributing the "Writing a Letter to the Editor" handout from the *Doing Democracy* toolkit and briefly reviewing with students how to use it. You may also want to encourage students to send their letters to a local newspaper.

Quicker Coverage

Eliminate the Amicus Brief After students examine all three exhibits in the Dexter case, reveal the Supreme Court decision and debrief the activity.

Eliminate the Processing Assignment Instead, conclude the lesson after asking the debriefing questions.

Focus on Exhibit B Distribute only the Exhibit B documents from Student Handout 16. Provide a brief introduction to the case and have teams examine the two documents. Then adjust the writing assignment by having students do the following:

- Take a position on this question: *Were the rights of Dwight Dexter upheld during the jury selection and trial? Why or why not?*

- Present two arguments, one paragraph each, in support of the position statement.

- Reference one constitutional article or amendment that supports the position.

Deeper Coverage

Learn More About the Case Before students learn the outcome of *Banks v. Dretke,* have them learn more about the case by examining documents at Cornell Law School's references page for *Banks v. Dretke,* including briefs submitted on behalf of the petitioner and respondent, amicus briefs, and newspaper articles (found at supct.law.cornell.edu/supct/background/02-8286_ref.html). Then facilitate a class discussion by asking, *What additional facts about the case did you learn? What questions did the Supreme Court consider? How do you think the Court decided in this case? Why?* Alternatively, divide the class into groups and assign each group a different document. Then have each group present key information to the class.

Research the Case Status After revealing the outcome of *Banks v. Dretke,* have students conduct an online search to learn about the current status of the case. At the time of publication, the case had not yet been retried and Delma Banks Jr. remained incarcerated in a federal prison in Livingston, Texas.

Assessment

Masters for the chapter assessment appear in the Lesson Masters.

Mastering the Content

1. D	2. A	3. B	4. A	5. B
6. A	7. C	8. D	9. C	10. B

Exploring the Essential Question

1. Possible answer:
   Crime: none or the Fourth Amendment
   Investigation: Fourth and Fifth amendments
   Arrest: Fourth, Fifth, and Sixth amendments
   Pretrial: Fifth, Sixth, and Eighth amendments
   Trial: Fifth and Sixth amendments
   Sentencing and Appeals: Eighth Amendment
   Corrections: Eighth Amendment

2. During the initial appearance, defendants hear the charges against them and are reminded of their rights. The judge may set bail at this time. At the preliminary hearing, the prosecutor calls witnesses and the judge decides whether there is enough evidence to go to trial. At the arraignment, defendants enter a plea of guilty or not guilty. If guilty, the judge sets a sentencing date. If not guilty, the judge sets a trial date.

3. Answers will vary. Accept any discussion of how one of the listed rights contributes to making the criminal system more just.

English Language Learners

Activate Prior Knowledge After staging the Preview activity, provide additional support for the idea of "rights of the accused" by discussing what rights students believe they have and asking them to reflect on what rights these students in trouble might now have. List ideas on board, and ask students to order them from most to least important.

Identify Key Examples Assist students in locating examples where it is debatable whether Dexter's rights were upheld by highlighting these items on Student Handout 16:

- Exhibit A, Document 1: The paragraph for July 24, 1 A.M.
- Exhibit B, Document 1: All of the "Objections raised in 2001 by the defense" and all of the "Reasons the prosecution gave."
- Exhibit B, Document 2: The pretrial comments.
- Exhibit C, Document 2: The third and fourth paragraphs.

Support the Writing of the Amicus Brief Consider these ideas:

- Provide a handout that briefly summarizes the three key precedents.
- Hold a class discussion and take notes on ideas to include in the amicus brief.
- Have students focus on just one exhibit in the Dexter case.
- Provide students with a word bank of required terms to use in the amicus brief.

Learners Reading and Writing Below Grade Level

Condense the Writing Assignment For the amicus brief, eliminate the requirements for references to the Constitution and Supreme Court precedents. Instead, ask students to write a three-paragraph brief with an introduction, a body paragraph, and a conclusion.

Create an Outline As a writing adaptation to the amicus brief, have students compose an outline to include the following:

- a clear thesis statement in response to the question, *How well were the rights of the accused, Dwight Dexter, upheld in the criminal justice system?*
- a topic sentence for each paragraph
- two pieces of evidence—facts, examples, or quotations—from the activity or text that support the topic sentence

Learners with Special Education Needs

Support the Case Analysis Have students complete the following matrix while examining the documents in Student Handout 16. They can refer to the matrix when writing the amicus brief.

Document	Criminal Stage	Were Dexter's rights upheld in this stage? Why or why not?
Exhibit A, Document 1: Sheriff's notes	Investigation	
Exhibit A, Document 2: Booking report	Arrest	
Exhibit B, Document 1: Jury selection	Jury selection	
Exhibit B, Document 2: Trial	Trial	
Exhibit C, Document 1: Appeals process	Appeals process	
Exhibit C, Document 2: Supreme Court	Supreme Court hearing	

Advanced Learners

Summarize Court Opinions Have students read the Supreme Court's majority and dissenting opinions from *Banks v. Dretke* (2004), summarize each opinion, and explain which they most agree with and why. The opinions can be accessed online at the Supreme Court's Oyez Web site.

National Constitution Center

Have students visit the National Constitution Center connections at www.teachtci.com to examine the Fourth Amendment's Search and Seizure Clause in more depth by exploring the Interactive Constitution. For each part of the Fourth Amendment highlighted, have students read the accompanying explanations. Then discuss these questions: *Do you agree with the Supreme Court's interpretation of the Fourth Amendment in* Kyllo v. the United States *(2001)? In* Board of Education v. Earls *(2002)?*

Internet Connections

For related research materials on the criminal justice system, refer students to Online Resources at www.teachtci.com.

Multimedia

Please follow school and district guidelines for showing films in the classroom.

The Plea This 90-minute Frontline documentary, accessible online, discusses the pros and cons of the use of plea bargains in the criminal justice system. It highlights the stories of four individuals who, despite maintaining their innocence, pled guilty in exchange for reduced sentences. The individuals discuss the challenges they face as convicted felons and the implications of a system that relies on plea bargains to expedite cases. Consider showing clips of this documentary when discussing plea bargains.

Gideon's Trumpet This 1980 movie by Robert E. Collins and starring Henry Fonda chronicles the trial and appeals process of Clarence Earl Gideon, a poor Florida handyman who was arrested for petty theft in 1961. Unable to afford a lawyer, Gideon was sentenced to five years in prison. Gideon himself appealed the sentence to the Supreme Court, arguing that the Constitution guaranteed him the right to counsel at the state's expense. The Court agreed and in a landmark 1963 decision extended the right to counsel to all criminal defendants. You may want to show this film to highlight the stages in the criminal justice system and the Sixth Amendment's guarantee of counsel. If pressed for time, consider showing just the original trial, Gideon's appeal to the Supreme Court from prison, and the Supreme Court hearing.

12 Angry Men This 1957 film by Sidney Lumet focuses on the jury deliberations in the capital murder case of an 18-year-old Latino. Eleven jurors immediately vote guilty; the twelfth convinces them to reconsider. The movie brings to life the important role of juries in the U.S. judicial system, as well as the right of the accused to be proven guilty beyond a reasonable doubt. Consider showing clips of the film when discussing the role of the jury in the criminal justice system.

Following are possible answers for each section of the Reading Notes.

Section 16.2

1. The act must be wrongful and do harm to other individuals or to society. The act must be carried out with intent. The crime must have been described and prohibited by law before the act was committed.

2. Misdemeanors are criminal offenses that are less serious than felonies. The circumstances or effects of a crime determine whether it is classified as a misdemeanor or felony.

3. Due process means the government cannot act unfairly, arbitrarily, or unreasonably in the treatment of criminal suspects. Procedural due process refers to law enforcement procedures. Substantive due process relates to the substance of a law rather than the way it is enforced.

4. Answers will vary.

Section 16.3

1. Possible answers:

   - Suspects have the right to be "secure in their persons, houses, papers, and effects" and protected from "unreasonable searches and seizures."

   - Police must conduct reasonable searches and seizures that do not go against a person's "reasonable expectation of privacy."

   - Searches without search warrants can be conducted only when special circumstances exist, such as at sobriety checkpoints or airports.

   - Search warrants must be based on probable cause and must describe the exact place to be searched and the items or persons to be seized.

   - The exclusionary rule protects suspects from evidence that is seized illegally.

2. Police, who did not have a valid search warrant, arrested Dollree Mapp for possession of obscene materials. In *Mapp v. Ohio* (1961), the Supreme Court held that the evidence had been obtained illegally and that all evidence obtained by searches and seizures in violation of the Constitution is inadmissible in a state court.

3. Police present evidence of probable cause to a judge. → The judge issues a search warrant. → Police conduct a search. → Police seize evidence and talk to witnesses. → Police present evidence to a prosecutor.

4. Answers will vary.

Section 16.4

1. Possible answers:

   - Arrest warrants must be issued by a judge and must be based on probable cause.

   - Upon arrest, suspects must be informed of the following rights: the right to remain silent, the right to an attorney, the right to have an attorney present during questioning, and the right to be appointed an attorney free of charge.

   - Any statements offered by a suspect before he or she is read the Miranda warnings cannot be offered as evidence in trial. Any evidence uncovered during an illegal confession is inadmissible.

   - Upon booking, suspects are informed of the charges against them.

   - Suspects have the right to make a phone call.

2. In 1963, Ernesto Miranda confessed to rape and kidnapping without being informed of his right against self-incrimination and his right to have an attorney present during questioning. In *Miranda v. Arizona* (1966), the Supreme Court concluded that the police interrogation of Miranda was done in an "atmosphere . . . of intimidation" and that for a confession to be considered valid, a suspect must be informed of his or her rights.

3. Police present evidence of probable cause to a judge. → The judge issues an arrest warrant. → The suspect is read the Miranda rights. → The suspect is arrested. → The suspect is booked.

4. Answers will vary.

Section 16.5

1. Possible answers:

   - Within 48 hours of arrest, suspects must have the opportunity to appear in court.

   - During the initial appearance, suspects are told the charges filed against them and that they can be appointed a lawyer at public expense.

   - In a preliminary hearing, the prosecutor must prove that there is probable cause that a crime was committed and that the suspect committed it.

   - Defendants accused of any serious violation of federal law are granted a federal grand jury hearing.

2. The defendant in *United States v. Salerno* (1987) argued that denying bail to suspects who were considered dangerous violated their constitutional rights. The Court disagreed and said that a judge could deny bail based on public safety.

3. The suspect makes an initial appearance in court. → The suspect is released on bail. → The grand jury hears the case. → The suspect accepts a plea bargain. → The suspect is arraigned.

4. Answers will vary.

Section 16.6

1. Possible answers:

   - The suspect has the right to a speedy and public trial.

   - A federal case must be brought to trial within 100 days or the case may be dismissed.

   - Judges may change the location of a trial or isolate the jury to ensure that a jury is not influenced by public opinion.

   - A jury must be impartial and consist of members of the local community.

   - If prosecutors try to exclude jurors based solely on race, they may be asked to explain or ordered to change their approach.

   - Prosecutors cannot use peremptory challenges to exclude jurors solely on the basis of gender.

   - The "Escobedo rule" disallows evidence gained from a confession made without an attorney present.

   - Defendants have the right to legal counsel.

   - Prosecutors must obey the rules of evidence and present evidence that is relevant and competent.

   - Defendants have the right to refrain from being witnesses against themselves.

   - To reach a guilty verdict, jurors must agree that the evidence supports, "beyond a reasonable doubt," the defendant's having committed the crime.

   - A defendant cannot be tried twice for the same crime.

2. Possible answers:

   - In *Batson v. Kentucky* (1986), the Supreme Court examined a case in which the prosecuting attorney used his peremptory challenges to exclude four black jurors, leaving an all-white jury to decide a case involving a black defendant. The Court determined that peremptory challenges used to exclude jurors on the basis of race could be challenged by the defendant.

   - In *Strickland v. Washington* (1984), the Court considered a case in which the defendant charged that his rights had been violated when his lawyer did not provide enough evidence to avoid the death sentence. The Court upheld the defendant's conviction but stated that defendants are entitled to "reasonably effective assistance" of counsel. The Court said that for defendants to claim ineffective counsel, they must show that errors made by the attorney were sufficient to prevent a fair trial.

3. Jurors are selected randomly and are sent a jury summons. → Jurors are challenged "for cause." → Lawyers issue peremptory challenges. → The prosecution and defense present evidence and call witnesses. → Jurors deliberate. → The jury foreman announces the verdict.

4. Answers will vary.

Section 16.7

1. Possible answers:

   • Judges consider many factors before issuing a sentence and try to make the punishment fit the crime and criminal.

   • A criminal has the right against "cruel and unusual punishment."

   • Prisoners who are insane, mentally handicapped, or minors cannot be executed.

   • Defendants have the right to appeal to a higher court if they believe the jury selection was flawed, their lawyer was ineffective, the law was not interpreted correctly, or their due process rights were denied.

   • The prosecution cannot withhold evidence.

2. In *Brady v. Maryland* (1963), the defendant appealed his conviction on the grounds that the prosecution concealed evidence that might have influenced the sentence. The Supreme Court decided that withholding evidence violates due process "where the evidence is material either to guilt or to punishment."

3. The judge requests a presentence report. → The judge chooses to apply an indeterminate sentence. → The defendant requests an appeal. → The appeals court denies appeal.

Section 16.8

1. Possible answers:

   • Prisoners must be given a basic standard of living.

   • Prisoners must be granted access to the parole process.

   • Prisoners are protected from discrimination on the basis of race, gender, or religion.

   • Prisoners have the right to receive mail, get adequate medical care, practice their religion, and exercise regularly.

2. In *Cutter v. Wilkinson* (2005), the Supreme Court said that prisoners cannot be denied their right to exercise their religious beliefs, even if those beliefs are not mainstream.

3. The prisoner is sent to a minimum-security prison. → The prisoner applies for parole. → The parole board hears testimony and examines evidence. → The prisoner is released.

4. Answers will vary.

The United States and the World

17 Creating American Foreign Policy 203
How should the United States conduct foreign policy?

Response Group

18 Confronting Global Issues 213
How effectively do international organizations respond to global issues?

Experiential Exercise

Creating American Foreign Policy

How should the United States conduct foreign policy?

Overview

Students examine the tools of American foreign policy, as well as the people, institutions, and worldviews that shape it.

Preview Students examine a list of U.S. foreign policy goals and identify which they believe are most and least important.

Activity In a Response Group activity, students assume the role of members of the National Security Council to advise the president on three foreign policy scenarios.

Processing Students analyze U.S. involvement in a current foreign policy event.

Objectives

In the course of reading this chapter and participating in the classroom activity, students will

- identify and give examples of U.S. foreign policy goals.
- identify the tools used to carry out U.S. foreign policy.
- describe the powers that the U.S. Constitution gives the president and Congress in the area of foreign affairs.
- analyze U.S. involvement in a current foreign policy event as reported in a news article.

Materials

Government Alive! Power, Politics, and You

Transparencies 17A–17I

CD Tracks 22–24

Lesson Masters

- Notebook Guide 17 (1 per student)
- Student Handouts 17A–17C (1 of each per student)
- Information Master 17 (1 transparency)

photograph of the president (optional)

Preview

Suggested time: 20 minutes

1   **Have students complete the Preview activity.** Distribute *Notebook Guide 17*. Students will examine a list of U.S. foreign policy goals and identify which they believe are most important and least important.

2   **Have students share their responses in pairs or with the class.**

3   **Explain the connection between the Preview and Chapter 17.** Tell students that the goals they just examined are some of those that U.S. leaders consider when creating a foreign policy, or a course of action with respect to another country. In this chapter, students will examine and evaluate how the United States creates and conducts foreign policy.

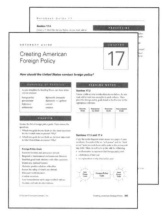

Notebook Guide 17

Reading

Speaking of Politics   Encourage students to use the following terms as they complete their Reading Notes for the chapter: *foreign policy, globalization, diplomacy, ambassador, diplomatic immunity, diplomatic recognition, summit,* and *sanction.*

1   **Introduce the Essential Question and have students read Section 17.1.**

2   **Have students read Sections 17.2 to 17.6 and complete the Reading Notes *before* conducting the classroom activity.** Consider breaking up the reading using the first option under "Quicker Coverage."

Response Group

Suggested time: 100 minutes

1   **Place students in mixed-ability groups of three and introduce the activity.** Tell students that they will now role-play members of the National Security Council, a group of senior advisers who counsel the president on matters of foreign policy. They have been called to an NSC meeting to advise the president on how to respond to three foreign policy scenarios. They will meet in the Situation Room, a secured conference room in the basement of the White House, to be briefed on the first scenario. (**Note:** To create additional suspense, meet students as they enter the classroom. Address them by last name and, in a stern tone, explain that they are entering the Situation Room and must turn off all electronic devices to ensure that they have no contact with anyone on the outside.)

2   **Conduct the first briefing.** Distribute *Student Handout 17A: National Security Briefing A* to each student. Then play CD Track 22, "National Security Briefing A," and have students follow along. (**Note:** The recording contains introductory information and details about the exhibits on the transparencies that are not printed on the handout.) When cued by the recording, project the corresponding exhibits on *Transparencies 17A–17C: Briefing A on Libya.* Consider pausing the recording after projecting each exhibit to give students an opportunity to examine it.

Student Handout 17A

Transparencies 17A–17C

3 Have groups prepare their recommendations. Encourage them to consider combining the given options or creating their own and to make an outline of their final proposals.

4 Facilitate a National Security Council meeting. Project *Information Master 17: Conducting an NSC Meeting*, and facilitate a lively meeting as follows:

Information Master 17

- Tape or project an image of the current president on a wall near the conference table (the inner circle). Tell students that the president is relying on them to provide the best thinking on what course of action the United States should pursue with respect to this scenario.

- Call on all spokespersons seated at the conference table (the inner circle) to share their policy recommendations.

- After all spokespersons have presented, call on NSC members in the outer circle to share their opinions on the policy recommendations.

- End the meeting by saying, "Ladies and gentlemen, thank you for your recommendations. The president will take these into consideration as he makes his final decision. The meeting is adjourned."

5 Update the foreign policy scenario. Share with students the following information: *The scenario you just analyzed occurred in October 2003. After intense diplomatic negotiations with British and U.S. leaders, Muammar al-Gaddafi admitted that Libya had developed a secret nuclear weapons program over several decades. Libya agreed to dismantle the program and allow international inspectors to oversee the destruction of its nuclear sites. Foreign policy analysts surmise that Gaddafi's decision was based on Libya's lack of preparation for a military confrontation with the United States.*

Student Handouts 17B and 17C

6 Debrief the foreign policy scenario. Ask,

- Do you believe that the United States pursued the appropriate course of action? Why or why not?

- How do you think the United States should respond to similar situations in the future?

7 Repeat Steps 2–6 for the remaining two briefings.

- *National Security Briefing B:* Use Student Handout 17B, CD Track 23, and *Transparencies 17D–17F: Briefing B on Darfur, Sudan.* After conducting the NSC meeting, share this information with students: *As of late 2007, ethnic cleansing continued in Darfur. Despite appeals by the president and secretary of state, Sudan would not allow UN peacekeeping forces into the country. In May 2007, the United States imposed new sanctions against Sudan and placed restrictions on foreign companies that did business with that country. It also issued an advisory warning U.S. citizens of the dangers of traveling to Sudan. In summer 2007, Sudan agreed to allow a UN peacekeeping force into Darfur. It is still unclear whether this force will be successful in stopping the violence.*

- *National Security Briefing C:* Use Student Handout 17C, CD Track 24, and *Transparencies 17G–17I: Briefing C on Piracy and Counterfeiting.* After conducting the NSC meeting, share this information: *As of late 2007, U.S.*

Transparencies 17D–17I

leaders and diplomats continued to pressure foreign governments to crack down on counterfeiting and piracy. The Department of Commerce continued its campaign to teach consumers how to protect themselves from counterfeited and pirated goods. Despite these attempts, widespread counterfeiting and piracy of U.S. goods continued, posing a hardship on the U.S. economy.

8 **Wrap up the activity.** Ask, *When do you think it is appropriate for U.S. leaders to use soft power foreign policy tools? Hard power foreign policy tools?*

Power, Politics, and You

1 **Have students read the "Power, Politics, and You" section of the chapter.** Explain that they will look at the pros and cons of globalization.

2 **Facilitate a class discussion.** Draw a spectrum on the board with ends labeled "Strongly Agree" and "Strongly Disagree." Read the first statement below aloud. Ask 8 to 10 volunteers to arrange themselves along the spectrum according to their personal beliefs. Then hold a brief discussion in which each student defends his or her placement. Repeat the process with new volunteers for the second and third statements.

- Globalization is turning the world into a consumer colony of the United States.

- Globalization will give us new ways not only to appreciate other cultures, but also to look on our own culture with fresh wonder and surprise.

- Globalization is an unstoppable force.

Processing

Suggested time: 20 minutes

Have students complete the Processing activity, in which they read a news article and analyze U.S. involvement in a current foreign policy event. Consider having students share their current events and analyses in pairs or with the class.

Quicker Coverage

Break Up the Reading Divide students into expert groups of four. Assign each group to read and to complete the corresponding Reading Notes for one of Sections 17.2 to 17.6. Allow students to meet in their groups for a few minutes to discuss the answers and to clarify any information they may have found confusing. Then ask students to number off within their expert groups. Form new jigsaw groups by having all number 1s, number 2s, and so on, meet. In each jigsaw group, have students share the information from their Reading Notes with the rest of the group.

Decrease the Number of Briefings Conduct only one or two of the briefings and corresponding NSC meetings.

Assign the Briefings for Homework Eliminate the CD tracks and transparencies, and have students read the briefings on Student Handouts 17A–17C for homework. Then conduct the NSC meetings in class.

Deeper Coverage

Conduct Additional Research Have groups research additional information about the scenarios in National Security Briefings B and C. Encourage them to gather current statistics to integrate into their foreign policy recommendations to the president. They might visit the Darfur Information Center Web site, maintained by the University of Pennsylvania's African Studies Center, at www.darfurinfo.org, and the U.S. Chamber of Commerce site truecosts.org.

Create an Additional National Security Briefing Using a current event, model the briefing after one in the lesson. Incorporate data and rich images.

Assessment

Masters for the chapter assessment appear in the *Lesson Masters*.

Mastering the Content

1. A	2. C	3. C	4. B	5. D
6. B	7. A	8. B	9. D	10. B

Exploring the Essential Question

1. isolationism: Washington
   containment: Truman
   human rights: Wilson
   antiterrorism: Bush

2. Possible answer: Both Wilson and Truman were concerned with freedom and were willing to commit the United States to assisting people in other countries to become free by military or other means. A person who supports disengagement would most likely view their statements with disapproval, fearing that these approaches to foreign policy would lead to future military involvement in other countries.

3. Possible answer: President Bush's declaration that nations harboring or supporting terrorism should be treated as hostile regimes best fits my foreign policy worldview. I think the greatest threat to our national security comes from terrorists rather than from hostile nations. To combat terrorism, we need to do all we can to discourage countries from supporting terrorists in any way.

English Language Learners

Familiarize Students with the Briefings Before the activity, review with students these overviews of the national security briefings and answer any questions.

Briefing A: A Libyan ship was stopped in the Mediterranean Sea. The ship carries machine parts that can be used to make nuclear weapons. Libya's president says the parts are used to supply electric power. The United States suspects that Libya is a terrorist nation and will use the parts to make nuclear weapons.

Briefing B: Darfur is a poor region in Sudan. Most people in Darfur are black Africans. The people in Sudan's government are mostly ethnic Arabs. In 2003, Darfur groups attacked government buildings. The government then supported attacks on Darfur villages. Over 2.5 million people in Darfur lost their homes. The government will not allow the United Nations to send troops.

Briefing C: U.S. companies have lost a lot of money because of counterfeiting and piracy. Most counterfeiting and piracy operations are in other countries, like China and Vietnam. The United States has tried to help other governments stop the counterfeiting and piracy of goods. However, these activities continue.

Replay the Recordings Have students listen to the CD track for each briefing more than once, following along on the corresponding handout and underlining phrases they find confusing. After each recording, discuss and clarify these phrases.

Learners Reading and Writing Below Grade Level

Photocopy the Transparencies Provide students with photocopies of the transparencies. During each briefing, pause the CD after projecting each exhibit. Then discuss the exhibit and have students annotate their copies with key information.

Assign Handouts for Homework Prior to each briefing, give students the corresponding copy of Student Handouts 17A–17C. Have them highlight key information and write at least three questions about the scenario.

Learners with Special Education Needs

Create a Cue Card Have students create cue cards to use when they are the spokesperson in the NSC meeting. The cards should list the reasons for the group's foreign policy recommendation.

Support the Processing Photocopy an article about a current foreign policy event. As students read the article, have them highlight key information. Then discuss the article with students before they answer the accompanying questions.

Advanced Learners

Create NSC Briefings Have students create their own NSC briefings by using the handouts as a model. Require that briefings reflect real historical or current scenarios. Briefings should include a map, a list of five country facts, two images, a graph or table, and three possible foreign policy options. Consider having pairs exchange briefings and write corresponding foreign policy recommendations.

U.S. Supreme Court Cases: You Make the Call

Have students read the summary of Case 10, *Missouri v. Holland,* which relates to the federal government's treaty powers, in the "U.S. Supreme Court Cases: You Make the Call" section of the Student Edition. Have volunteers share key facts from the case and the question before the Court. Then facilitate a Response Group–type discussion asking students to "make the call" on how the Court should decide the case and why. Finally, have students read the actual Supreme Court decision.

Internet Connections

For related research materials on U.S. foreign policy, refer students to Online Resources at www.teachtci.com.

Multimedia

Please follow school and district guidelines for showing films in the classroom.

The West Wing, **Season 6, Episode 111, "NSF Thurmont"** In this episode, the president must decide how to respond to an attack on U.S. officials in the Palestinian-controlled territory of Gaza. The president learns that 82 percent of the American people, as well as most members of his staff and Congress, favor an immediate military attack. He considers the military option as well as arranging for a summit at Camp David. Consider showing this episode when discussing the pros and cons of using soft and hard power foreign policy tools.

Thirteen Days **(PG-13)** This film, directed by Roger Donaldson, highlights the 13 days of the Cuban missile crisis and focuses on the decision-making process of President Kennedy and his advisers. Although the film has been criticized for taking liberties with historical events, it conveys the complexities of foreign relations and the role of the president in shaping foreign policy. Consider showing clips of this film when discussing the role of the president in creating foreign policy.

Following are possible answers to the questions in the Reading Notes.

Section 17.2

Security Goals	Peacekeeping Goals	Economic Goals	Humanitarian Goals
• Defend the nation from attacks by other countries. • Combat terrorism. • Protect our national borders. • Maintain positive relations with allies. • Ensure the safety of Americans abroad.	• Support the peacekeeping work of the United Nations. • Mediate disputes among nations. • Eliminate world dictators. • Mediate civil wars in other nations.	• Promote the economic prosperity of Americans. • Protect the right of Americans to buy goods from other countries and to sell goods to other countries. • Increase Americans' access to raw materials and resources from other parts of the world. • Establish good trade relations with other countries.	• Promote freedom and democracy abroad. • End poverty and promote human rights. • Respond to international environmental disasters. • Send humanitarian aid to impoverished nations.

Section 17.3

Soft power tools

- Diplomacy is the art of conducting negotiations between countries. It is used to represent the interests of the home country while developing foreign relations with the host country.

- A summit is a high-level meeting between heads of state. It is used to address issues of concern to both countries.

- A treaty is an agreement between two or more countries. It is used to solve a problem peacefully.

- Cross-border trade relations are trade relations between countries. The establishment of such relations can be used to signal one government's approval of another government, as well as a desire for more contact between countries.

- Foreign aid is assistance to less wealthy countries in the form of cash, equipment, or personnel. It is used to assist in the long-term development of poor countries, to promote security, and to help victims of human-made and natural disasters.

- Cultural exchanges are visits to another country by educators, scientists, businesspeople, or performing artists. Such exchanges help promote goodwill between countries.

Section 17.4

Hard power tools

- Intelligence refers to the information that a government collects about the activities and intentions of other countries. Intelligence gathering can be overt or covert.

- A covert action is a secret operation that supports a country's foreign policy. It is used to influence events in another country.

- A boycott is a refusal to buy goods from a country, or a refusal to take part in an international event, as a form of protest against another country's policies or actions.

- A sanction is an action, such as a tariff or trade barrier, taken against one or more countries. It is used to force a government to change its policies.

- A military alliance is an agreement made by countries to defend one another in case of an attack. Countries join alliances for mutual protection.

- Armed force is war. It is used as a last resort to pressure other countries to change their policies.

Section 17.5

Presidential Foreign Powers	Congressional Foreign Powers
to negotiate treaties	to approve treaties (Senate)
to appoint ambassadors to other countries	to approve presidential appointments (Senate)
to serve as commander in chief of the military	to declare war and control funding for war
to direct administration of foreign policy in the areas of diplomacy, intelligence, national security, and the economy	to pass laws that affect U.S. relations with other countries
	to conduct oversight hearings and investigations into foreign policy issues

Edward Corwin described this division of powers as "an invitation to struggle" because neither the president nor Congress has complete power over foreign affairs. The framers intended this so that neither branch could act effectively in foreign affairs without the other.

Section 17.6

Answers will vary.

Confronting Global Issues

How effectively do international organizations respond to global issues?

Overview

Students examine the structure, purpose, and work of international organizations.

Preview Students consider the advantages and disadvantages of international organizations responding to global climate change.

Activity In an Experiential Exercise, students assume the role of delegates to the United Nations to debate a fictitious draft resolution on global climate change.

Processing Students research an international organization and evaluate its effectiveness in responding to a global issue.

Objectives

In the course of reading this chapter and participating in the classroom activity, students will

- identify the purposes and functions of various types of international organizations.
- contrast the strengths and limitations of international organizations.
- debate a global issue from the perspective of a specific country.
- evaluate the goals and work of an international organization.

Materials

Government Alive! Power, Politics, and You

Transparencies 18A and 18B

Lesson Masters

- Notebook Guide 18 (1 per student)
- Student Handout 18A (1 per student)
- Student Handout 18B (1 per pair of students, copied onto heavy paper or cardstock)
- Student Handout 18C (1 per pair of students)
- Information Master 18 (1 transparency)

Preview

Suggested time: 15 minutes

1 **Introduce the Preview.** Project *Transparency 18A: Global Temperature Change* and have students inspect the graph. Ask, *What interesting details do you notice about the graph?* Point out that the right ends of the graphed lines represent three projections of future temperature change.

2 **Have students complete the Preview.** Distribute *Notebook Guide 18,* and have students answer the Preview questions.

3 **Have students share their responses in pairs or with the class.**

4 **Explain the connection between the Preview and Chapter 18.** Explain that global climate change is just one issue that international organizations might respond to. One advantage of international organizations is that they can pool the resources of many nations to respond to such issues. At the same time, international organizations are often criticized for failing to fully resolve such issues as poverty, disease, and global climate change. In this chapter, students will examine how effectively international organizations respond to global issues.

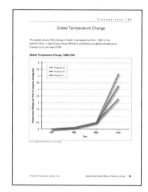

Transparency 18A

Reading

Speaking of Politics Encourage students to use the following terms as they complete their Reading Notes for the chapter: *intergovernmental organization (IGO), nongovernmental organization (NGO), global warming, collective security, sustainable development, convention, greenhouse effect,* and *protocol.*

1 **Introduce the Essential Question and have students read Section 18.1.** Then ask students to consider possible answers to the Essential Question: *How effectively do international organizations respond to global issues?*

2 **Have students read Sections 18.2 to 18.7 and complete the Reading Notes *before* conducting the classroom activity.** Consider breaking up the reading using the first option under "Quicker Coverage."

Notebook Guide 18

Experiential Exercise

Suggested time: 120 minutes

1 **Place students in pairs and introduce the activity.** Explain that in this activity students will assume the roles of delegates to the United Nations. They will review, amend, and debate a proposed resolution from the perspective of a UN member state during a General Assembly session.

2 **Distribute materials.** Distribute *Student Handout 18A: UN Draft Resolution* to each student and one page of *Student Handout 18B: Position Cards of UN Member States* to each pair. (**Note:** There are 16 position cards. For fewer than 16 pairs, eliminate countries in this order: Canada, Philippines, Australia, Bolivia, Germany, Saudi Arabia. Alternatively, consider assigning some countries to a single student. If you have more than 32 students, create some groups of three.)

Student Handouts 18A and 18B

3 **Have pairs prepare for the General Assembly session.** Explain that during the General Assembly session, pairs will debate a draft resolution on global climate change from the perspective of their country. Project *Transparency 18B: UN Draft Resolution* and review the resolution with the class. Then distribute *Student Handout 18C: Preparing for the General Assembly Session* and provide pairs adequate time to prepare.

4 **Conduct the General Assembly session.** Assume the role of chair. Project the steps on *Information Master 18: Conducting the General Assembly Session* one at a time as the class follows along. Here are some additional tips for conducting the session:

- Encourage students to speak in third person and from the perspective of their country ("China believes . . ."). This will reinforce the idea that students are representing countries, as well as add authenticity to the activity.

- Prior to Step 2, review the position table with students to make sure they recorded accurate information.

- After collecting the amendments at the end of Step 2, place them in the order you feel will elicit the most debate in Step 3.

5 **Debrief the activity.** Ask,

- How did it feel to participate in the General Assembly session? What was the most rewarding part of the process? The most frustrating?

- The draft resolution and the information on the country cards are realistic but fictitious. In what ways do you think this session was realistic? In what ways do you think it was unrealistic?

- What is challenging about passing a UN resolution? Do you think the process should be changed? Why or why not?

- Based on your experience in the activity, how well do you think international organizations are able to respond to global issues?

Power, Politics, and You

Have students read the "Power, Politics, and You" section of the chapter. Then facilitate a class discussion by having them respond to the questions below. Consider having students discuss the questions in pairs or small groups first.

- Do you think that Free the Children is an effective international organization? Why or why not?

- What global issue "hits you in the heart"? Why?

- What might you do to respond to that issue?

Transparency 18B

Student Handout 18C

Information Master 18

Processing

Suggested time: 30 minutes

Have students complete the Processing activity, in which they research an international organization and evaluate its effectiveness in responding to a global issue. Consider having students share their research in pairs or with the class.

Quicker Coverage

Break Up the Reading Divide students into groups of three, and assign each group one of Sections 18.2 to 18.7 (or part of a section). Tell groups they will become experts on their assigned section and present the answers to those Reading Notes to the class. After students read and complete their Reading Notes, have each group transfer their answers onto a transparency. Tell groups to determine who will explain each component of the notes and to find interesting examples, facts, and statistics from the text to incorporate into their presentations.

Eliminate the General Assembly Session Instead, have students assume the roles of U.S. delegates to the United Nations. Divide them into groups of three and have them discuss the draft resolution on Student Handout 18A from the perspective of just the United States. Then hold a class discussion in which students debate whether the United States should sign and ratify the draft resolution. Consider making a transparency of the U.S. position card on Student Handout 18B to facilitate the discussion.

Deeper Coverage

Write Individual Resolutions Have pairs write their own resolutions on global climate change from the perspective of their assigned countries, using Student Handout 18A as a model. Encourage them to conduct additional research by visiting such Web sites as the CIA's *The World Factbook* and their country's ministry of foreign affairs. Then conduct the General Assembly session, making these changes:

- *Student Handout 18C:* Change all references to "amendment" to "resolution."
- *Information Master 18:* Change all references to "amendment" to "resolution." and, in Step 3, delete the last three items. Debate as many resolutions as time permits. Consider allowing students to propose and vote on amendments to the resolutions.

Assessment

Masters for the chapter assessment appear in the *Lesson Masters*.

Mastering the Content

1.	A	2.	B	3.	A	4.	D	5.	A
6.	B	7.	C	8.	B	9.	D	10.	A

Exploring the Essential Question

1. Possible answer: The Environmental Defense Fund and Human Rights Watch both use advocacy campaigns to achieve their goals. This approach makes sense for the Environmental Defense Fund because environmental protection is mainly a function of governments. It makes sense for Human Rights Watch because most violations of human rights are committed by governments.

2. Possible answer: The International Red Cross and Save the Children focus on humanitarian work. They might need to coordinate their efforts when responding to a disaster in order to avoid duplication of each other's relief work.

3. Answers will vary.

English Language Learners

Activate Prior Knowledge Before having students complete the Preview, introduce the concept of global climate change. Use an image, such as a polar bear standing on a small portion of ice, to elicit discussion. Then discuss the Preview questions as a class before students answer them independently.

Provide a Template for the Activity Offer the following template to help students formulate their opening statements during the General Assembly.

The country of _____ (name of country) is a

_____ (developed/developing) nation with a population

of _____. Our country _____ (opposes/

supports) this resolution as it is currently written. We propose an amend-

ment that would _____ (describe amendment).

Learners Reading and Writing Below Grade Level

Support the Processing Provide additional support for the Processing assignment by giving students printouts of material from an international organization such as the Sierra Club or CARE. Highlight examples of how the organization is working to address a global issue and ways in which they could get involved in the organization.

Support the Reading Notes Help students complete the Reading Notes using one of these options:

- Use the Guide to Reading Notes to create a cloze worksheet. Omit key terms or ideas in each answer, and have students fill in the blanks.

- Reduce the number of questions for each section. The following questions focus on the main ideas of each section: Section 18.2: Questions 2 and 3; Section 18.3: Question 2; Section 18.4: Questions 1 and 3; Section 18.5: Question 1; Section 18.6: Questions 1 and 2.

Learners with Special Education Needs

Streamline the Activity Limit the number of countries in the General Assembly session to six and increase the number of students per group. Choose three countries against the resolution (United States, Australia, China) and three in support of the resolution (Iceland, Great Britain, Zambia). Help groups formulate their amendments by suggesting the following amendment topics:

- *United States:* Set a later target date.
- *Australia:* Reduce emissions reduction rates for all countries.
- *China:* Exempt developing nations from the resolution.
- *Iceland:* Set an earlier target date.
- *Great Britain:* Increase emissions reduction rates for all countries.
- *Zambia:* Allocate all UN funds for global climate change to developing countries.

Design a Flyer For the Processing, have students design an illustrated flyer highlighting a global issue, an international organization that addresses it, and examples of how the organization is responding to it. Have students share their flyers with one another and discuss whether they would consider joining that organization.

Advanced Learners

Debate an Actual Resolution During the activity, have students debate an actual resolution from the General Assembly or the Security Council. Provide students with a copy of a resolution and give them time to research their country's position. Current resolutions can be downloaded from the UN General Assembly and Security Council Web sites.

Internet Connections

For related research materials on international organizations, refer students to Online Resources at www.teachtci.com.

Multimedia

Please follow school and district guidelines for showing films in the classroom.

UN Security Council and General Assembly Webcasts These webcasts, which vary in length and subject matter and are updated daily when the United Nations is in session, offer a glimpse into the inner workings of the United Nations. Consider showing current clips of meetings in the General Assembly and Security Council after students read Section 18.2. Webcasts can be downloaded for free from the UN Web site.

An Inconvenient Truth **(PG)** In this 2006 documentary, former vice president Al Gore describes the causes and effects of global climate change. He calls on nations around the world to work together on this issue and offers suggestions for what individuals can do. Consider showing parts of this documentary prior to the activity to provide additional background to the subject of the draft UN resolution.

Hotel Rwanda **(PG-13)** This 2004 film by director Terry George provides a personal account of the Rwandan genocide of the 1990s. The story unfolds in a hotel frequented by wealthy foreigners. When Hutu extremists initiate a campaign of terror against the minority Tutsis, the hotel turns into a refuge for local Tutsis. UN peacekeepers, unable to quell the violence, flee along with the tourists, leaving the hotel employees and refugees to fend for themselves. Consider showing this film, or clips of this film, when discussing the role of international organizations in responding to human rights violations.

Following are possible answers to the questions in the Reading Notes.

Section 18.2

1. Illustrations will vary. The four goals are to save succeeding generations from war, to reaffirm faith in human rights, to establish conditions under which treaties and other sources of international law can be maintained, and to promote social progress and better standards of living.

2. Main activities of the UN:

   - Sponsoring peacekeeping missions in more than a dozen countries.

   - Helping stop the proliferation of nuclear weapons.

   - Promoting sustainable development by finding ways to meet the needs of the world's people without exhausting natural resources.

   - Ending hunger and poverty, achieving universal primary education, promoting gender equality, and reducing child mortality.

3. Strengths of the UN:

   - The UN is a central forum for debating global issues.

   - Since it is such a large organization, the UN has the resources to coordinate efforts to deal with short-term crises like natural disasters as well as tougher, longer-term problems like poverty.

   - The UN coordinates peacekeeping operations in locations throughout the world.

   Limitations of the UN:

   - Rulings from the General Assembly and Security Council are not always legally binding.

   - The UN has no standing army and must rely on member states to carry out peacekeeping missions.

   - The UN has been rocked with corruption scandals and charges of mismanagement and waste.

4. Answers will vary.

Section 18.3

1. IGOs and their objectives:

   - The Organization of Petroleum Exporting Countries (OPEC) works to create a stable market for oil at the best possible price for its members.

   - The North American Free Trade Agreement (NAFTA) works to promote trade among Canada, the United States, and Mexico.

   - Members of the North Atlantic Treaty Organization (NATO) share military resources and strategies for protecting their region.

   - The African Union (AU) promotes democracy and sustainable development among its members.

2. Strengths of IGOs:

   - Groups of nations cooperate to achieve common objectives.

   - Nations can share resources, expand trade, and increase national security.

   Limitations of IGOs:

   - Decisions by IGOs may conflict with one nation's foreign policy or national interests.

   - Nations must sometimes surrender some of their sovereignty to abide by an IGO's decisions.

3. Answers will vary.

Section 18.4

1. Purposes of NGOs:

   - to tackle problems that governments cannot deal with effectively

   - to work in the world's least developed countries

   - to deliver assistance in the form of teaching or medical care

   - to provide information and analyses to governments about global issues

   - to speak out on their areas of concern

2. Answers will vary.

3. Strengths of NGOs:

- They take a hands-on approach to problems.
- They understand the needs of the people at the grass roots.
- They can effectively make the case to governments and donors that their cause deserves attention and funding.
- They can bring help to disaster survivors much faster than government relief agencies or IGOs can.

Limitations of NGOs:

- They often lack the personnel and resources to carry out large-scale, long-term relief efforts.
- They are less organized and less well funded than governments or IGOs.
- They sometimes have problems coordinating their efforts.
- They often face corruption and civil unrest in other countries.

4. Answers will vary.

Section 18.5

1. The Universal Declaration of Human Rights guarantees the rights to life, liberty, and equal protection under the law as well as the rights to work, to own property, to get an education, and to enjoy a decent standard of living. The Convention on the Rights of the Child guarantees the rights to life and survival as well as protection from abuse and exploitation, from economic exploitation, from work that is hazardous or interferes with education, and from work that is harmful to children's health or physical, mental, spiritual, moral, or social development.

2. Answers will vary.

3. Answers will vary.

Section 18.6

1.

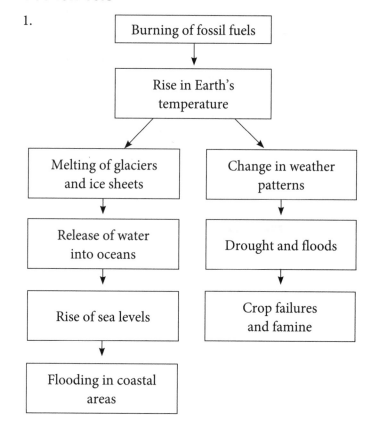

2. The United States did not sign the Kyoto Protocol because it felt that meeting the emissions reduction target would hurt the U.S. economy. It also felt that developing nations should be forced to accept mandatory cuts.

3. Ways U.S. governments and NGOs are confronting climate change:

- President Bush announced a plan to reduce U.S. gasoline consumption by 20% over the next 10 years. He also increased funding of research on science and technologies related to climate change.
- The California Global Warming Solutions Act of 2006 pledges to reduce carbon emissions by substantial amounts by 2020 and by 2050.
- The Sierra Club encourages cities to take steps to reduce carbon dioxide emissions.
- The Environmental Defense Fund used TV ads to educate the public on the problem.
- The Natural Resources Defense Council has launched a campaign to urge Americans to cut their electricity use.

One-Semester Course, Conventional Schedule

This pacing guide suggests how many instructional days to allot to each chapter, including activities and assessment, for teaching the course in 50-minute classes, 5 times a week (250 minutes/week).

Unit 1: Power, Authority, and Government

1 The Nature of Power, Politics, and Government	3 days
2 Comparing Forms of Government	4 days

Unit 2: Foundations of American Government

3 The Roots of American Democracy	4 days
4 The United States Constitution	5 days
5 The Bill of Rights and Civil Liberties	5 days
6 Federalism: National, State, and Local Powers	4 days

Unit 3: Political Participation and Behavior

7 Citizen Participation in a Democracy	3 days
8 Parties, Interest Groups, and Public Policy	5 days
9 Public Opinion and the Media	5 days
10 Political Campaigns and Elections	6 days

Unit 4: The Legislative Branch

11 Lawmakers and Legislatures	3 days
12 Congressional Lawmaking	5 days

Unit 5: The Executive Branch

13 Chief Executives and Bureaucracies	4 days
14 The Federal Budget	3 days

Unit 6: The Judicial Branch

15 Courts, Judges, and the Law	3 days
16 The Criminal Justice System	5 days

Unit 7: The United States and the World

17 Creating American Foreign Policy	4 days
18 Confronting Global Issues	4 days

One-Semester Course, Block Schedule

This pacing guide suggests how many instructional days to allot to each chapter, including activities and assessment, for teaching the course in 100-minute classes, twice a week, plus one 50-minute class (250 minutes/week).

Unit 1: Power, Authority, and Government

1 The Nature of Power, Politics, and Government	1.5 days
2 Comparing Forms of Government	2 days

Unit 2: Foundations of American Government

3 The Roots of American Democracy	2 days
4 The United States Constitution	2.5 days
5 The Bill of Rights and Civil Liberties	2.5 days
6 Federalism: National, State, and Local Powers	2 days

Unit 3: Political Participation and Behavior

7 Citizen Participation in a Democracy	1.5 days
8 Parties, Interest Groups, and Public Policy	2.5 days
9 Public Opinion and the Media	2.5 days
10 Political Campaigns and Elections	3 days

Unit 4: The Legislative Branch

11 Lawmakers and Legislatures	1.5 days
12 Congressional Lawmaking	2.5 days

Unit 5: The Executive Branch

13 Chief Executives and Bureaucracies	2 days
14 The Federal Budget	1.5 days

Unit 6: The Judicial Branch

15 Courts, Judges, and the Law	1.5 days
16 The Criminal Justice System	2.5 days

Unit 7: The United States and the World

17 Creating American Foreign Policy	2 days
18 Confronting Global Issues	2 days

Unit 1: Power, Authority, and Government	
Chapter 1 The Nature of Power, Politics, and Government *Why should you care about power, politics, and government?*	Students will • collect, evaluate, and employ information from primary and secondary sources. • synthesize information from multiple sources to draw conclusions. • use methods of social science investigation to answer questions about society. • use social studies vocabulary and terminology correctly. • build consensus within a group. • work in groups to analyze issues and make decisions.
Chapter 2 Comparing Forms of Governments *How should political and economic power be distributed in a society?*	Students will • evaluate government data using charts, tables, graphs, and maps. • analyze information by identifying cause-and-effect relationships. • analyze information by comparing and contrasting. • synthesize information from multiple sources to draw conclusions. • evaluate the effectiveness of governments. • draw connections between particular historical events and larger social, economic, and political trends and developments.
Unit 2: Foundations of American Government	
Chapter 3 The Roots of American Democracy *What ideas gave birth to the world's first modern democratic nation?*	Students will • evaluate the consequences of past events and decisions. • collect, evaluate, and employ information from primary and secondary sources. • analyze information by sequencing and categorizing. • interpret past events and issues within the context in which those events unfolded. • understand the meaning, implication, and effects of historical events.
Chapter 4 The United States Constitution *How and why did the framers distribute power in the Constitution?*	Students will • evaluate the effectiveness of governments. • analyze information by summarizing, making generalizations and predictions, and drawing inferences and conclusions. • interpret past events and issues within the context in which those events unfolded. • analyze and interpret information. • understand the meaning, implication, and effects of historical events.

Chapter 5 The Bill of Rights and Civil Liberties *How are your rights defined and protected under the Constitution?*	Students will • evaluate the consequences of past events and decisions. • evaluate conflicting sources, materials, and arguments about interpretations of the past. • evaluate the effectiveness of governments. • analyze information by summarizing, making generalizations and predictions, and drawing inferences and conclusions. • take, defend, explain, and evaluate positions on issues or public policies. • create written, oral, and visual presentations of social studies information.
Chapter 6 Federalism: National, State, and Local Powers *How does power flow through our federal system of government?*	Students will • analyze information by comparing and contrasting. • acquire and organize information from books, maps, almanacs, news sources, data sets, public records, and other sources. • analyze information by summarizing, making generalizations and predictions, and drawing inferences and conclusions. • engage in constructive conversation about matters of public concern and work toward a decision. • create written, oral, and visual presentations of social studies information.
Unit 3: Political Participation and Behavior	
Chapter 7 Citizen Participation in a Democracy *How can you make a difference in a democracy?*	Students will • take, defend, explain, and evaluate positions on issues or public policies. • identify a problem and develop a solution. • develop and implement an action plan for a situation or an issue requiring a decision. • engage in constructive conversation about matters of public concern and work toward a decision. • interpret past events and issues within the context in which those events unfolded.
Chapter 8 Parties, Interest Groups, and Public Policy *Political parties and interest groups: How do they influence our political decisions?*	Students will • analyze information by comparing and contrasting. • identify bias, prejudice, propaganda, point of view, and frame of reference. • take, defend, explain, and evaluate positions on issues or public policies. • analyze political platforms. • create written, oral, and visual presentations of social studies information.

Chapter 9 Public Opinion and the Media *To what extent do the media influence your political views?*	Students will • evaluate the validity of information. • identify bias, prejudice, propaganda, point of view, and frame of reference. • analyze political platforms. • evaluate relationships. • transfer information from one medium to another, including written to visual and statistical to written or visual, using computer software as appropriate. • create written, oral, and visual presentations of social studies information.
Chapter 10 Political Campaigns and Elections *Elections and voting: Why should they matter to you?*	Students will • collect, evaluate, and employ information from primary and secondary sources. • take, defend, explain, and evaluate positions on issues or public policies. • analyze political platforms. • engage in constructive conversation about matters of public concern and work toward a decision. • build consensus within a group.

Unit 4: The Legislative Branch

Chapter 11 Lawmakers and Legislatures *What makes an effective legislator?*	Students will • evaluate government data using charts, tables, graphs, and maps. • construct and interpret charts, graphs, tables, diagrams, maps, and timelines. • collect, evaluate, and employ information from primary and secondary sources. • evaluate the effectiveness of governments. • transfer information from one medium to another, including written to visual and statistical to written or visual, using computer software as appropriate.
Chapter 12 Congressional Lawmaking *How do laws really get made?*	Students will • synthesize information from multiple sources to draw conclusions. • identify issues or problems and alternative solutions. • take, defend, explain, and evaluate positions on issues or public policies. • generate and evaluate alternatives to public policies. • engage in constructive conversation about matters of public concern and work toward a decision. • work in groups to analyze issues and make decisions.

Unit 5: The Executive Branch	
Chapter 13 Chief Executives and Bureaucracies *What qualities do modern presidents need to fulfill their many roles?*	Students will • collect, evaluate, and employ information from primary and secondary sources. • synthesize information from multiple sources to draw conclusions. • formulate and test hypotheses. • analyze information by summarizing, making generalizations and predictions, and drawing inferences and conclusions. • interpret past events and issues within the context in which those events unfolded. • respond to questions and feedback about presentations knowledgeably and civilly.
Chapter 14 The Federal Budget *Does the federal government budget and spend your tax dollars wisely?*	Students will • evaluate government data using charts, tables, graphs, and maps. • construct and interpret charts, graphs, tables, diagrams, maps, and timelines. • synthesize information from multiple sources to draw conclusions. • identify issues or problems and alternative solutions. • take, defend, explain, and evaluate positions on issues or public policies. • analyze information by summarizing, making generalizations and predictions, and drawing inferences and conclusions.
Unit 6: The Judicial Branch	
Chapter 15 Courts, Judges, and the Law *How is the U.S. judicial system organized to ensure justice?*	Students will • evaluate government data using charts, tables, graphs, and maps. • collect, evaluate, and employ information from primary and secondary sources. • synthesize information from multiple sources to draw conclusions. • interpret the meaning and significance of information. • evaluate the effectiveness of governments.
Chapter 16 The Criminal Justice System *From doing the crime to doing time: How just is our criminal justice system?*	Students will • synthesize information from multiple sources to draw conclusions. • evaluate the validity of information. • evaluate the effectiveness of governments. • analyze information by summarizing, making generalizations and predictions, and drawing inferences and conclusions. • analyze and interpret information.

Unit 7: The United States and the World	
Chapter 17 Creating American Foreign Policy *How should the United States conduct foreign policy?*	Students will • interpret the meaning and significance of information. • analyze and interpret information. • identify issues or problems and alternative solutions. • evaluate government data using charts, tables, graphs, and maps. • synthesize information from multiple sources to draw conclusions.
Chapter 18 Confronting Global Issues *How effectively do international organizations respond to global issues?*	Students will • identify issues or problems and alternative solutions. • take, defend, explain, and evaluate positions on issues or public policies. • generate and evaluate alternatives to public policies. • identify a problem and develop a solution. • engage in constructive conversation about matters of public concern and work toward a decision. • relate current events to the physical and human characteristics of places and regions.

This document correlates the chapters in *Government Alive! Power, Politics, and You* to national standards for civics and government, grades 9–12.

I. What are civic life, politics, and government?

A. What is civic life? What is politics? What is government? Why are government and politics necessary? What purposes should government serve?

1. Defining civic life, politics, and government	Chapters 1, 2, 3, 4, 6, 7, 8, 10
2. Necessity of politics and government	Chapters 1, 2, 3
3. Purposes of politics and government	Chapters 1, 2, 3, 4, 5, 7

B. What are the essential characteristics of limited and unlimited government?

1. Limited and unlimited governments	Chapters 1, 2, 3, 4, 6, 11, 13, 15
2. The rule of law	Chapters 3, 4, 5, 11, 15, 16
3. Civil society and government	Chapters 1, 4, 7, 8, 9, 10
4. Relationship of limited government to political and economic freedom	Chapters 1, 2, 3, 4, 5

C. What are the nature and purposes of constitutions?

1. Concepts of "constitution"	Chapters 2, 3, 4
2. Purposes and uses of constitutions	Chapters 2, 4, 5, 6, 11, 13, 15, 16, 17
3. Conditions under which constitutional government flourishes	Chapters 2, 4, 7, 8, 9, 10

D. What are alternative ways of organizing constitutional governments?

1. Shared powers and parliamentary systems	Chapters 2, 3, 4, 6
2. Confederal, federal, and unitary systems	Chapters 2, 3, 4, 6
3. Nature of representation	Chapters 2, 3, 4, 6, 8, 10, 11, 12

II. What are the foundations of the American political system?

A. What is the American idea of constitutional government?

1. American idea of constitutional government	Chapters 3, 4, 5, 6
2. How American constitutional government has shaped the character of American society	Chapters 4, 5, 6, 7, 8, 9, 10

B. What are the distinctive characteristics of American society?

1. Distinctive characteristics of American society	Chapters 3, 5, 6, 7, 8, 9, 10
2. Role of volunteerism in American life	Chapters 7, 8, 10, 18
3. Role of organized groups in political life	Chapters 7, 8, 9, 10, 17, 18
4. Diversity in American society	Chapters 6, 7, 8, 9, 10, 11

C. What is American political culture?	
1. American national identity and political culture	Chapters 1, 2, 3, 7, 9, 17, 18
2. Character of American political conflict	Chapters 1, 3, 6, 7, 8, 10, 12, 14, 17
D. What values and principles are basic to American constitutional democracy?	
1. Liberalism and American constitutional democracy	Chapters 2, 3, 4, 7, 8
2. Republicanism and American democracy	Chapters 2, 3, 4, 5, 8
3. Fundamental values and principles	Chapters 1, 3, 4, 5, 6, 7, 8, 9, 13, 15, 16
4. Conflicts among values and principles in American political and social life	Chapters 1, 3, 5, 7, 8
5. Disparities between ideals and reality in American political and social life	Chapters 3, 4, 5, 6, 7, 8, 9, 10, 11, 14, 16

III. How does the government established by the Constitution embody the purposes, values, and principles of American democracy?

A. How are power and responsibility distributed, shared, and limited in the government established by the U.S. Constitution?	
1. Distributing governmental power and preventing its abuse	Chapters 1, 2, 3, 4, 5, 6, 8, 11, 13, 15, 17
2. American federal system	Chapters 4, 6, 7, 8, 11, 13, 15, 16
B. How is the national government organized and what does it do?	
1. Institutions of the national government	Chapters 3, 4, 11, 12, 13, 14, 15, 16, 17
2. Major responsibilities of the national government in domestic and foreign policy	Chapters 4, 6, 8, 11, 12, 13, 14, 17, 18
3. Financing government through taxation	Chapters 4, 6, 11, 14
C. How are state and local governments organized and what do they do?	
1. The constitutional status of state and local governments	Chapters 4, 5, 6
2. Organization of state and local governments	Chapters 6, 8, 11, 13, 15
3. Major responsibilities of state and local governments	Chapters 6, 11, 13, 14, 15
D. What is the place of law in the American constitutional system?	
1. Place of law in American society	Chapters 3, 4, 5, 7, 15, 16
2. Judicial protection of the rights of individuals	Chapters 4, 5, 7, 10, 15, 16

E. How does the American political system provide for choice and opportunities for participation?	
1. The public agenda	Chapters 8, 9, 10
2. Public opinion and behavior of the electorate	Chapters 8, 9, 10
3. Political communication: television, radio, the press, and political persuasion	Chapters 5, 9, 10, 11, 13, 14
4. Political parties, campaigns, and elections	Chapters 6, 8, 9, 10, 11, 13
5. Associations and groups	Chapters 1, 7, 8, 9, 11
6. Forming and carrying out public policy	Chapters 8, 11, 13, 14, 17

IV. What is the relationship of the United States to other nations and to world affairs?

A. How is the world organized politically?	
1. Nation-states	Chapters 2, 18
2. Interactions among nation-states	Chapters 17, 18
3. International organizations	Chapter 18

B. How do the domestic politics and constitutional principles of the United States affect its relations with the world?	
1. Historical context of U.S. foreign policy	Chapters 17, 18
2. Making and implementing U.S. foreign policy	Chapters 17, 18
3. Ends and means of U.S. foreign policy	Chapters 17, 18

C. How has the United States influenced other nations, and how have other nations influenced American politics and society?	
1. Effects of American concept of democracy and individual rights on the world	Chapters 17, 18
2. Political developments	Chapters 7, 17, 18
3. Economic, technological, and cultural developments	Chapter 17
4. Demographic and environmental developments	Chapters 7, 18
5. U.S. and international organizations	Chapter 18

V. What are the roles of the citizen in American democracy?

A. What is citizenship?	
1. The meaning of citizenship in the United States	Chapters 4, 5, 6, 7, 10
2. Becoming a citizen	Chapter 7

B. What are the rights of citizens?	
1. Personal rights	Chapters 3, 4, 5, 7, 15, 16
2. Political rights	Chapters 3, 4, 5, 6, 7, 9, 10
3. Economic rights	Chapters 2, 3, 4, 5, 6, 7, 8, 14, 17
4. Relationships among personal, political, and economic rights	Chapters 2, 7, 8, 10
5. Scope and limits of rights	Chapters 4, 5, 9, 16, 17

C. What are the responsibilities of citizens?	
1. Personal responsibilities	Chapters 1, 5, 7
2. Civic responsibilities	Chapters 7, 8, 9, 10, 14, 15, 16

D. What civic disposition or traits of private and public character are important to the preservation and improvement of American constitutional democracy?	
1. Dispositions that lead the citizen to be an independent member of society	Chapters 1, 7
2. Dispositions that foster respect for individual worth and human dignity	Chapters 1, 3, 5, 8, 18
3. Dispositions that incline the citizen to public affairs	Chapters 1, 2, 3, 7
4. Dispositions that facilitate thoughtful and effective participation in public affairs	Chapters 1, 3, 7, 11

E. How can citizens take part in civic life?	
1. Relationship between politics and the attainment of individual and public goals	Chapters 1, 7, 8, 9, 10
2. Difference between political and social participation	Chapters 7, 8, 10
3. Forms of political participation	Chapters 1, 3, 5, 7, 8, 10
4. Political leadership and careers in public service	Chapters 10, 11, 12, 13, 14, 16, 17
5. Knowledge and participation	Chapters 1, 7, 8, 9, 10

Source: Center for Civic Education.

Placard

Chapter 11
21, 22: U.S. Congressman Mark Steven Kirk, "Kirk and Bass to Lead Republican Mainstream Tuesday Group," Nov. 18, 2004, at United States House of Representatives, www. house.gov.
23, 24: Republican Study Committee, "RSC to Unveil Conservative Check Card," July 7, 2004, at www.house.gov.

Lesson Guide

111: QYA Design Studio **183:** QYA Design Studio **184:** QYA Design Studio **185:** QYA Design Studio

Placards

Photographs

Cover: © Randy Santos/dcstockimages.com **i:** © Randy Santos/dcstockimages.com **1:** David J. & Janice L. Frent Collection/Corbis **2:** The Granger Collection, New York **3:** Corbis **4:** David J. & Janice L. Frent Collection/Corbis **5:** David J. & Janice L. Frent Collection/Corbis **6:** David J. & Janice L. Frent Collection/Corbis **7:** David J. & Janice L. Frent Collection/Corbis **8:** David J. & Janice L. Frent Collection/Corbis **19 TL:** Getty Images **21:** AP Photo **24 R:** Republican Study Committee **29:** ©John Trever, The Albuquerque Journal and PoliticalCartoons.com **33:** Bettmann/Corbis **35:** AP Photo **37:** Getty Images **39:** Bettmann/Corbis **41:** Jack Novak/SuperStock **43:** AFP/Getty Images **45:** Bettmann/Corbis **47:** Corbis **49 L:** Jim West/The Image Works **49 R:** Mark Kegans/Getty Images **49 C:** Getty Images **51 C:** Tim Boyle/Getty Images **51 L:** Colin Braley/Reuters **51 R:** John Bazembre/AP Photo **53 L:** Courtesy of E. Houts **53 R:** Dadan Tri/Corbis **53 C:** Romeo Ranoco-Reuters/Corbis **55 C:** AFP/Getty Images **55 L:** Internal Revenue Service **55 R:** Getty Images **57 L:** Published with the permission of the National Pollution Prevention Roundtable. **57 R:** Gerry Broome/AP Photo **57 C:** Phillip James Corwin/Corbis **59 R:** Gala/SuperStock **59 C:** Getty Images **59 L:** RF/SuperStock

Art

11: QYA Design Studio **12:** QYA Design Studio **13:** QYA Design Studio **14:** QYA Design Studio **17:** QYA Design Studio **18:** QYA Design Studio **25:** QYA Design Studio **26:** QYA Design Studio **27:** QYA Design Studio **28:** QYA Design Studio **31:** QYA Design Studio **32:** QYA Design Studio **49:** Gary Undercuffler **50:** Gary Undercuffler **51:** Gary Undercuffler **52:** Gary Undercuffler **53:** Gary Undercuffler **54:** Gary Undercuffler **55:** Gary Undercuffler **56:** Gary Undercuffler **57:** Gary Undercuffler **58:** Gary Undercuffler **59:** Gary Undercuffler **60:** Gary Undercuffler